CONTENTS

GW00650276

Contact us...

Editor: Graham Sleeman
editor@gethooked.co.uk
Distribution: jane@gethooked.co.uk
Advertising: mandi@gethooked.co.uk

Tel: 01271 860183
Fax: 01271 860064

www.gethooked.co.uk
www.westcountryseaangling.co.uk

 Find us on Facebook @gethookedguide

Cover Picture: Rudd - John Bailey

Published by
Diamond Publications Ltd
PO Box 59, Bideford, Devon EX39 4YN
Tel: 01271 860183 Fax: 01271 860064
Email: info@diamondpublications.co.uk

www.diamondpublications.co.uk

Diamond Publications   © Copyright

ISBN 978-0-9549175-5-3
Published November 2013

Welcome...

To the 18th edition of the Get Hooked Guide to Angling in South West England, published in partnership with the Environment Agency and Angling Trust.

Hello to readers old and new, it's been a while but it's good to be back.

Once again we have updated our definitive guide to coarse and game angling in the West Country. Regular readers may note a slight change to the title this year as we have moved our sea fishing section to a web based format at www.westcountryseaangling.co.uk

That's not to say there won't be a paper edition, keep an eye on our web sites for the latest news. Also, if you are interested in transferring some of your freshwater skills to saltwater, (many are doing so) there are experts within our feature on pages 160-161 who can offer tuition and guiding.

So what's been happening since the last edition? The national drive to encourage more people into the sport continues - lots of information within these pages. More organisations and many volunteers are getting actively involved in improving fisheries. Much of this work is focussed on improving river/wetland habitat and water quality, the key to so much: cheaper water bills, flood alleviation, better invertebrate and insect populations and thus more fish. It's a total win situation, lend them your support - financial, moral or physical - wherever you can.

Yet again the information in this edition has been exhaustively updated to provide you with the definitive guide to game and coarse fishing with over 900 fishing venues listed, along with informative articles and a mine of other useful fishing related information. As ever, if you know of a fishery or club not listed please let us know by phoning (01271 860183), emailing (info@gethooked.co.uk) or by using the form on our website **www.gethooked.co.uk**
Remember directory listings in paperback and online are free of charge!

We know the information in the guide is current at the time of publishing but please be aware this publication has a long shelf life and prices, rules and regulations will change over time. Check our website for the latest information and contact the fishery direct if in any doubt. Please mention our name when calling or make your enquiry direct from **www.gethooked.co.uk** You can also talk to us about anything fishing related via Twitter and Facebook @gethookedguide

We are a lucky bunch here in the West Country, as many of the contributors within these pages will testify. World famous, iconic rivers for coarse and game angling. Equally renowned stillwaters, 'that' coastline. There is nowhere better to be an angler. Of course you do not need to live here to enjoy the spoils and there are many establishments advertising here and on the website that will cater for all your accommodation needs. If you are a local why not pass the guide on to friends from outside the area. There is plenty of fishing to go round.

Before we meet again in these pages try to introduce someone to fishing. It need not be difficult and it's a skill they will keep for life, as you will the memory of their first fish. Although, as us old hands will tell you, it's not all about the fish. There are times I find a quiet hour by the riverbank an almost complete panacea. Relaxing, refreshing, invigorating - hard to beat.

Whether you are picking up this guide for the first time or you are a regular reader (we started in 1994 and I've just realised 2014 will be 20 years!), remember....

enjoy your fishing

Graham Sleeman - Editor
editor@gethooked.co.uk

Mark Lloyd returns a fresh run salmon

We love fishing!
Let's make it even better

The Angling Trust and the Environment Agency have teamed up with Diamond Publications to produce this excellent Angling Guide for the South West.

There's something in here for everyone - local or tourist, beginner or expert, game or coarse.

The guide covers Cornwall, Devon, Dorset, Somerset, Bristol, South Gloucestershire, most of Wiltshire and a small part of West Hampshire. Get Hooked is a one-stop-shop for fishing enthusiasts, with details of where to fish, types of water, species and charges, as well as tackle shops, accommodation and tuition. There are also interesting articles extolling the benefits of fishing in the West Country.

We want to make sure that every angler knows the best places to go fishing and we think this edition of Get Hooked is better value than ever. Regularly updated information on each fishery is also available on the website at:

www.gethooked.co.uk

The Environment Agency and Angling Trust are working closely together to improve your fishing. We strongly support the Get Hooked Angling Guide and believe that it really helps to get more people fishing. We've not included Environment Agency byelaws in this issue because they are about to be reviewed and simplified to make fishing easier. However, all the up-to-date byelaws are available on the Get Hooked website or by going to the Environment Agency website at:

www.environment-agency.gov.uk

Please also join the Angling Trust and Fish Legal now to support our work fighting for fish and fishing! The Angling Trust is the representative body for game, coarse and sea anglers in England and campaigns on all the issues affecting fish stocks and fishing. Fish Legal takes action through the courts to stop pollution and to win compensation for its member clubs and riparian owners. Join to support our campaigns and legal action to protect fish stocks and our programmes to increase the number of anglers fishing for fun and in competitions. We need YOUR support to do more. Please join today and benefit from free insurance and discounts on permits, tackle, books and your favourite angling magazines.

www.anglingtrust.net

Tell your friends about this guide, try some new venues and get someone new hooked on fishing this year!

Have a great year!

Mark Lloyd

MARK LLOYD
Chief Executive – Angling Trust

Martin Williams

MARTIN WILLIAMS
Environment Agency
Strategic Fisheries Specialist

3

Environment Agency

We are the Environment Agency. It's our job to look after your environment and make it a better place for you, and for future generations.

We tackle flood and pollution incidents, reduce industry's impact on the environment, clean up rivers, coastal waters, and contaminated land and improve wildlife habitats. Visit our website at:

www.environment-agency.gov.uk

to find out more about our work and your local environment.

Rod Licences: 0844 800 5386
General enquiries: 03708 506 506

To report an environmental incident please call our incident hotline on 0800 80 70 60

You must have a valid Environment Agency rod licence if you are aged 12 or over and fish for salmon, trout, freshwater fish, smelt or eel in the south west.

Rod fishing rules tell you when you can fish (open and closed seasons); where you can fish; how you can fish; and what fish you can take.

Some fishing rules are local, covering specific waters; others apply to the whole of South West Region; and some national rules cover the whole of England and Wales. Angling clubs and private fisheries often have their own rules which you must respect. The Environment Agency are continually reviewing the rules around fishing.

ROD FISHING OPEN SEASONS

FISHERY DISTRICT	RIVER	Starts	Ends
SALMON			
Avon (Devon)	Avon (Devon)	15 Apr	30 Nov
	Erme	15 Mar	31 Oct
Axe (Devon)	Axe, Otter, Sid	15 Mar	31 Oct
	Lim	1 Mar	30 Sept
Camel	Camel	1 Apr	15 Dec
Dart	Dart	1 Feb	30 Sept
Exe	Exe	14 Feb	30 Sept
Fowey	Fowey, Looe, Seaton	1 Apr	15 Dec
Tamar & Plym	Tamar, Tavy, Lynher	1 Mar	14 Oct
	Plym, Yealm	1 Apr	15 Dec
Taw & Torridge	Taw, Torridge	1 Mar	30 Sept
	Lyn	1 Feb	31 Oct
Teign	Teign	1 Feb	30 Sept
Frome (Dorset) & Piddle		1 Mar	31 Aug
All other rivers in Wessex		1 Feb	31 Aug
MIGRATORY TROUT			
Avon (Devon)	Avon (Devon)	15 Apr	30 Sept
	Erme	15 Mar	30 Sept
Axe (Devon)	Axe, Otter, Sid	15 Apr	31 Oct
	Lim	16 Apr	31 Oct
Camel	Camel, Gannel Menahyl, Valency	1 Apr	30 Sept
Dart	Dart	15 Mar	30 Sept
Exe	Exe	15 Mar	30 Sept
Fowey	Fowey, Looe, Seaton, Tresillian	1 Apr	30 Sept
Tamar & Plym	Tamar, Lynher, Plym, Tavy, Yealm	3 Mar	30 Sept
Taw & Torridge	Taw, Torridge, Lyn	15 Mar	30 Sept
Teign	Teign	15 Mar	30 Sept
All rivers in Wessex		15 Apr	31 Oct
BROWN TROUT			
	Camel & Fowey	1 Apr	30 Sept
	Other rivers in Devon and Cornwall Area	15 Mar	30 Sept
	All rivers in Wessex Areas	1 Apr	15 Oct
	Enclosed stillwaters	No statutory closed season	
	All other stillwaters in Devon and Cornwall Area	15 Mar	12 Oct
	All other stillwaters in Wessex Area	17 Mar	14 Oct
RAINBOW TROUT			
	Camel & Fowey	1 Apr	30 Sept
	Other rivers in Devon and Cornwall Area	15 Mar	30 Sept
	All rivers in Wessex Area	1 Apr	15 Oct
	All reservoirs, lakes & ponds	No statutory closed season	
GRAYLING, COARSE FISH & EELS			
	Rivers, Streams, Drains (including the Glastonbury Canal) and some stillwater Sites of Special Scientific Interest	16 Jun	14 Mar
	Ponds, Lakes, Reservoirs and all other Canals	No statutory closed season	

Please check the Get Hooked website for the most complete and up to date rules
www.gethooked.co.uk

STOP THE SPREAD

STOP THE SPREAD

INVASIVE AQUATIC SPECIES

CHECK-CLEAN-DRY

Are you unknowingly spreading invasive species on your water sports equipment and clothing?

Invasive species can affect fish and other wildlife, restrict navigation, clog up propellers and be costly to manage. You can help protect the water sports you love by following three simple steps when you leave the water.

CHECK

Check your equipment and clothing for live organisms - particularly in areas that are damp or hard to inspect.

CLEAN

Clean and wash all equipment, footwear and clothing thoroughly.

If you do come across any organisms, leave them at the water body where you found them.

DRY

Dry all equipment and clothing - some species can live for many days in moist conditions.

Make sure you don't transfer water elsewhere.

For more information go to www.direct.gov.uk and search for Check Clean Dry

ANGLING TRUST
THE VOICE OF ANGLING

CanoeEngland
Something for Everyone

BRITISH ROWING

RYA

efra
Department for Environment
Food and Rural Affairs

Environment Agency

NATURAL ENGLAND

NNSS
GB non-native species secretariat

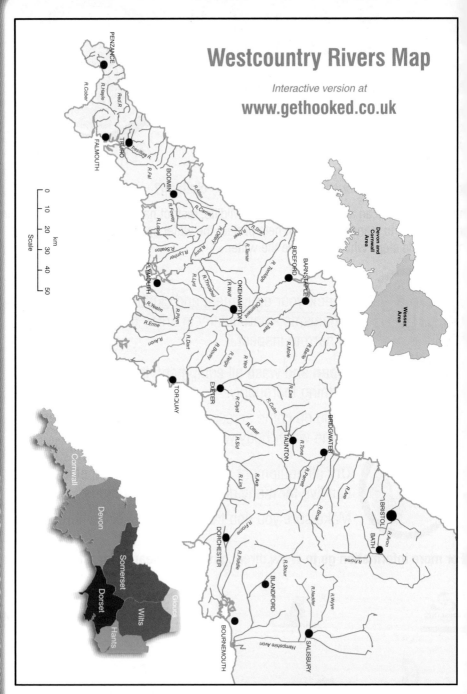

Westcountry Rivers Map

Interactive version at

www.gethooked.co.uk

South West Update

ANGLING TRUST

My name is Dean Asplin and I am the South West Angling Trust development officer. I have been asked by the team at Get Hooked to write a few words to bring you all up to date about what we (the Angling Trust) have achieved in this wonderful sport so far and the direction we are going in over the next few years.

Well where to start? I was first employed by the Angling Development Board back in 2009 (now the Angling Trust) to help deliver the very first Angling whole sport plan agreed and funded by Sport England. My role was also part funded by the Environment Agency to help increase angling participation within the South West. It has been a frantic four years but I am very pleased to announce that we have achieved everything we set out to achieve, plus much more.

South West achievements for 2009 - 13:

- 20 new ClubMark accredited angling clubs across the region.
- South West Angling participation through Angling Trust supported programmes gradually increased year on year. In 2009: 750 people had a go at angling; in 2013 this figure had increased to 3500.
- 4 x County angling action groups were set up.
- 250 new coaches were trained and deployed.
- 10 flagship National Fishing Month events were launched.
- Approximately 40 school club links / sportivate projects were delivered.
- Promotion of club and coaches increased.
- New funding support was found and communicated to clubs and coaches.

- A Scout fishing badge initiative was set up, offering £150 per completed programme.
- 30 talented juniors entered the Team Southern coarse fishing selection events with 10 making the team and 1 being invited to a team England selection day.
- Social media was embraced for communication purposes; you can find me on Facebook and Twitter: Angling Trust Dean Asplin
- For the first time Angling was fully represented and had a voice at all sports forums and national meetings along with all the other National Governing Bodies of sport. *Plus much more!*

Well that's a glimpse of the successes we have had over the last few years, now I would like to tell you about the exciting new Angling Whole Sport Plan 2013-17 and the National Angling strategy.

The Angling Trust has secured more than £1 million a year for the next four years from Sport England and the Environment Agency to get more people fishing more often and to help put the National Angling Strategy into action. In April 2013 we began an ambitious four year programme of work; for this to be successful we need the help and support of fisheries, clubs, coaches and volunteers. By getting involved, you will have opportunities to drive up your club membership, support club and fishery development and improve ticket sales at fisheries. Most importantly, our work will offer volunteers the opportunity to put something back into angling and

to enjoy the unbelievably rewarding experience of helping others learn new skills.

Our funding partners have set us distinctly different challenges. The Environment Agency funding will be targeted at delivering the four aims of the National Angling Strategy which we set out on the basis of the results of our surveys of more than 29,000 anglers and 780 organisations last year.

'**Getting the fishing habit**' is all about introducing new people to fishing through National Fishing Month and Take a Friend Fishing and encouraging people to fish more often through new competitions, social fishing events and coach development.

'**Transforming and changing lives**' involves working with our members and the voluntary sector to use angling to help people develop new skills and self confidence or to recover from trauma or illness.

'**Creating Community Waters**' will see small grants and funding advice being provided to clubs, fisheries and voluntary organisations to restore and improve access to fisheries, while '**Hands up for the Environment**' is concerned with improving fish stocks, which was identified as a priority for increasing angling participation in our surveys.

Sport England, the government agency set up to help people and communities across the country create a sporting habit for life, has set the Angling Trust the target of increasing weekly participation amongst existing anglers aged 26 years and above and anglers with disabilities. Our performance will be measured by the results of the Active People Survey which measures weekly levels of sport participation.

So, how will the Angling Trust rise to the challenge set by Sport England?

Angling is the sixth biggest sport measured by once per month participation but only 14% of these anglers participate weekly. We now have a better understanding of the barriers to weekly participation and want to provide opportunities and incentives for the one million occasional anglers to take part more often and create a habit for life.

Using data from the 2012 National Angling Survey, we have designed four very exciting

national programmes. These programmes are supportive of each other and structured to overcome the recognised barriers to regular participation.

CLUB FISH

This programme will help Angling Trust member clubs and fisheries increase and retain membership and ticket sales, in the short, medium and long term.

Our Regional Officers are working closely with clubs and fisheries to secure funding and identify volunteer and coach development opportunities. This work also involves the design and promotion of four six-week bespoke programmes of activity at the member club or fishery. These sessions are designed to encourage existing & potential members and customers to fish more often.

LET'S FISH

This is all about group participation delivered in partnership with member fisheries. It is designed to increase regular participation and improve ticket sales.

To build on the massive success of the volunteer Sports Makers at last year's Olympics the Angling Trust will train proficient anglers as Volunteer Champions to help our Regional Officers organise, promote and run three hour group recreational angling sessions specifically targeted at existing anglers aged over fifty years and those with disabilities.

These recreational sessions will offer affordable social angling opportunities that provide someone to go fishing with and will be designed to be easy and fun to do. The sessions will not be coached but coaches who have trained as volunteer champions may well help run informal competitions and fun challenges over the six week programmes.

Let's Fish partner fisheries are currently planning fun events such as Summer Carp Fishing challenges for anglers with disabilities, over 50's midweek matches and winter pairs competitions.

THE NATIONAL COMPETITION LEAGUE

This represents a modern all discipline National League framework designed as an incentive for regular anglers to compete more frequently in competitions.

This will allow anglers fishing in existing com-

The first South West Volunteer Champions receive their certificates

petitions between June and May each year to accumulate points from winning and competing. It involves coarse, sea and game disciplines in individual competition leagues in two separate formats, the National Club League (NCL) and The National Fishery League (NFL), all managed by the Angling Trust.

Member clubs or fisheries are invited to register any number of competitions for an annual admin charge of £25. Any individual anglers fishing these matches then simply register with the Angling Trust to qualify for annual ranking points. There is no charge for this entry.

This new framework will ultimately increase the number of competitions, club memberships and the level of weekly participation.

It costs nothing for an individual to enter, but they are encouraged to fish more often because they have the chance to compete against each other on a virtual basis at national, regional, county levels in addition to the usual reward of a one off competition win.

TEAM ENGLAND TALENT PATHWAY:

Sport England is funding the Angling Trust to work with young anglers and identify those showing most potential and select a squad for further coaching. Coaches will be looking at angler's technical, tactical and mental skills and attributes while fishing in a competitive environment. All anglers will receive personalised feedback on their performance which will highlight strengths and areas for development. If selected, anglers will be invited to attend a series of coaching sessions

and Angling Trust talent coaches, some of whom are experienced international anglers will facilitate their learning throughout the programme. Those anglers will then have the opportunity to apply or be selected for an England trial in their chosen discipline, game, coarse or sea.

For information or to get involved in the Talent Pathway programme in your region please visit www.anglingtrust.net or contact Talent Development Manager, Ben Thompson at: ben.thompson@anglingtrust.net

Through these new programmes we are committed to increasing the number, diversity and frequency of angling participation, provide an excellent sporting experience for existing anglers and develop pathways so young anglers with talent can reach their full potential.

The funding provided by our partners provides a genuine opportunity to grow participation in our wonderful sport and to develop and secure its future; with your help we can ensure that this becomes reality.

To find out how you, your club or your fishery can help support the Angling Trust with this exciting work please contact Clive Copeland, Head of Participation via clive.copeland@anglingtrust.net or if you are based in the South West please contact me directly:

dean.asplin@anglingtrust.net

or phone 07854 239731

Getting Involved!

John Bailey

I approve of books like this one. Anything that makes angling more accessible, particularly for children and beginners, I have to commend from the bottom of my heart. I've got to the stage in my angling life where I realise that fishing must, once again, be the largest participant sport in the country if it is to have a really powerful voice. Of course, many things have militated against the young going fishing over the last twenty to forty years. There is an increasing clamour for the attention of the young from all manner of electronic sources. Moreover, there's now a perception that for a child under the age of sixteen or so to go out on his or her own is to invite one of any manner of disasters. For lucky oldies like me, fishing was a way of escape from our parents and adults but now it seems fishing can only be done in the presence of parents and adults.

Never mind, we want to get more people fishing. That's why I was so happy to be a part of the Fishing in the Footsteps of Mr Crabtree team. That's why I'm pleased that the first series of television programmes has done so well. That's why I'm pleased that we are now in the midst of filming the second series with more series to come on the horizon. I'm not saying that these

are the most important television programmes ever made about angling but, hopefully, they're beginning to strike a chord with the young. That's what this is all about. Fishing has guided my life, I like to think, for the better. I would love to be a part of a project that convinces more children to follow the same path. Fishing, I believe, is a truly, utterly, worthy pastime that brings a lifetime of pleasure and endless layers of contentment.

It's this belief that makes me proud to be an Ambassador for the Angling Trust. I had initial doubts but now I feel the Trust has found its way. To claim to be the voice of angling you really have to be big and bold enough to call the shots and the Trust is growing in stature each and every week. We need the Trust. We need the Trust to protect what we've got and improve our fisheries well into the future. The Trust could and should be a colossal organization, at least equalling the RSPB. It should have the money that the RSPB controls, the clout and the easy access to the ear of politicians. Anglers might still have numerical superiority over birdwatchers but we do not have their influence. This must change. Oh, by the way, I also speak as a member of the RSPB which allows me to say that I often feel they come from a ridiculously prejudiced point of view.

So cheers to this guide from Diamond Publications. If it serves its purpose of helping anglers who are already in the sport but also bringing in new blood then I will certainly be proud to have been a part of the process.

Wild trout fishing for all

Mike Weaver fishes Blackabrook on Dartmoor

MIKE WEAVER looks back on the development of the Westcountry Angling Passport and reveals some of his favourite beats...

When the season opened back in the spring of 2000, there was suddenly a sharp increase in the availability of fishing opportunities for any angler in search of wild trout in the South West. The launch of Angling 2000 by the Westcountry Rivers Trust introduced a brand new concept in getting a day on the river at a very modest price. All you had to do was get the free Angling 2000 guide, purchase a book of tokens, make a selection from around a dozen beats on small rivers in Devon and Cornwall, and then head for the river.

Well over a decade later this scheme has gone from strength to strength and is now known as the Westcountry Angling Passport, with over 50 river beats available in 2013. Such a good idea was never going to stick in the South West and it quickly spread to the Wye and Usk, followed by the Eden, the Peak District streams, the Ribble, the Severn, the Annan in Scotland and even across the water to Kerry in Ireland.

So much for history - so what does the scheme have to offer the angler in 2013? Wild trout fishing on rivers remains at the core of the project but there are also opportunities to fish for salmon and sea trout. The Passport now includes salmon beats on rivers like the Taw, Torridge and Fowey that are available through the Booking Office, where you can book your fishing online or by telephone.

For me it is the wild trout fishing on small to medium streams that is the big attraction of the Passport and since the scheme started I have cast a fly on many of the beats on offer. So here are some of the stretches of river that have given me so much pleasure over the years.

Shortly after the launch of Angling 2000 I fished the Woodford beat on the upper Torridge and hit it at the peak of the black gnat hatch in May. The tiny black flies were swarming over the river and right from the word go the brown trout were eagerly taking them – both the natural insects and my attempts to imitate them. That splendid day produced more than 40 trout, starting with a fish of 12 inches and concluding with another of the same size. Since then the Passport scheme has added the Lane Barton beat that overlaps and continues well downstream on the opposite bank, so there is now nearly 3 km of river bank to fish in the Woodford Bridge area.

The three Passport beats on the Ottery, which flows down to the Tamar from the west, include around 6 km of fishing, with plenty of grayling as well as the wild brownies. I have enjoyed many visits to all three beats but if I had to stick with one it would be the topmost beat at Wiggaton near the village Canworthy Water. This is a lengthy beat offering an endless variety of small pools and riffles and the access is easy, with a public footpath running alongside the top half of the beat. My last visit as the 2012 season drew to a close found few trout rising except, fortunately, to my dry fly - and on the deeper pools I located several small pods of grayling that came readily to a beadhead nymph. The biggest brown was but 10 inches and the top grayling only an inch longer but catching over 20 fish in such a peaceful spot was what the Passport scheme is all about.

The Little Dart, a tributary of the Taw, has been in the Passport scheme for many years and offers three token beats on the upper, middle and lower river. Over the years I have visited the 1600 - metre Essebeare beat near Witheridge many times and it has never let me down. As you fish up the quiet and beautiful valley it is easy to lose touch with time as one beguiling pool or glide follows another. The wild trout come readily to a dry fly and only the mewing of a buzzard or the harsh cry of a raven is likely to disturb the peace.

At the other end of the Little Dart, not far above its confluence with the Taw, is Park Mill, where the highlights of my last visit were first taking two trout of 10 inches on the same cast - one on the dropper and the other on the point - and then catching the best fish of the day on the tiny Huntacott Stream, which you could jump across in many places.

When I came to live in Devon more than 40 years ago the first river that I fished was the West Dart, part of the Duchy of Cornwall's Dartmoor Fishery, for the princely sum of two shillings and sixpence a day – that is 12.5p in the currency of today. Several years ago this fishery joined the Westcountry Angling Passport scheme and continues to offer over 25 km of fishing on eight varied moorland rivers, ranging from the big pools and runs on the West Dart to tiny tumbling streams like Blackabrook or the upper East Dart.

Since 2012 anglers have been able to use their Passport tokens on the waters of the Upper Teign Fishing Association, bringing another 12 km of trout fishing into the scheme. Most anglers go for the ever popular stretches above and below Fingle Bridge but the waters at the top of the fishery around Chagford and at the bottom in the Dunsford Nature Reserve are lightly fished and well worth exploring.

In well over a decade I have only scratched the surface of what the Passport scheme has to offer and as the 2013 trout season started I was looking forward to exploring some of the more recent additions; The Castle Hill Estate Fishery on the Bray and Garramarsh Farm on the Mole, both on the edge of Exmoor, were high on the short list for early visits. A trip to the top of the Exe Valley to fish the Little Exe at Week Bridge and the Batherm at Westons near Bampton were also likely prospects. As ever the opportunities exceed the time available for fishing.

At the time of writing the Westcountry Angling Passport offered 51 river beats plus all of the streams in the Duchy of Cornwall's Dartmoor Fishery, and the tokens can also be used on the reservoirs of the South West Lakes Trust and at Drift Reservoir.

Full details can be found on the web site:
www.westcountryangling.com

Into a good trout on the Teign near Fingle Bridge

CORNWALL

Find us on Facebook

@gethookedguide

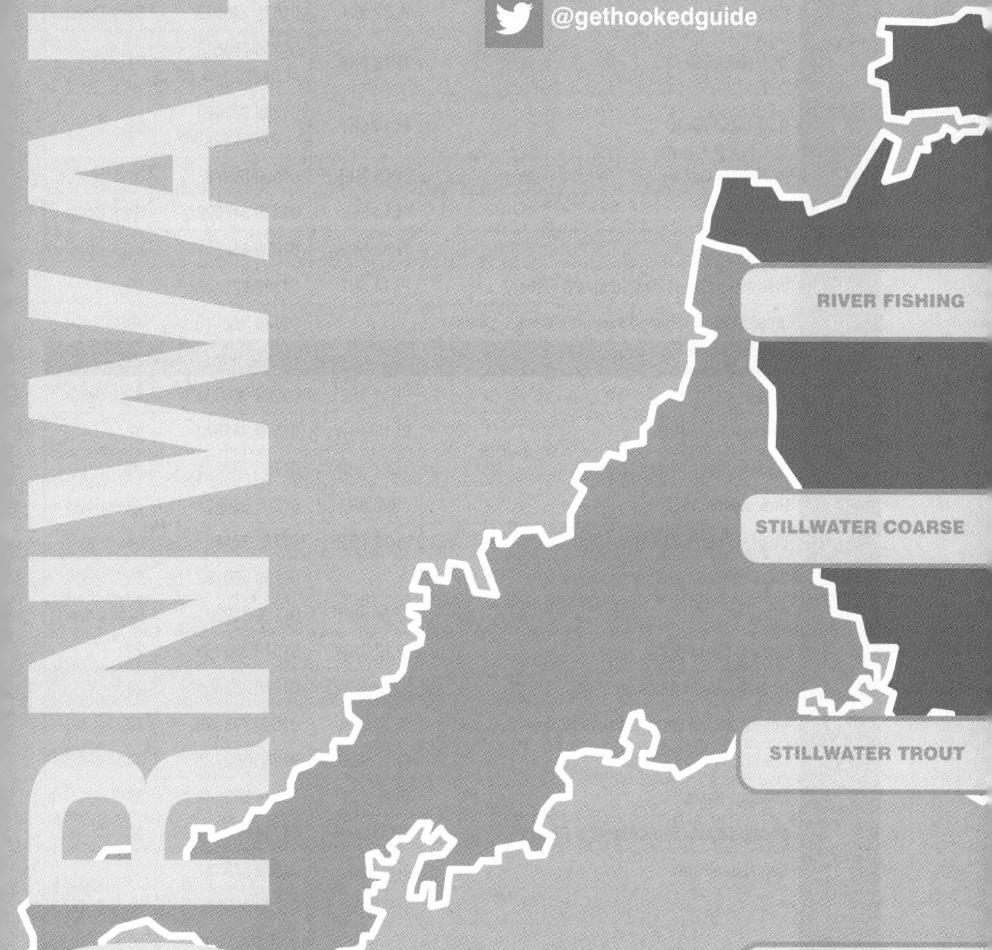

RIVER FISHING

STILLWATER COARSE

STILLWATER TROUT

WHERE TO STAY

ADVERTISER LOCATION MAP

Map No	Advertiser	Sat Nav	Phone	Advert Page
	Game Fishing			
1	Bake Lakes (Game & Coarse)	PL12 5BW	07798 585836	27
2	Colliford	PL14 6PZ	01579 346522	Back Cover
3	Crowdy	PL32 9XJ	01579 346522	Back Cover
4	Drift Reservoir	TR19 6AB	01736 786613 or 07976 184109	31
5	Rivermead Farm	PL14 6HT	01208 821464 or 07774 224962	32
6	Rose Park Fishery	PL15 7RF	01566 86278	31
7	Siblyback	PL14 6ER	01579 346522	Back Cover
8	Stithians	TR16 6NW	01209 860301	Back Cover
9	Wainsford Riverside Cottages & Fishery	PL14 6HT	01208 821432	32
10	Westcountry Angling Passport (Game & Coarse)		01579 372140	19
	Coarse Fishing			
11	Argal	TR11 5PE	01209 860301	Back Cover
12	Badham Farm Holidays	PL14 4RW	01579 343572	32
13	BK Fisheries	TR27 6HS	01736 753275	22
14	Boscathnoe	TR20 8RZ	01209 860301	Back Cover
15	Bosinver Farm Cottages	PL26 7DT	01726 72128	34
16	Bude Canal Angling Association		07799 560152	20
17	Bussow	TR26 3AH	01209 860301	Back Cover
18	Cadson Manor Farm	PL17 7HW	01579 383969	22
19	Houndapitt Farm Cottages	EX23 9HW	01288 355455	20
20	Lower Dutson Farm Cottages (Coarse & Game)	PL15 9SP	01566 776456	32
21	Lower Lynstone Lakes	EX23 0LR	01288 352726	34
22	Meadow Lakes	PL26 7JG	01726 882540	33
23	Middle Boswin Farm (Game & Coarse)	TR13 0HR	01209 860420	30
24	Nanteague Farm	TR4 9DJ	01872 540351	33
25	Porth	TR8 4JS	01209 860301	Back Cover
26	Snowland Leisure Group & Angling Centre	PL24 2AE	01726 825058 or 07598 392278	26
27	Trebellan Park Coarse Fishery	TR8 5PY	01637 830522	32
28	Trevornick Holiday Park	TR8 5PW	01637 830531	32
29	Upper Tamar	EX23 9SB	01288 321712	Back Cover
30	White Acres Country Park	TR8 4LW	01726 862526	25 & 33
31	Wooda Farm Holiday Park	EX23 9HJ	01288 352069	34
32	Woodlay Holidays	PL14 4RB	01503 220221	24

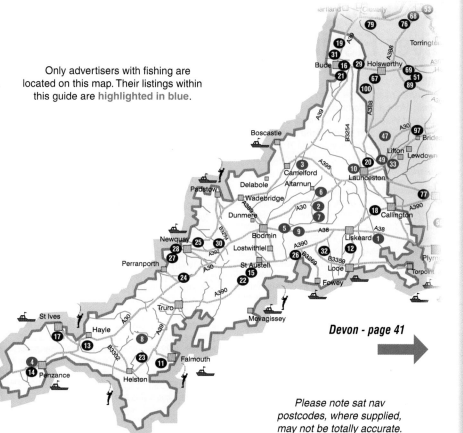

Only advertisers with fishing are located on this map. Their listings within this guide are highlighted in blue.

Devon - page 41

Please note sat nav postcodes, where supplied, may not be totally accurate.

Cornwall River Fishing

CAMEL

The Camel rises on the north west edge of Bodmin Moor and flows past Camelford to its estuary at Wadebridge. The run of Salmon tends to be late with some of the best fishing in November and December. Sea Trout in summer. Brown Trout in upper reaches and tributaries.

Bodmin Anglers Association (Camel)

Contact: Ivan Lyne, Ivy Cottage, Dunmere, Bodmin. *Tel:* 01208 72306. *Water:* 12 miles on River Camel. *Species:* Salmon, Sea Trout. *Permits:* Mrs S. Odgers, Gwendreath, Dunmere, Bodmin, Cornwall PL31 2RD. Rogers Tackle Shop, above Stan May's Store, Higher Bore Street, Bodmin. Stan Spry, Wadebridge. *Charges:* From £15 per day and £40 per week. Children under 16 half price. *Season:* 1 May to 30 November. Juniors half price membership details available from the secretary. *Methods:* Fly, bait or spinner restrictions apply on certain beats at certain times of year.

Butterwell

Contact: Tyson Jackson, Butterwell, Nr Nanstallon, Bodmin. *Sat Nav:* PL30 5LQ. *Tel:* 01208 831515. *Water:* 1.5 miles River Camel, mainly double bank. *Species:* Sea Trout (to 10lb 8oz) & Salmon (to 25lb). 5 year average 75 Salmon and 140 Sea Trout. *Permits:* On site. *Charges:* £25/£30 day, maximum 4 rods/day. Priority given to residents staying at owners self catering cottages or guest house. *Season:* 1 May - 30 August, night fly fishing only for Sea Trout. 1 September - 15 December for Salmon. *Methods:* Any method for Salmon after 1st September.

River Camel Fisheries Association

Contact: Tyson Jackson, Butterwell, Nr Nanstallon, Bodmin. *Tel:* 01208 831515. *Water:* The association represents all major riparian owners and fishing clubs on the River Camel and agrees fish limits, conservation policy and enhancement projects in co-operation with the Environment Agency. *Species:* Migratory fish. *Permits:* See individual clubs and riparian owners. *Season:* May 1st to December 15th.

Tresarrett Fishery

Contact: Mr Pope, Tresarrett Manor Farm, Blisland, Bodmin. *Tel:* 01208 850338. *Water:* 0.75 miles on the Camel. *Species:* Salmon, Sea Trout and Brown Trout. *Permits:* You must have a valid EA licence. *Charges:* From £10 - £20 depending on time of year. Please phone before travelling. *Season:* May 1 to August 31 for Brown and Sea Trout. Until December 15 for Salmon. *Methods:* Fly only to June 1. All legal methods after.

Wadebridge and Dist. Angling Association

Contact: Adrian Halling, Eco Mens Wear, 1 Orchard Walk, Eddystone Road, Wadebridge. *Tel:* 01208 813666. *Water:* 10 miles River Camel, 1 mile River Allen. *Species:* Salmon to 20lb, Sea Trout to 8lb. *Permits:* Day/Week permits and Membership forms, Ego Menswear, Eddystone Road, Wadebridge: 01208 813666. Rogers Tackle Shop, Stan Mays Store, Higher Bore Street, Bodmin: 01208 78006. *Charges:* May to Sept - Day £15/Week £60. October to Nov - Day £25/Week £100. *Season:* Visitor permits limited to three per day in October and November. *Methods:* No maggots permitted. Fly and spinning, natural baits on some beats. Circle hooks only when worming for Salmon. Please use barbless circle hooks.

Westcountry Angling Passport (Camel)

Contact: Westcountry Rivers Trust, Rain-Charm House, Kyl Cober Parc, Stoke Climsland, Callington. *Tel:* 01579 372140. *Water:* 1250m of single right hand bank on the Camel at Tresarrett. 1400m of single left hand bank on the De Lank at South Penquite and 1500m of single right hand bank on the Allen at Lemail Mill. *Species:* Salmon, Brown Trout & Sea Trout on Camel. Brown Trout - De Lank. Brown Trout & Sea Trout on Allen. *Permits:* From: Snowbee UK, Plymouth, PL7 5JY - 01752 334933. Tamar Field and Stream, Lifton, PL16 0AA - 01566 780512. Devil's Stone Inn, Beaworthy, EX21 5RU - 01409 281210. Homeleigh Garden Centre, Launceston, PL15 9SP - 01566 771878. Blisland Inn, Bodmin, PL30 4JK - 01208 850739. Fly Fishing Tackle co uk, Crediton, EX17 2AW - 01363 777783. Hart Flyshop, Exebridge, TA22 9AY - 01398 323008. Lance Nicholson, Dulverton, TA22 9HB - 01398 323409. Tolley's of Tavistock, Tavistock, PL19 0HE - 01822 617186. *Charges:* From £5 to £12.50 per rod per day. *Season:* Camel - 1 May to 30 September. De Lank - 1 April to 30 September. Allen - 1 May to 30 September. *Methods:* Fly spinner and worm.

FAL

The Fal rises on the Goss Moor and flows down to join with the Truro and Tresillian Rivers entering the Carrick Roads estuary. Salmon have been making a few rare appearances back to the River due to an improvement in water quality, but the Fal is predominately a Brown Trout river with some Sea Trout present.

Westcountry Angling Passport (Fal & Tresillian)

Contact: Westcountry Rivers Trust, Rain-Charm House, Kyl Cober Parc, Stoke Climsland, Callington. *Tel:* 01579 372140. *Water:* 1000m mixed double/single on Fal at Grogarth. 2000m of right hand single bank on the Tresillian at Geens Mill and Tregeagle. *Species:* Brown Trout and Sea Trout. *Permits:* From: Snowbee UK, Plymouth, PL7 5JY - 01752 334933. Tamar Field and Stream, Lifton, PL16 0AA - 01566 780512. Devil's Stone Inn, Beaworthy, EX21 5RU - 01409 281210. Homeleigh Garden Centre, Launceston, PL15 9SP - 01566 771878. Blisland Inn, Bodmin, PL30 4JK - 01208 850739. Fly Fishing Tackle co uk, Crediton, EX17 2AW -

River Inney Brown Trout
Pic - The Editor

01363 777783. Hart Flyshop, Exebridge, TA22 9AY - 01398 323008. Lance Nicholson, Dulverton, TA22 9HB - 01398 323409. Tolley's of Tavistock, Tavistock, PL19 0HE - 01822 617186. *Charges:* From £5 to £7.50 per rod per day. *Season:* 1 April - 30 September. *Methods:* Fly spinner and worm.

FOWEY

Rises near the highest point of Bodmin Moor from which it flows south, then turns to the west, and finally south again through Lostwithiel to its long estuary. A late Salmon river. Also good Sea Trout fishing and some Trout fishing.

Fowey River Association
Contact: Jon Evans (sec.), Polgeel, Polbrock, Washaway, Bodmin. *Tel:* 01208 812447. *Mobile:* 07732 921015. *Water:* An association of representatives of angling clubs and riparian owners on the Fowey whose aim is to secure and maintain the well-being of the river and its ecology. It exists largely as a pressure group and negotiating body on behalf of its members. *Species:* Salmon and Sea Trout. *Permits:* No fishing permits sold through the Association. For membership details please contact the secretary at the above address. *Season:* Salmon 1st April - 15th December. *Methods:* E.A. Byelaws apply. Catch restrictions: Salmon 1/ day, 2/week, 5/season; Sea Trout 4/day, all Sea Trout to be returned in September.

Lanhydrock Angling Association ♿
Contact: The National Trust, Property Office, Lanhydrock House, Bodmin. *Tel:* 01208 265950. *Water:* 2 miles on River Fowey. *Species:* Sea Trout, Salmon. *Permits:* Available

from the above telephone number. *Charges:* £17.50 Daily, £35 Weekly. *Season:* 1 April - 30 September, Sea Trout 31 August. *Methods:* Artificial bait only. Disabled anglers please contact office to discuss suitability.

Liskeard and District Angling Club (Fowey)
Contact: Mr Paul Jordan. *Water:* 23 miles of Rivers: Fowey, Lynher, Inny, Seaton and West Looe; Map of waters provided with ticket. *Species:* Salmon to 20lb (typically 5-12lb) & Sea Trout to 10lb (typically 2-4lb). *Permits:* Visitor tickets (available until 30 November for winter Salmon) and membership application forms from: Lashbrooks Tackle Shop, Bodmin, Tel: 01280 78006. Fishing Mayhem, Goldenbank Nursery, Plymouth Road, Liskeard, Tel: 0844 800 2630. *Charges:* Adult: £20/day, £55/week, Membership £85 (OAP £72). Joining fee £15. Membership limited to 250 adults. *Season:* River Fowey 1 April - 15 December; Sea Trout season closes end September. *Methods:* Spinning, fly fishing or bait. Artificials only on one beat. No groundbait, no maggots.

Rivermead Farm
Rivermead Farm, Twowatersfoot, Liskeard. *Sat Nav:* PL14 6HT. *Tel:* 01208 821464. *Mobile:* 07774 224962. *Water:* Half a mile on River Fowey. *Species:* Salmon, Sea Trout and Brown Trout. *Permits:* Only from Rivermead Farm. Pre-booking required. Fishing is also available via the Westcountry Rivers Trust Passport Scheme, Tel: 01579 372140. *Charges:* April - September £20 per day. October - December £20 per day. *Season:* April 1 to December 15. *Methods:* Methods allowed before 16th June are Fly and Spinner only, with worm additionally thereafter. Circle hooks only to be used when worming.

LERRYN

Largest tributary of the Fowey.

Westcountry Angling Passport (Lerryn)
Contact: Westcountry Rivers Trust, Rain-Charm House, Kyl Cober Parc, Stoke Climsland, Callington. *Tel:* 01579 372140. *Water:* 1200m of right hand single bank. Flexible day permits for Brown Trout and Sea Trout at Collon Barton. *Species:* Brown Trout and Sea Trout. *Permits:* From: Snowbee UK, Plymouth, PL7 5JY - 01752 334933. Tamar Field and Stream, Lifton, PL16 0AA - 01566 780512. Devil's Stone Inn, Beaworthy, EX21 5RU - 01409 281210. Homeleigh Garden Centre, Launceston, PL15 9SP - 01566 771878. Blisland Inn, Bodmin, PL30 4JK - 01208 850739. Fly Fishing Tackle co uk, Crediton, EX17 2AW - 01363 777783. Hart Flyshop, Exebridge, TA22 9AY - 01398 323008. Lance Nicholson, Dulverton, TA22 9HB - 01398 323409. Tolley's of Tavistock, Tavistock, PL19 0HE - 01822 617186. *Charges:* £5 per rod per day. *Season:* Brown Trout/Sea Trout 1 April to 30 September. *Methods:* Fly, spinner and worm.

LYNHER

Rises on Bodmin Moor and joins the Tamar estuary opposite Plymouth. Brown Trout and runs of Salmon and Sea Trout.

Liskeard and District Angling Club (Lynher)
Contact: Mr Paul Jordan. *Water:* 23 miles of Rivers: Fowey, Lynher, Inny, Seaton and West Looe; Map of waters provided with ticket. *Species:* Salmon to 16lb & Sea Trout to 6lb (some very big ones April/May). *Permits:* Visitor tickets and membership application forms from: Lashbrooks Tackle Shop, Bodmin, Tel: 01208 78006. Fishing Mayhem, Goldenbank Nursery, Plymouth Road, Liskeard, Tel: 0844 800 2630. *Charges:* Adult: £20/day, £55/week, Membership £85 (OAP £72). Joining fee £15. Membership limited to 250 adults. *Season:* River Lynher & Inny; 1 March - 14 October; Sea Trout season closes end September. *Methods:* Spinning, fly fishing or bait. No groundbait, no maggots.

River Lynher Association
Contact: Arthur White (Hon.Secretary), River Lynher Association, 14 Wadham Road, Liskeard. *Tel:* 01579 345428. *Water:* Consultative body for the River Lynher. Membership comprises riparian owners, angling clubs, lessees of fishing rights, individual anglers and others interested in the Lynher valley environment. *Species:* Salmon, Sea Trout, Trout. *Permits:* Not applicable. *Charges:* £5 annual membership. Riparian owners £20.

Westcountry Angling Passport (Lynher)
Contact: Westcountry Rivers Trust, Rain-Charm House, Kyl Cober Parc, Stoke Climsland, Callington. *Tel:* 01579 372140. *Water:* 650m of left hand bank at Berrio Mill. *Species:* Brown Trout, Salmon and Sea Trout. *Permits:* From: Snowbee UK, Plymouth, PL7 5JY - 01752 334933. Tamar Field and Stream, Lifton, PL16 0AA - 01566 780512. Devil's Stone Inn, Beaworthy, EX21 5RU - 01409 281210. Homeleigh Garden

Centre, Launceston, PL15 9SP - 01566 771878. Blisland Inn, Bodmin, PL30 4JK - 01208 850739. Fly Fishing Tackle co uk, Crediton, EX17 2AW - 01363 777783. Hart Flyshop, Exebridge, TA22 9AY - 01398 323008. Lance Nicholson, Dulverton, TA22 9HB - 01398 323409. Tolley's of Tavistock, Tavistock, PL19 0HE - 01822 617186. *Charges:* £7.50 per rod per day. *Season:* Brown Trout - 15 March to 30 September. Salmon - 1 March to 14 October. Sea Trout - 3 March to 30 September. *Methods:* Fly, spinner and worm.

MENALHYL

Small stream starting near St. Columb Major and entering the sea north of Newquay. Brown Trout fishing.

St. Mawgan Angling Association
Contact: Mr P. Parkinson, 17 Challis Avenue, St. Mawgan, Newquay. *Tel:* 01637 860517. *Water:* Stretch of Menalhyl around Mawgan Porth. *Species:* Brown Trout. *Charges:* Limited day tickets from The Merrymoor, Mawgan Porth. Club membership restricted to those in parish of St. Mawgan. *Season:* April 1st - end September. *Methods:* See details on site.

SEATON

Small river to the east of Looe with good Sea Trout but very few Brown Trout.

Liskeard and District Angling Club (Seaton & West Looe)
Contact: Mr Paul Jordan. *Water:* Seaton River, West Looe River; Map of waters provided with ticket. *Species:* Good small waters for Sea Trout (typically 2 to 4lbs). *Permits:* Visitor tickets and membership application forms from: Lashbrooks Tackle Shop, Bodmin, Tel: 01208 78006. Fishing Mayhem, Goldenbank Nursery, Plymouth Road, Liskeard, Tel: 0844 800 2630. *Charges:* Adult: £20/day, £55/week, Membership £85 (OAP £72). Joining fee £15. Membership limited to 250 adults. *Season:* As for River Fowey 1 April - 15 December; Sea Trout season closes end September. *Methods:* Spinning, fly fishing or bait. No groundbait, no maggots.

TAMAR

The Tamar rises near the north coast, and for most of its course forms the boundary between Devon and Cornwall. It is always a lowland stream flowing through farmland and this fact is reflected in the size of its Trout which have a larger average size than those in the acid moorland streams. Around Launceston, the Tamar is joined by five tributaries - Ottery, Carey, Wolf, Thrushel and Lyd - which offer good Trout fishing, as does the Inny which enters a few miles downstream. There is a

good run of Salmon and Sea Trout, the latter being particularly numerous on the Lyd. There are also Grayling in places.

Arundell Arms
Contact: Adam Fox-Edwards, The Arundell Arms, Lifton, Devon. *Sat Nav:* PL16 0AA. *Tel:* 01566 784666. *Water:* 20 miles of private fishing on Rivers Tamar, Lyd, Carey, Thrushel, Wolf, Ottery and Lew. Also 3 acre private lake stocked with Rainbow and Brown Trout (Residents only). *Species:* Rivers: Salmon, Sea Trout and Brown Trout & Grayling. Lake: Rainbow & Brown Trout. *Permits:* Arundell Arms. Cockpit Tackle Shop open 9-10am and 6.30-7.00pm daily in the season. Day permits available for non-residents on river beats. *Charges:* £30 Trout fishing on Rivers, Salmon up to £40. Lake £38 (Residents only). *Season:* Salmon March 1st to October 14th. Trout March 15th to September 30th. Sea Trout March 3rd to September 30th. Grayling June 16th to March 14th. Lake open all year. *Methods:* Fly only on lake and rivers. Spinning (for Salmon only) permitted on River Tamar.

Bradridge Farm
Contact: BW and A Strout, Boyton, Launceston. *Sat Nav:* PL15 9RL. *Tel:* 01409 271264. *Mobile:* 07748 666993. *Water:* Stretch on River Tamar. *Charges:* Please enquire for further details.

> Remember a ♿ means the fishery has disabled facilities - contact them direct for further details

Bude Angling Association
Contact: Mr L. Bannister, 2 Creathorne Road, Bude. *Tel:* 01288 353986. *Water:* 3 miles on the upper reaches of the River Tamar. *Species:* Brown Trout (wild) and occasional Grayling. *Permits:* Day tickets from Waterfront Tackle on the canal wharf. *Charges:* £5 day, week tickets available £15. *Season:* March 15th - Sept 30th. *Methods:* Fly only.

Dutson Tamar Fishery
Contact: Mr Broad, Lower Dutson Farm, Launceston. *Tel:* 01566 776456. *Water:* Half a mile on the River Tamar at Launceston. *Species:* Brown Trout, Salmon, Grayling and occasional Sea Trout. *Permits:* From farm. *Charges:* £10 per day. *Season:* 1 March - 14 October, Salmon as current EA Byelaws. *Methods:* See current EA Byelaws.

Launceston Anglers Association
Contact: Colin Hookway, 7 Grenville Park, Yelverton, Devon. *Tel:* 01822 855053. *Water:* 6 miles on River Tamar and Carey, 7 miles River Inny. *Species:* Brown Trout, Sea Trout, Salmon, Grayling. *Permits:* Launceston Sports, 1 Market Street, Launceston, PL15 8EP, Tel: 01566 774127. Lewannick Post Office, Lewannick, PL15 7QD. Tel: 01566 782269 (open 6 and a half days a week). *Charges:* Salmon & Sea Trout; Day £15, Week £40. Brown Trout: Day £7.50, Week £25, Juniors £2 a day. Day tickets valid for 24 hours from time of purchase. Annual membership from £70. *Season:* From 1 March to 14 October. Winter Grayling on some beats. *Methods:* Brown Trout - fly only, Salmon & Sea Trout - any method subject to byelaws. Grayling - fly only.

Stillwater Coarse

BODMIN

East Rose Farm
Contact: Matthew Morris, East Rose Farm, St. Breward, Bodmin Moor. *Sat Nav:* PL30 4NL. *Tel:* 01208 850674. *Water:* Complex of four lakes. *Species:* Tench, Carp, Bream, Crucian Carp, Roach, Rudd - ranging in size up to 12lb. *Permits:* Day tickets from Farmhouse at East Rose. *Charges:* £6 Adults, £4 under 16, disabled and OAP. *Season:* No closed season, no night fishing. *Methods:* No keepnets. Barbless hooks only.

Hengar Manor
Contact: Hengar Manor Country Park, St Tudy, Bodmin. *Sat Nav:* PL30 3PL. *Tel:* 01208 850302. *Mobile:* 07940 432902. *Water:* 3 Lakes: 1 acre, 1.5 acres and 0.5 acre. *Species:* Carp to 25lb, Bream, Tench, Roach, Rudd. *Charges:* Please phone for prices. *Season:* Open all year dawn to dusk. *Methods:* Barbless hooks, no keepnets.

Lakeview Coarse Fishery &
Old Coach Road, Lanivet, Bodmin. *Sat Nav:* PL30 5JJ. *Tel:* 01208 831808 extn 4. *Water:* Three lakes, 3.5 acres in total. *Species:* 12 in total inc. Carp to 25lb, Tench to 8lb, Bream to 5lb, Roach, Rudd, Dace, etc. Eels to 5lb, Perch to 5lb. *Permits:* Permits from main reception available after 8 am though you may set up before 8 am. Bailiff makes regular visits around the lakes. *Charges:* £11 a day adult. OAP/ concessions / under 16 £6. Children must be accompanied by an adult. Permits will not be issued without a valid rod and line licence. Please bring it with you. *Season:* Open all year dawn till dusk. Closed Christmas Day. *Methods:* No nuts. No night fishing, 12lb maximum line strength, Barbless Hooks. We have 15 disabled pegs, on site toilets.

Lostwithiel Hotel Golf and Country Club
Contact: Trudy Gilruth, Lower Polscoe, Lostwithiel, Nr Bodmin. *Sat Nav:* PL22 0HQ. *Tel:* 01208 873550. *Water:* 2.5 acre lake. *Species:* Common, Mirror and Crucian Carp 5lb. Roach, Eels. Also some unidentified large fish at 15lb plus. *Charges:* Day ticket £5. *Methods:* Barbless or micro barb hooks only. No keepnets. All fish to be returned.

Prince Park Lake
Contact: John Brown, Prince Park Farm, St Wenn, Nr Bodmin. *Sat Nav:* PL30 5SP. *Tel:* 01726 890095. *Water:* Half acre pond. *Species:* Crucian Carp to over 3lb, Common to 9lb, Tench, Roach, Bream to 4lb and Golden Rudd. *Permits:* Please telephone before travelling. *Charges:* £6 Adults, £5 Juniors/OAP. *Season:* Phone for opening times. *Methods:* Nets must be dipped, barbless hooks only, no boilies.

BUDE

Bude Canal Angling Association &
Contact: Mr Paul Braund, 15 Southfield Road, Bude. *Mobile:* 07799 560152. *Water:* Bude Canal (1.25 miles). *Species:*

Mirror, Common, Crucian Carp, Bream, Tench, Roach, Rudd, Perch, Eels, Gudgeon, Dace. *Permits:* Available from the Crescent Post Office, The Crescent, Bude (adjacent to Falcon Bridge). The Post Office is open from 07.30am seven days a week. *Charges:* Seniors day £5, Seniors week £20, Junior & OAP day £2.50, Junior & OAP week £10. *Season:* All year. *Methods:* Micro barb or barbless hooks only, Strictly one rod only. No camping or any equipment deemed to be associated with camping. Unhooking mats advised.

Hele Barton Coarse Fishery
Contact: Jonathan Chapman, Hele Barton, Week St. Mary, Bude. *Sat Nav:* EX22 6XR. *Tel:* 01288 341622. *Water:* 1.5 Acre Lake. Well stocked with Carp (common, mirror, leather and ghost) and Tench. Lots of Carp in the 1lb to 8lb category and a decent number up to 15lbs. *Species:* Carp to 15lb. Tench to 5.5lb. *Permits:* Pay at Self Service Kiosk in car park. *Charges:* All day ticket (dawn to dusk): £5 one rod, £6 two. Concessions - Under 16's, OAP etc. £3.50 one rod, £4.50 two rods. Evening Fishing (4pm to dusk) £2.50. Night Fishing by arrangement. *Season:* Open all year. *Methods:* Barbless hooks only (Micro barb hooks and flattened barbed hooks are still barbed hooks). No fixed rigs/leads (which could tether fish). No keepnets or carp sacks. No nuts and pulses except sweetcorn. No fires. No radios. Under 14's to be accompanied by an adult at all times. Anglers must have a suitable landing net and disgorger.

STILLWATER COARSE

Houndapitt Farm
Contact: Mr Heard, Houndapitt Farm, Sandymouth, Bude.
Sat Nav: EX23 9HW. *Tel:* 01288 355455. *Water:* 3 Ponds:
0.25 acre lake and two small ponds. *Species:* Golden Tench,
Rudd, various Carp. Common Tench and Mirror. *Charges:*
£5 per day. *Season:* All year. *Methods:* Barbless hooks.

Killock Fishery
Contact: Mr Barry Vickery, Killock Farm, Atlantic Highway,
Kilkhampton, Bude. *Sat Nav:* EX23 9PZ. *Tel:* 01288 321739.
Water: 2 acre lake. *Species:* Mirror and Common Carp,
Bream, Tench and Crucians. *Permits:* On site. *Charges:* £5.
Season: All year. *Methods:* No night fishing. Full rules at lake.

Lower Lynstone Lakes
Contact: John & Clare Hicks, Trelowen, Lynstone, Bude. *Sat
Nav:* EX23 0LR. *Tel:* 01288 352726. *Water:* Two 0.6 acre
lakes 0.75 miles from Bude. *Species:* Mirror and Common
Carp to 20lb, Tench, Crucians. *Permits:* On site. *Charges:*
£5 per day (1 rod). £3.50 under 16s and over 60s. *Season:*
Closed January 1st to February half term. Open 7.30am to
dusk. *Methods:* Barbless hooks only. No boilies, keepnets or
fixed rigs. No radios. Children under 14 must be accompanied
by an adult.

Upper Tamar Lake &
Contact: South West Lakes Trust. *Sat Nav:* EX23 9SB. *Tel:*
01288 321712. *Water:* Reservoir 81 acres. *Species:* Carp
to 40lb, Bream to 10lb. 100lb plus bags of Bream, 30lb plus
bags of Rudd. Lake record 46lb Mirror Carp. Perch to 5lb.

*Common Carp for a
holidaymaker at Cadson Manor*

21

STILLWATER COARSE

Regular competitions - Booking number Tel: 01566 771930. *Permits:* Self service on site. Fishing is also available via the Westcountry Rivers Trust Passport Scheme, Tel: 01579 372140. *Charges:* Full day £6.50, conc. £5, 24 hour £12, Season tickets available from Summerlands Tackle (01237 471291) and Centre on site - additional fisheries £35 each. *Season:* Open all year, 24 hours a day. *Methods:* Follow the wind in summer months. Dam area good in winter for Carp. Shallow end for stalking. Method feeder for larger Bream.

Whalesborough Lake &
Contact: Paul Braund, 15 Southfield Road, Bude. *Sat Nav:* EX23 0JD. *Mobile:* 07799 560152. *Water:* 1.5 acre lake. *Species:* Common Carp 10lbs, Mirror Carp 5lbs, Roach 1lb, Tench 1lb, Bream 1lb. *Permits:* Day tickets available from Weir Cafe situated by lake. *Charges:* £5 per day. Concessions £2.50. *Season:* Open all year. *Methods:* Barbless hooks only.

CALLINGTON

Polhilsa Farm
Contact: P. Barriball, Polhilsa Farm, Callington. *Sat Nav:* PL17 8PP. *Tel:* 01579 370784. *Water:* 2 acre lake. *Species:* Bream, Carp, Rudd and Eels. *Permits:* From the above or from Westcountry Angling Passport. *Charges:* £5. *Season:* Open all year. *Methods:* No Carp in keepnets, barbless hooks only.

DELABOLE

Ferndale Fishery
Contact: Ashley Davey, Rockhead, Delabole. *Sat Nav:* PL33 9BU. *Tel:* 01840 211017. *Mobile:* 07790 246580. *Water:* Three half acre lakes set in a sheltered valley 3 miles off the North Cornwall coast. *Species:* Roach to 1.5lb, Rudd to 1.5lb, Bream to 5lb and Carp to 21lb, Tench to 2lb & Crucian Carp 1.5lb. *Charges:* Adult Day 1 rod £5, Adult Day 2 rods £6. Under 14's/OAP 1 rod £4, Under 14's/OAP 2 rods £5. Adult after 5, 1 rod £4, Adult after 5, 2 rods £5. Under 14's/OAP 1 or 2 rods £4. Night fishing £10 per person. You must be 18 to fish Ferndale at night. Under 18's must be supervised by an adult. Please contact Ashley on number above to book Night fishing. *Season:* Open all year. Times as specified at lakes. *Methods:* Barbless hooks and no keepnets.

FALMOUTH

Argal &
Contact: South West Lakes Trust Fishery Assistant. *Sat Nav:* TR11 5PE. *Tel:* 01209 860301. *Water:* Reservoir 65 acres. *Species:* Carp to 40lb, Pike to over 30lb (no live baiting), Bream to 15lb, Tench & Eels. Re stocked with Carp in 2009. *Permits:* Self service on site or online from our website. Fishing is also available via the Westcountry Rivers Trust Passport Scheme, Tel: 01579 372140. *Charges:* Full day £6.50. Concession/child (12 -16 years) £5. 24 hour £12. Season tickets available from Stithians Centre and Summerlands Tackle (01237 471291) - additional fisheries £35 each. *Season:* Open all year 24 hours a day. *Methods:* Good quality boilies work well.

HAYLE

Billy Knott Fisheries (BK Fisheries) &
Contact: Billy Knott, Green Lane, St Erth, Nr Hayle *Sat Nav:* TR27 6HS. *Tel:* 01736 753275. *Mobile:* 07919 130244. *Water:* 3 acre lake (Bill's Pool). 2 acre lake (Billy's Pool). *Species:* Bill's Pool - Big Carp to 30lb plus, Bream 12lb, Roach over 2lb, Rudd, Perch over 5lb, Tench, Common, Mirror, Koi, Ghost and Crucian Carp. Billy's Pool - Large head of Carp to 18lb, Bream 5lb, Roach, Rudd, Orfe, Perch over 5lb. *Permits:* Available from onsite buildings. Toilets for disabled - Gents and Ladies. Local Authority approved. Full tackle and bait hire. *Charges:* £7 per day. £6 juniors. Eve. after 5pm £5.50. £4.50 juniors. Night permits available - Adult £20, Junior £15. Coaching available from qualified Sport England coach. *Season:* Open all year. *Methods:* Pole, waggler, feeder, bomb. No barbed hooks. No keepnets (except in matches). No nuts, beans or meat baits. Disabled platforms and Disabled toilets.

Marazion Angling Club &
Contact: Mr Barry Little, 32 Trehayes Meadow, St Erth, Hayle. *Tel:* 01736 756767. *Water:* St. Erth Fishery (3 acres), Trevabyn Pond, Plain-An-Gwarry, Marazion 0.5 acres, approx 18 pegs. Children's classes run most Saturday's. *Species:* Carp, Bream, Tench, Roach, Rudd, Perch, Golden Orfe, Golden Rudd, Gudgeon. *Permits:* Available in local shops: Newtown Angling Centre, Praa Sands. West Cornwall

Angling, Penzance. County Angler, Camborne. Post Office, St. Erth. Plus many more outlets (Please phone for more details). *Charges:* Membership fees: Full Senior £60, Ladies £50, Juniors (up to 16) £20, OAP & Disabled £50, Out of county £500. Family (2 adults & 2 children) £90. Ticket prices: Day £6 - Ladies, Seniors. OAP and Disabled £5. Juniors £3.50. Student 16 to 19 in full time education £25. *Season:* Open all year dawn till dusk, night fishing by appointment only, matches held regularly throughout the year. *Methods:* Barbless hooks, full rules & byelaws displayed at lake side (best baits: maggot, worm, pellet, sweetcorn, meat, boilies).

Trevabyn Fishery &

Contact: Ryan Curnow, Plain-an-Gwarry, Marazion. *Sat Nav:* TR17 0DR. *Water:* 0.5 acre lake with 14 swims. *Species:* Carp, Tench, Rudd, Roach and Bream. *Permits:* From fishery. *Charges:* £4 tuition including rod and bait hire. *Methods:* Barbless hooks only, 10lb mainline limit. Disabled parking close to lake.

HELSTON

Garras Lakes &

Contact: Geoffrey and Pam Benney, Tregear Farm, Garras, Helston. *Sat Nav:* TR12 6LW. *Tel:* 01326 221868. *Water:* 0.5 acres. *Species:* Carp 20lb, Rudd 2lb, Roach 2lb, Tench 3lb, Perch 3lb, Gudgeon, Crucians 3lb, Bream 3lb. *Permits:* On the bank. *Charges:* £6 per day - 2 rods. *Season:* Open all year dawn to dusk. No night fishing. *Methods:* Barbless hooks only. Fishing close to car park for disabled. Unfortunately no toilets on site.

Middle Boswin Farm (Coarse)

Contact: Jonno, Middle Boswin Farm, Porkellis, Helston. *Sat Nav:* TR13 0HR. *Tel:* 01209 860420. *Mobile:* 07815 956095. *Water:* One Coarse Lake. *Species:* Roach 2lb, Rudd 1.5lb, Bream 4lb, Tench 3lb, Perch 2lb, Hybrid (Roach/Bream) 2.5lb plus single figure Mirror and Common Carp. *Permits:* Day tickets available on bank. *Charges:* Adult £5, concessions/junior £4. *Season:* Winter; Dawn to dusk, Summer 7am - 9 pm. *Methods:* Barbless hooks only, no fixed legers, no cereal groundbait, cat food, hemp or nuts, no Trout pellets. No keepnets (except Matches) or Carp sacks. Baited rods must not be left unattended. Max 2 rods per person.

LAUNCESTON

Adamsfield Fishery &

Contact: Mr Roger Pooley, Adamsfield Farm, Canworthy Water, Launceston. *Sat Nav:* PL15 8UD. *Tel:* 01566 781243. *Water:* 2 acre and 1.25 acre lakes. *Species:* Carp to 28lb, Tench to 6lb, Roach to 3lb, Perch to 5lb, Bream, Orfe to 1lb, Chub to 5lb. *Permits:* Members only. Details on application. *Season:* Open all year. *Methods:* No keepnets, ground bait in feeders only, barbless hooks, boilies to 10mm only (shop bought).

Remember a & means the fishery has disabled facilities - contact them direct for further details

Dutson Water &

Contact: Mr Broad, Lower Dutson Farm, Launceston. *Sat Nav:* PL15 9SP. *Tel:* 01566 776456. *Water:* 0.75 acre lake. *Species:* Carp 22lb, Tench to 6lb 2oz, Bream to 5lb 2oz, Rudd, Perch to 3lb 4oz etc. *Permits:* Available at farm. *Charges:* Day ticket £10. *Season:* Open all year. *Methods:* No Groundbait, Barbless hooks only.

East Kitcham Farm

Contact: Chris and Carol Budge, St Giles on the Heath, Launceston. *Sat Nav:* PL15 9SL. *Tel:* 01566 784325. *Mobile:* 07734 166316. *Water:* Half acre pond. *Species:* Carp, Tench and Bream. *Charges:* £5 day, night fishing by arrangement only. *Season:* All year. *Methods:* Full rules on site and must be followed.

St. Leonards Coarse Fishing Lake

Contact: Andy Reeve, St. Leonards Equitation Centre, Polson, Launceston. *Sat Nav:* PL15 9QR. *Tel:* 01566 775543. *Mobile:* 07860 431225. *Water:* 0.75 acre lake. *Species:* Tench, Crucian, Leather, Mirror and Common Carp. *Permits:* From house. *Charges:* £5 per rod per day. *Season:* Open all year. *Methods:* Barbless hooks only.

STILLWATER COARSE

STILLWATER COARSE

Harry with an 11lb Mirror Carp from Bill's pool at BK Fisheries

LISKEARD

Badham Farm &

Contact: Mr Jan Sroczynski, Badham Farm, St Keyne, Liskeard. *Sat Nav:* PL14 4RW. *Tel:* 01579 343572. *Water:* 0.5 acre lake and 1 acre lake. *Species:* Carp 15lb, Roach 2lb and Rudd 2lb in small lake. Carp 8lb, Roach 1lb, Trout in acre lake. *Charges:* £5 per rod per day. *Season:* Open all year dawn to dusk. *Methods:* Barbless hooks only, no boilies, no keepnets, landing nets to be used at all times, no groundbait.

LOOE

Tregoad Park

Contact: Reception, St Martins, Looe. *Sat Nav:* PL13 1PB. *Tel:* 01503 262718. *Water:* Two lakes (80 metres long). *Species:* Carp, Roach, Bream. *Permits:* Local Post Office. *Charges:* £6 adult. £4 child. *Season:* Open all year. *Methods:* Please observe full rules on site.

NEWQUAY

Goonhavern Fishery

Contact: S. Arthur, Oak Ridge Farm, Bodmin Road, Goonhavern. *Sat Nav:* TR4 9QG. *Tel:* 01872 540345. *Water:* 2 acres. *Species:* Carp, Tench, Rudd, Roach, Perch. *Permits:* On the bank. *Charges:* £5 Adults. £4 Children and OAP. *Season:* Open all year. *Methods:* Barbless hooks, no Carp keepnets.

Gwinear Pools &

Contact: Charlie and Rhona Nichol, Gwinear Farm, Cubert, Newquay. *Sat Nav:* TR8 5JX. *Mobile:* 07802 400050. *Water:* Five acre complex. 3 match lakes with Carp up to 13.5lb. Specimen Lake - Carp up to 30lb. Matches Sunday, Tuesday, Friday. For match enquiries phone Roger Baker 07766 930909. *Species:* Carp 34lb, Roach, Bream, Perch, Rudd, Tench. *Charges:* Day tickets from £5. *Season:* No close season. *Methods:* Barbless hooks only, no keepnets, no meat products.

Legonna Farm Fishery

Contact: Mr Trebilcock, Legonna Farm, Lane, Newquay. *Sat Nav:* TR8 4NJ. *Tel:* 01637 872272. *Mobile:* 07833 596120. *Water:* 1 acre lake. *Species:* Tench, Roach, Rudd, Perch, Carp to 20lbs. *Permits:* Day tickets from farm. *Charges:* Adult £5 (2 rods), Junior (2 rods) £5. OAP £5 (2 rods). Children under 14 to be accompanied by an adult. *Season:* No close season. *Methods:* Barbless hooks, no nuts of any type, no litter, no large fish in keepnets.

Mawgan Porth Pools and Lakes &

Contact: Ms Janet Reynolds, Retorrick Mill, Mawgan Porth, Newquay. *Sat Nav:* TR8 4BH. *Tel:* 01637 860770. *Water:* 2 lakes - 1.5 acre 47 peg lake, plus specimen pool with 11 pegs. *Species:* Carp, Tench, Bream, Gold and Blue Orfe. *Permits:* On site. Disabled toilet on site, all paths and pegs disabled angler friendly. *Charges:* £7 (one rod/pole). Pension day every Thursday £6 (one rod). *Season:* Open all year, 7.30am to dusk. *Methods:* Nets provided by fishery. No tiger nuts. 2 kilo groundbait max. Full list of rules at fishery. No keepnets except for competitions. No meat.

STILLWATER COARSE

Mid Cornwall Fisheries

Contact: Kevin. *Sat Nav:* TR8 4PP. *Mobile:* 07779 285550. *Water:* Three Lakes at Gunnabarn near Summercourt. 3 acre specimen Carp lake. 20 peg silvers match lake. 24 pegs Joans Carp match lake. *Species:* Specimen lake has over 80 double figure Carp with 50 over 20lb and 30lb. Silvers lake heavily stocked with silver fish, some Tench and some very large Perch. Joans lake heavily stocked with Carp to 8lb and Tench. *Charges:* Carp lake yearly membership only at £250 plus £30 key deposit. Silvers lake £6 per day. Joans lake £6 per day. Barn Match Club membership at £50 per year gives access to both match lakes. *Season:* Open all year. *Methods:* Full rules on site. Keepnets only in matches.

Oakside Fishery & Fish Farm

Contact: Brian & Sandra Hiscock, Whitecross, Newquay. *Sat Nav:* TR7 3BT. *Mobile:* 07773 224243. *Water:* 3 acre lake. *Species:* Carp to 30lb, Tench 10lb, Rudd, Bream 10lb+, Perch, Roach 2lb, Crucians 2lb. *Permits:* Pay kiosk, checked by bailiff. *Charges:* Adult £6 (Two rods), Junior, OAP, Disabled £5 (Two rods). *Season:* All year round. *Methods:* Barbless hooks, no tiger nuts or peanuts and no Carp in keepnets.

Penvose Farm Holidays &

Contact: Jonathan Bennett, St. Mawgan, Nr. Newquay. *Sat Nav:* TR8 4AE. *Tel:* 01637 860277/432. *Mobile:* 07811 531881. *Water:* 5 acres of water set in a beautiful valley. *Species:* Carp (Common 15-16lb, Mirror 16-19lb, Ghost 19.5-22lb), Tench (Green 3-4lb, Golden 1lb) Bream 2lb,

Crucians 1.5lb, Rudd 1.5lb, Roach 1lb. *Permits:* Post Office nearby. *Charges:* Adults £6. Under 14 £5. *Season:* No closed season, fishing dawn till dusk. *Methods:* Anglers must hold a valid licence. All nets to be dipped in solution tanks, no keepnets except for matches, landing nets must be used. Ground bait up to 2kg maximum. Barbless hooks only.

Porth &

Contact: South West Lakes Trust. *Sat Nav:* TR8 4JS. *Tel:* 01209 860301. *Water:* Reservoir 40 acres. *Species:* Carp to 32lb, Bream to 10lb 16oz, Perch to 4lb, Roach to 2lb, Rudd, Pike to 24lb - no livebaiting. Mixed bags of 130lb have been caught. Re stocked with Carp in 2009. *Permits:* Self service on site or online from our website. Fishing is also available via the Westcountry Rivers Trust Passport Scheme, Tel: 01579 372140. *Charges:* Full day £6.50. Concession/child (12 -16 years) £5. 24 hour £12. Season tickets available from Summerlands Tackle (01237 471291) - additional fisheries £35 each. *Season:* Open all year, 24 hours a day. *Methods:* Method feeder with worm tip for good mixed bags. Pole and Waggler also productive.

Trebellan Park & Fisheries

Contact: Mr Eastlake, Cubert, Newquay. *Sat Nav:* TR8 5PY. *Tel:* 01637 830522. *Water:* 3 lakes ranging from 1 to 2.5 acres. *Species:* Carp 30lbs, Roach 3-4lbs, Rudd 3-4lbs, Tench 3-4lbs. *Permits:* Permits on the bank. Bailiff collects. *Charges:* Day tickets - £6 for 1 rod, £10 for 2 rods. Season ticket (12 months) £90. *Season:* Open all year. No night

STILLWATER COARSE

Josh swings in another Rudd on Downacarey Lake

fishing. *Methods:* No keepnets, barbless hooks only, no ground baiting, no high protein baits, no night fishing, no cat or dog meat.

White Acres Country Park ♿
Contact: Tackle Shop, White Acres Country Park, Newquay. *Sat Nav:* TR8 4LW. *Tel:* 01726 862519. *Water:* 15 lakes totalling approx. 36 acres. *Species:* Wide range of almost all species (no Pike or Zander). *Permits:* Available from Fishing Lodge. Residents fish all year and non-residents can fish Friday and Saturday. Specimen Lakes are resident only. *Charges:* Please call for info. £10 Adult, £5 Junior. *Season:* Fishery open all year round. *Methods:* Barbless hooks only, some keepnet restrictions, no peas, nuts, or beans. No catmeat or Trout Pellet. No bloodworm or joker.

PADSTOW

Borlasevath
Contact: Robert Hurford, Borlasevath Manor Farm, St. Wenn, Bodmin. *Sat Nav:* PL30 5PW. *Mobile:* 07973 767147. *Water:* 10 acres of water (5 lakes). *Species:* Carp, Bream, Tench, Rudd. *Season:* Open all year. *Methods:* Barbless hooks. All children under 14 years to be accompanied by an adult. No keepnets.

Remember a ♿ means the fishery has disabled facilities - contact them direct for further details

PAR

Snowland Angling Centre ♿
Par Farm, Par. *Sat Nav:* PL24 2AE. *Mobile:* 07598 392278. *Water:* 3 lakes. Lodge and Brunel mainly silver fish (total 50 pegs) plus new specimen lake. *Species:* Carp to 20lb+, Tench to 2lb+, Rudd, Roach, Bream 4lb Crucians up to 2lb. *Permits:* Season and day tickets available. *Charges:* £5 per day. Concessions for disabled and OAP. *Season:* Dawn to dusk. *Methods:* Barbless hooks only. No braid, floating baits, boilies or cat meat. All Carp, Tench and Bream to be landed in a net. No keepnets from 1st April - 31st October with exception to organised matches.

PENZANCE

Boscathnoe
Contact: South West Lakes Trust Fishery Assistant. *Sat Nav:* TR20 8RZ. *Tel:* 01209 860301. *Water:* Reservoir 4 acres. *Species:* Common and Mirror Carp to 37lb. Crucian Carp, Bream, Roach, Rudd and Tench stocked. *Permits:* Newtown Angling, Germoe, Penzance (01736 763721), West Cornwall Angling, Penzance (01736 362363), County Angler, Camborne (01209 718490), Heamoor Post Office (01736 363083), Ayr Newsagents, St. Ives (01736 791800), Sandy's Tackle, Redruth (01209 214877) or online from our website. *Charges:* Full day £6.50. Concession/child (12 -16 years) £5. 24 hour £12. Season tickets available from Stithians Centre and Summerlands Tackle (01237 471291) - additional fisheries £35 each. Fishing is also available via the Westcountry Rivers Trust Passport Scheme, Tel: 01579

372140. *Season:* Open all year, 24 hours a day. *Methods:* No child under 14 years may fish unless accompanied by an adult over 18 years. No child under 16 may fish overnight unless accompanied by an adult over 18 years, and then only with permission of parent or legal guardian (letter to this effect must be produced).

Tindeen Fishery &

Contact: J. Laity, Bostrase, Millpool, Goldsithney, Penzance. *Sat Nav:* TR20 9JG. *Tel:* 01736 763486. *Water:* Two lakes approx. 1 acre each. *Species:* Carp, Roach, Rudd, Gudgeon, Perch to 5lb, Tench, Carp to 30lbs. *Permits:* From above address. *Charges:* Adults £5, Juniors (under 12) £2.50, Extra rod £1. *Season:* Open all year, night fishing by arrangement. *Methods:* Barbless hooks to be used. Easy access for disabled persons with suitable fishing platforms.

Wheal Gray

Contact: Lands End Angling Syndicate. *Tel:* 01326 280069. *Mobile:* 07952 040715. *Water:* 3.5 acre lake. Old clay pit, depths to 45ft. very snaggy and weedy. *Species:* Carp to upper twenties, Roach and Rudd over 2lbs. Perch over 4lb 8oz. *Permits:* Application forms by telephone or email. Waiting list once syndicate full. *Charges:* No day tickets. Annual membership £100 discounted to £50 for those in full time education. 20 syndicate places available. Guest tickets available for members. *Season:* March 1st - February 28th. *Methods:* Minimum 12lb line, Max 3 rods. No boats but bait boats allowed. Min. 42 inch net and unhooking mats compulsory.

Woonsmith Lagoon &

Contact: Kenneth Roberts, Woonsmith Farm, Nancledra, Penzance. *Sat Nav:* TR20 8LP. *Tel:* 01736 796925. *Water:* 1 acre lake. *Species:* Carp, Tench, Roach, Rudd and Bream. *Permits:* Day, week and season permits available from West Cornwall Angling, Penzance. Tel: 01736 362363. *Charges:* Adult Day £5. Child Day £3. £4 Senior Day. £20 Week Ticket. £50 Season Ticket. *Season:* January to December. *Methods:* Barbless hooks only. No Carp or fish over 3lb in keepnets. No night fishing. Full list of rules on application.

SALTASH

Bake Fishing Lakes (Coarse) &

Trerulefoot, Saltash. *Sat Nav:* PL12 5BW. *Mobile:* 07798 585836. *Water:* 9 lakes totalling over 15 acres, Coarse and Trout. *Species:* Mirror 28lb, Common over 30lb, Ghost 24lb, Crucian Carp, Tench 7lb, Bream 8lb 4oz, Roach, Rudd. *Permits:* On site. *Charges:* From £7 per day (adult, 2 rods) reductions for OAP and under 16s. Season permits available. Full prices on application. *Season:* 8am to dusk. Open all year. *Methods:* Barbless hooks. No nuts. No keepnets for specimen fish. Landing mats.

Bush Lakes &

Contact: Irene Renfree, Bush Farm, Saltash. *Sat Nav:* PL12 6QY. *Tel:* 01579 351102. *Water:* 3 Lakes from half to one acre. *Species:* Carp to 30lb plus, Tench to 3.5lb, Rudd to

1.5lb, Roach to 1.5lb, Bream, Perch to 4.5lb. *Charges:* Day ticket £9 - 2 rods. Day tickets currently available but water may be syndicated. Please check before travelling. *Season:* Open all year. *Methods:* Barbless hooks, unhooking mat, no nets for big Carp. No keepnets.

Club Brunel

Contact: Vincent Riley, 81 Brentford Avenue, Whitleigh, Plymouth, Devon. *Tel:* 01752 207434. *Mobile:* 07837 684125. *Water:* One acre coarse lake abundantly stocked. Small, friendly club welcoming new members. *Species:* Carp to 20lb, Bream to 8lb, Roach to 2lb, Rudd to 2lb, Crucians, Tench to 3lb. *Permits:* Membership only. No day tickets. Please contact the above. *Charges:* £25 per year. *Season:* Open all year. *Methods:* All methods produce well. Floating crust account for many large catches in warmer months. Meat, worm and corn on pole or feeder for Bream and Carp. Maggot and caster over hemp for large bags of Roach and Rudd but expect to feed heavily as there are an abundance of smaller bits to get through.

Trewandra Lake

Contact: Mr & Mrs S.F. Delbridge, Berry Park, Trewandra Farm, Tideford, Saltash. *Sat Nav:* PL12 5JA. *Tel:* 01752 851258. *Mobile:* 07833 666899. *Water:* One acre lake. *Species:* Carp to 22lb. Tench to 6lbs. Roach to 2.5lbs and Bream to 5lbs. *Permits:* Local Post Office. *Charges:* £6 Day, Children £3. Evening Ticket £4, £2 Children. Children 13 years and under must be supervised by an adult at all times. *Season:* Open all year (dawn to dusk). Toilet available June, July and August only. Night fishing by arrangement only. *Methods:* No dogs allowed, barbless hooks, no keepnets for Carp, no tiger nuts and no peanuts.

ST AUSTELL

Court Farm Holidays

Contact: Simon or Bill Truscott, Court Farm Holidays, St Stephen, St Austell. *Sat Nav:* PL26 7LE. *Tel:* 01726 823684. *Mobile:* 07973 773681. *Water:* Natural Spring fed 0.75 acre lake. *Species:* Crucian Carp, Grass, Roach, Tench, Perch. *Permits:* You must have a valid EA Rod Licence. *Charges:* Day tickets £6. *Season:* Open all year. *Methods:* Barbless hooks only. No boilies. No keepnets.

When did you last look at a fish this close - incredible! Pic - The Editor

STILLWATER COARSE

Glenleigh Farm Fishery &

Contact: Mr & Mrs J. Kneller, Glenleigh Farm, Sticker, St Austell. *Sat Nav:* PL26 7JB. *Tel:* 01726 73154. *Mobile:* 07850 313132. *Water:* One acre lake. *Species:* Carp (Common, Ghost, Mirror, Leather), Tench, Rudd, Roach, Eels, Gudgeon, Perch. *Permits:* Tickets from lakeside, permits from Sticker post office. *Charges:* £6.50 day, £4.50 young person (7-16). £4 evening, £3 young person (7-16). *Season:* Open all year dawn to dusk. *Methods:* Barbless hooks. No nuts, peas or beans. Max 2 rods per person. Mats to be used. No groundbait. No keepnets. Parking available adjacent to lake, allowing easy access for disabled persons. Disabled friendly fishing platforms.

Meadow Lakes Coarse Fishery &

Contact: Rachel Nation, Hewas Water, St Austell. *Sat Nav:* PL26 7JG. *Tel:* 01726 882540. *Water:* Total of 4 lakes: Two 2 acre lakes. Two 1 acre lakes. *Species:* Ghost Carp 26lb, Common Carp 18lb, Mirror Carp 10lb, Bream 4lb 8oz, Roach and Rudd 2lb, Eels 6lb, Tench 1lb and Perch 4lb 5oz. *Permits:* From reception. *Charges:* £10 per day. *Season:* March-January. *Methods:* Anyone aged 12 or over must have a rod licence. Barbless hooks only. No boilies. No nuts or cat meat. No night fishing. Eels must be returned back to lake alive. Parking is not allowed near the lakes unless you have a blue disabled badge.

Roche (St Austell) Angling Club &

Contact: Alan Goddard. *Tel:* 01726 843624. *Water:* 6 freshwater lakes in St Austell area. *Species:* Roach, Perch, Rudd, Tench, Eels, Carp, Pike & Bream. *Permits:* Fishing restricted to members and their guests only. Membership applications available from membership secretary direct. *Charges:* Full annual membership £85 with a £50 joining fee, concessionary £42.50 plus initial joining fee. Membership to Game and Sea sections only at reduced rates. *Season:* Open all year. *Methods:* As specified in club byelaws.

ST COLUMB MAJOR

Meadowside Fishery

Contact: Mick Brown, Meadowside Farm, Winnards Perch, St. Columb. *Sat Nav:* TR9 6DH. *Tel:* 01637 880544. *Mobile:* 07800 740561. *Water:* 3 lakes mixed coarse fishery. *Species:* Carp 24lb, Roach 2lb, Perch 3lb, Rudd 1lb, Tench 5lb, Bream 6lb. *Permits:* Annual season ticket (guest allowed). *Charges:* Adult 2 rods £80, 3 rods £100. Conc. £60 2 rods. Guest day £10. *Season:* No close season, 7.30am to dusk. *Methods:* Barbless hooks, no keepnets. Mat, weigh sling and landing net for Carp supplied.

Retallack Waters &

Contact: Chris Day, Winnards Perch, St Columb Major. *Sat Nav:* TR9 6DE. *Tel:* 01637 882400. *Water:* 3 lakes totalling an area of over 10 acres. *Species:* Carp, Tench, Pike, Bream. *Permits:* Night fishing available. *Charges:* Please phone for prices. *Season:* Open all year. *Methods:* Barbless hooks only. Unhooking mats and specimen landing net required on specimen lake. Dogs allowed by prior arrangement, please phone first.

ST IVES

Amalwhidden Farm Coarse Fishery

Contact: Neil Hodder, Towednack, St. Ives. *Sat Nav:* TR26 3AR. *Tel:* 01736 796961. *Mobile:* 0784 2089760. *Water:* 3 ponds - 1.5 acre lake, 1.2 acre lake, 0.5 acre lake. *Species:* Mirror Carp, Common Carp, Ghost Carp, Crucian Carp. Tench, Perch, Bream, Rudd, Roach and Gudgeon. *Charges:* Day tickets £5 1 rod, £7 2 rods - Adults. *Season:* No closed season. *Methods:* No Carp sacks, barbless hooks only, no night fishing. No keepnets, no cat food, no meat, no trout pellets and no particle baits.

Bussow

Contact: South West Lakes Trust Fishery Assistant. *Sat Nav:* TR26 3AH. *Tel:* 01209 860301. *Water:* Reservoir 7 acres. *Species:* Rudd to 1.5lb. Roach, Perch, Bream and Carp to 28lb. Recently restocked with Carp. *Permits:* Ayr Newsagents, St. Ives (01736 791800), Newtown Angling Centre (01736 763721). Sandy's Tackle, Redruth (01209 214877), West Cornwall Angling, Penzance (01736 362363), Heamoor Post Office, County Angler, Camborne (01209 718490) or online from our website. Fishing is also available via the Westcountry Rivers Trust Passport Scheme, Tel: 01579 372140. *Charges:* Full day £6.50. Concession/child (12 -16 years) £5. 24 hour £12. Season tickets available from Stithians Centre and Summerlands Tackle (01237 471291) - additional fisheries £35 each. *Season:* Open all year 24 hours a day.

Nance Lakes &

Contact: Mrs Ellis, Nance Lakes, Trevarrack, Lelant, St Ives. *Sat Nav:* TR26 3EZ. *Tel:* 01736 740348. *Water:* Three lakes, various sizes. *Species:* Carp, Roach, Bream and Tench. *Charges:* £5 per day. Evening tickets - £3 after 5pm. *Season:* Open all year 8am to 5pm. *Methods:* Barbless hooks, no keepnets unless competition. Disabled angler friendly pegs. Plenty of nearby parking.

TORPOINT

Millbrook &

Contact: Mark or Rebecca Blake, Tregonhawke Farm, Millbrook, Torpoint. *Sat Nav:* PL10 1JH. *Tel:* 01752 823210. *Water:* 1 acre water in sheltered, wooded valley. 150 year old reservoir. *Species:* Perch, Tench, Ghost Carp, Crucians, Common Carp, Mirror Carp, Roach, Rudd, Bream. *Permits:* In front of owners house on approach road to water in old red

phone box. *Charges:* £6.50 per day up to 2 rods. *Season:* No closed season. 6am to 8pm. *Methods:* Barbless hooks only. Keepnets are permitted, but not for Carp, landing nets and disgorgers to be used. Parking very close to lake and disabled friendly pegs. Please telephone for further information. Toilet facilities.

TRURO

Mellonwatts Mill Coarse Fishery

Pensagillas Farm, Grampound, Truro. *Sat Nav:* TR2 4SR. *Tel:* 01872 530808. *Mobile:* 07967 827340. *Water:* 2 acre lake. *Species:* Carp to 25lb, Common & Mirror, Roach, Tench, Golden Rudd. *Charges:* Day ticket £5, Evening £3. *Season:* Open all year.

Nanteague Farm Fishing

Contact: Viv George, Marazanvose, Zelah, Truro. *Sat Nav:* TR4 9DJ. *Tel:* 01872 540351. *Water:* 1.5 acre lake. *Species:* Carp to 25lb, Roach, Rudd, Bream and Perch. *Permits:* Limited season tickets by prior arrangement. Please telephone/e-mail. No day tickets.

Threemilestone Angling Club (Coarse Lakes) &

Contact: Mrs T. Bailey, 9 Sampson Way, Threemilestone, Truro. *Tel:* 01872 272578. *Mobile:* 07734 445133. *Water:* Langarth Pools (2 Pools). *Species:* Carp, Tench, Roach, Rudd, Bream, Perch, Goldfish. *Permits:* At lakeside. *Charges:* New members welcome. Family membership £60, Junior/ Disabled/OAP £30, Adult £40. Day tickets: Seniors £5, Juniors £3. *Season:* Open all year, no night fishing. *Methods:* Barbless hooks only, no peanuts etc.

Tory Farm Angling &

Contact: David Worlledge, Tory Farm, Ponsanooth, Truro. *Sat Nav:* TR3 7HN. *Tel:* 01209 861272. *Mobile:* 07971 859570. *Water:* 3.5 acre lake. *Species:* Mirror, Common, Wild and Ghost Carp to 20lb. Crucian to 2.5lb. Tench to 6lb. Rudd to 2.25lb. *Charges:* Please telephone for details. Annual membership £100. No day tickets unless by previous arrangement. £10 day ticket. *Season:* Open all year. *Methods:* Barbless hooks only, no keepnets, unhooking mats to be used. No nut baits. Hemp-specialist prepared only. Wheelchair friendly.

Stillwater Trout

BODMIN

Colliford Lake
Contact: South West Lakes Trust. *Sat Nav:* PL14 6PZ. *Tel:* 01579 346522. *Water:* Reservoir 911 acres. *Species:* Brown Trout. *Permits:* Jamaica Inn 01566 86250 and Colliford Tavern 01208 821335 or online from our website. Fishing is also available via the Westcountry Rivers Trust Passport Scheme, Tel: 01579 372140. *Charges:* Full day £14, Conc. £12, Child £5. Season tickets available from Summerlands Tackle (01237 471291). *Season:* 15 March - 12 October. *Methods:* Catch & release option (barbless hooks only). Fly fishing only from bank, wading not advisable.

Temple Trout Fishery &
Contact: Mr Julian Jones, Temple Trout Fishery, Temple Road, Temple, Bodmin. *Sat Nav:* PL30 4HW. *Tel:* 01208 821730. *Mobile:* 07787 704966. *Water:* 2.7 acre Mallard lake. Plus 4.5 acre Teal 'any method' lake. *Species:* Rainbows (18lb 9oz) & Brown Trout (16lb 6oz). *Permits:* At fishery. *Charges:* Club membership available - entitles members to 10% discount on tickets to fish. £150.00 for 25 Trout. Mallard Lake: Day £27.50, 5 fish. £24.50, 4 fish. Half day £20, 3 fish. Evening £14.50, 2 fish. Under 16 & disabled £15, 2 fish all day. Teal Lake: £82.50 for 25 fish. 5 fish £15, 4 fish £13.50, 3 fish £11, 2 fish eve £9. *Season:* Open all year round 8 am to dusk. In winter open Weds, Thurs, Sat and Sun or by appointment. *Methods:* Fly only on 2.7 acre lake. Any legal method on 4.5 acre lake. A sporting ticket is available on 4.5 acre lake.

BOSCASTLE

Orchard Lake
Contact: Justin, Trafalgar Farm, Lesnewth, Boscastle. *Sat Nav:* PL35 0BW. *Tel:* 01840 250070. *Mobile:* 07969 699572. *Water:* 0.75 acre stillwater stocked with Rainbow, Brown and Blue Trout. Average stocked size 2.5lb. *Species:* Largest to date: Rainbow 13lb 4oz, Brown 6lb 1oz, Blue 5lb 8oz. Largest bag to date 27lb 8oz. *Charges:* £35 full day 6 fish. £30 full day 4 fish. £20 half day ticket 4 hours 3 fish. Catch and release permitted after bag limit reached. *Season:* Open all year. 9am to 6pm. Evening ticket by prior arrangement. *Methods:* Fly fishing only.

CAMELFORD

Crowdy
Contact: South West Lakes Trust. *Sat Nav:* PL32 9XJ. *Tel:* 01579 346522. *Water:* Reservoir 115 acres. *Species:* Wild Brown Trout. *Permits:* Fishing is also available via the Westcountry Rivers Trust Passport Scheme, Tel: 01579 372140. *Charges:* Free to holders of a valid Environment Agency Licence. Bag limit of 4 fish over seven inches. *Season:* 15 March - 12 October. *Methods:* Angling by spinning, fly or bait.

HAYLE

Tree Meadow Trout Fishery
Contact: John Hodge, Tree Meadow, Deveral Road, Fraddam, Hayle. *Sat Nav:* TR27 5EP. *Tel:* 01736 850899. *Mobile:* 07971 107156. *Water:* Two lakes. 4 acres in total. Sedge lake to 14lb, Willow lake up to 25lb plus. *Species:* Rainbow and Brown Trout. Also Blue, Brook and Tiger Trout. *Permits:* At Lodge Shop. *Charges:* Contact for details. *Season:* Open all year 9am to dusk. *Methods:* Catch and release after fish limit. Max hook size 10.

HELSTON

Middle Boswin Farm (Trout)
Contact: Jonno, Middle Boswin Farm, Porkellis, Helston. *Sat Nav:* TR13 0HR. *Tel:* 01209 860420. *Mobile:* 07815 956095. *Water:* 1 acre lake. *Species:* Rainbow trout, brown trout and blue trout. *Permits:* On the bank. *Charges:* 2 fish - £17.50. Concession £15. Extra fish POA. *Season:* Open all year *Methods:* Fly Fishing only.

LAUNCESTON

Rose Park Fishery
Contact: Rose Park Fishery, Trezibbett, Altarnun, Launceston. *Sat Nav:* PL15 7RF. *Tel:* 01566 86278. *Water:* Two lakes. 2 acre and half acre. Small lake Browns and Rainbows. *Species:* Rainbow 13lb, Wild Browns 2.5lb. *Permits:* From the fishery. *Charges:* Rainbows £2.25 per lb, Browns £3 per lb. Fishing charge £6. *Season:* Open all year from 8am till dusk. *Methods:* Fly fishing. No catch and release.

LISKEARD

Siblyback &
Contact: South West Lakes Trust, Angling and Watersports Centre, Commonmoor, Liskeard. *Sat Nav:* PL14 6ER. *Tel:* 01579 346522. *Water:* Reservoir 140 acres. *Species:* Rainbow fishery. Boats available including Wheelyboats. To guarantee boats please book at least 24hrs in advance via the centre. Rod average 2012: 3.6 fish per rod per day. Fishery record 9lb 6oz. *Permits:* Angling and Watersports Centre or online from our website. Fishing is also available via

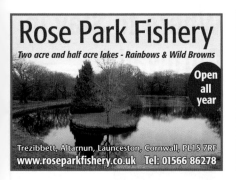

STILLWATER TROUT

the Westcountry Rivers Trust Passport Scheme, Tel: 01579 372140. *Charges:* Full day £20, Concession £17, Evening £16. Catch and Release Tickets £13. Child £5. Boats £15 per day. Season permits also available from Summerlands Tackle (01237 471291). *Season:* 15 March - 31 October. *Methods:* Catch and release available (barbless hooks must be used), fly fishing only.

PENZANCE

Drift Reservoir
Contact: David Williams (Water Bailiff), C/O The Estate Office, Chyandour, Penzance. *Sat Nav:* TR19 6AB. *Tel:* 01736 786613. *Mobile:* 07976 184109. *Water:* 65 acre reservoir. *Species:* Brown and Rainbow Trout. *Permits:* Self Service at reservoir. West Cornwall Angling, Penzance. Newtown Angling, Germoe and The Estate Office, Chyandour. Fishing is also available via the Westcountry Rivers Trust Passport Scheme, Tel: 01579 372140. *Charges:* Day ticket £10, 2 fish - catch and release £12, 3 fish - catch and release £15. Week ticket £40, Season - £150. Float tubing £3 plus day ticket price. Contact the Water Bailiff David Williams for more details. *Season:* 1 April to mid November. *Methods:* Fly fishing only. Catch and release.

REDRUTH

Cast Fly Fishing Club
Contact: Graeme Clement. *Tel:* 01326 212369. *Water:* Membership of 50, fishing Stithians and other waters. Monthly competitions. Juniors and ladies welcome. Tuition can be arranged. Club boat available at £2 per day. *Species:* Rainbows and Browns. Browns are wild fish, some Blues are occasionally stocked. *Charges:* Please phone above. *Season:* Please telephone for info pack. *Methods:* Fly fishing only.

Stithians &
Contact: South West Lakes Trust, Angling & Watersports Centre, Redruth. *Sat Nav:* TR16 6NW. *Tel:* 01209 860301. *Water:* Reservoir 274 acres. *Species:* Rainbow & Brown Trout Fishery to 6lb. Boats available including a Wheelyboat (must be booked in advance) via the centre. *Permits:* Angling & Watersports Centre or online from our website.

Fishing is also available via the Westcountry Rivers Trust Passport Scheme, Tel: 01579 372140. *Charges:* Full day £17, Concession £14.50, Evening £13, Child £5, Boats £15 per day. Season permits also available from Stithians Centre and Summerlands Tackle (01237 471291). *Season:* 15 March - 31 October. *Methods:* Fly fishing only. Catch and release available - barbless hooks must be used.

SALTASH

Bake Fishing Lakes (Trout) &
Trerulefoot, Saltash. *Sat Nav:* PL12 5BW. *Mobile:* 07798 585836. *Water:* 9 lakes totalling over 15 acres, Coarse and Trout. Troutmaster Water. *Species:* Rainbow 16lb 7oz, Brown Trout 10lb. *Permits:* On site. *Charges:* Catch and Release ticket £18 per day. Catch only £7.50 plus £6.50 per fish, £17 - 2 fish, £21 - 3 fish, £25 - 4 fish, £29 - 5 fish. *Season:* 8am to dusk. *Methods:* Catch and release. Barbless or debarbed hooks when releasing.

ST AUSTELL

Innis Fly Fishery &
Contact: Mrs Pam Winch, Innis Fly Fishery, Innis Moor, Penwithick, St. Austell. *Sat Nav:* PL26 8YH. *Tel:* 01726 852382. *Mobile:* 07773 282724. *Water:* 15 acres (3 lakes), stream fed enclosed water. *Species:* Rainbow Trout. *Charges:* 5 fish £27. 3 fish £22. 2 fish £15. Catch and release £20. 2 fish plus catch and release £20. Parent and Child 5 fish shared bag £27. *Season:* Dawn to Dusk - All year. *Methods:* Fly only and kill to bag limit. Catch and release restricted to Carbis and Sterrick lakes on barbless hooks only.

WHERE TO STAY

Where to Stay in Cornwall

Robyn with her first Rainbow from Middle Boswin

WHERE TO STAY

Anne Voss Bark
1928 - 2012

An Appreciation by Michael McCarthy for the International Fario Club

The old saying that there's more to fishing than catching fish was perhaps as well exemplified as ever by the case of Anne Voss Bark, the châtelaine of the Arundell Arms in Devon. Anne's obituaries have rightly stressed her many qualities: her indefatigable building of a wonderful hotel, her own passion for angling, her unceasing work in defence of West Country rivers, and the warmth that accompanied her perfect, pre-War manners - but somehow none seems to me to have quite captured what it was that made her exceptional.

For it wasn't her obvious offerings, elevated though they were, the comfort she provided, her marvellous food, her twenty miles of Tamar tributaries, even the friendship she so readily gave to those who came within her orbit, and I say that as someone who knew her well for thirty years and counted her as a friend for most of that time.

Rather, it was somehow the way in which she exemplified what it was all worth - I mean, what the experience she provided was worth.

At the heart of it of course was fishing, fishing these exquisite, granite spate rivers running off Dartmoor down through their hidden green combes. Every day you fished the Arundell Arms waters, the river was yours entirely, with everything that came with it: the explosion of wild flowers in April and May, the kingfishers, grey wagtails and dippers in the stream, the buzzards mewing in the sky, the otters that you knew were there, somewhere, and the shadowy, silvery shapes beneath the surface, the brown trout, the salmon, and the peal, to give the sea trout, the Arundell Arms' special fish, its West Country name.

Fishing these wonderful watercourses was exciting and pleasurable, yet there was something deeper: it was a particularly intense way of experiencing nature. To be there in the wild river, hunting, with everything hunting around you, the birds, the mammals, the fish, the insects, was to be truly at one with the natural world, it was to live, if only briefly, at a higher level, and Anne instinctively understood that. For what she offered above all, beyond hospitality, beyond friendship, was a presiding intelligence; and this was an intelligence which saw, and which made you realise, that to come to her world, and take what it had to offer, was not just enjoyable; it was civilising.

I spent many hours on the Lyd, and the Thrushel, and the Carey, and one might think that nothing could have added to their perfection, but if I look back I know that in my time, something did, and I give thanks for it; it was the presence of the presiding spirit of these waters, poised and benign, the goddess of the springs, as the Romans would have said, Anne Voss Bark.

The Salmon & Trout Association

Introduction

The Salmon & Trout Association (S&TA) was established in 1903 to address the damage done to our rivers by the polluting effects of the Industrial Revolution. For 110 years, the Association has worked to protect fisheries, fish stocks and the wider aquatic environment. In 2008, S&TA was granted charitable status, primarily because it was able to show that its work had historically been for a much wider benefit than just its immediate membership. S&TA's charitable objectives now empower it to use its professional influencing skills to address all issues affecting the management of salmonid and other fish species of UK origin, water, and the environment upon which all aquatic life depends.

S&TA's work is vitally important now, because there has never been more pressure on our freshwater and marine environments. For example, in a recent assessment of our rivers by the Environment Agency, less than 30% were of good ecological status. Many wild fish stocks have declined alarmingly since the 1980s and some invertebrate populations - the food for fish and bird life and an indicator of the health of aquatic habitats - have collapsed by as much as 70% in some areas.

S&TA aims to challenge this situation by using well balanced arguments, supported by peer-reviewed scientific evidence and environmental law, to influence all relevant issues affecting the aquatic environment and its dependent species, at both national and international level. S&TA's influencing role is supported by a science department and educational programme, and the beneficiaries of its work are not just anglers, but all those who have an interest in the wellbeing of our rivers, lakes and wetlands, and the wildlife they support.

There are numerous organisations that focus on conservation. However, S&TA stands alone as a national campaigning charity focusing on these issues from a fisheries viewpoint. It is vital that the Association makes its voice heard if we are to raise the status of fisheries within the wider environmental field, by using fish species and their habitat as the logical natural indicator to the health of the aquatic environment. Our work is vital for the future health of wild brown trout, sea trout and salmon stocks, but is also relevant to all other freshwater species in the UK.

Charitable Objectives

S&TA's objectives are straightforward:

- Management and conservation of salmon, trout and all other fish species of UK origin

- Management and conservation of ecosystems necessary for them to thrive

- Scientific research to underpin all our work

- Education

Working with others

S&TA promotes a conservation-based agenda in consultation and co-operation with other like-minded fisheries and environmental organisations, including the Atlantic Salmon Trust, Game and Wildlife Conservation Trust, Wild Trout Trust, Association of Rivers Trusts, Rivers & Fisheries Trusts of Scotland, WWF, the Wildlife Trusts, the Wildlife & Wetlands Trust and RSPB.

S&TA worked with other organisations to produce the 'Blueprint for Water', a ten point ask of Government to achieve a sustainable aquatic environment by 2015 for people and the environment. The Blueprint is now 'housed' within Wildlife & Countryside Link, a collection of nearly 40 environmental organisations representing some 8 million members.

S&TA's Head of Science, Janina Gray, is Vice Chair of Link's Water Group and so S&TA has considerable influence over determining water policy and delivery to national decision makers.

Many of the Blueprint issues have already been incorporated into Defra and EA water policy, but the document is regularly updated and S&TA continues to exert influence to ensure all recommendations are adopted.

S&TA has taken this partnership approach a stage further by announcing a close working collaboration with the Game & Wildlife Conservation Trust (GWCT), a charity with a strong fisheries scientific department based at a unique laboratory infrastructure on the River Frome in Dorset. GWCT also has an experimental 2,000 acre farm at Loddington in Leicestershire, which is undertaking tremendous work in seeking to find solutions to the impact of agricultural practices on river and lake systems, which could be crucially important to delivery of measures designed to achieve good ecological status in our waterways under the EU Water Framework Directive (WFD).

Looking to the future

Our strategic objective is to combat what we see as:

- a lack of awareness of the threats facing our aquatic environments and their dependant species;

- where awareness exists, there is a lack of political commitment to protecting the aquatic environment. Instead, there seems a remorseless quest for 'sustainable development', which usually translates into sustaining development, rather than making development sustainable.

Our aim is to increase knowledge and understanding of the threats facing aquatic ecosystems. Our particular focus in the foreseeable future includes:

- pressing for management policies which prevent deterioration in our rivers and stillwaters, the resource upon which freshwater aquatic life depends.

- focussing on the whole of the chalkstream environment in England, which constitutes more than 80% of the total global resource. Unless we can protect this unique habitat we cannot hope to protect other less high profile river systems.

- pressing for water to be managed more effectively by reducing excessive abstraction, and land management practices which reduce diffuse pollution and sedimentation, thereby cutting down the amount of nutrients and chemicals which are deposited in rivers and lakes.

- achieving revised Good Practice Guidelines for Hydropower scheme applications which have environmental protection at their heart, rather than unconditional promotion of an industry which will only ever contribute marginally to renewable energy but has the potential to severely impact river ecosystems, and especially impede migration of fish and the natural dynamics of rivers.

- combating non-sustainable Fish farming practices. The Association has appointed an environmental lawyer, Guy Linley-Adams, to lead our Aquaculture Campaign to convince the Scottish Government and fish farming industry to adopt measures which will ensure that salmon farming is genuinely sustainable. The ultimate goal is to bring all units within close containment systems, thereby cutting out any interaction between farmed and wild fish, so halting the impact on wild salmon and sea trout from sea lice infestations and escapee hatchery fish interbreeding with native salmon, thereby destroying gene pools which have evolved since the Ice Age.

- expanding our burgeoning scientific network to undertake research to underpin our work, and continue using a robust legal approach to relevant issues, focusing especially on European environmental legislation.

- continuing to host the Riverfly Partnership (RP), a collection of angling, fisheries and conservation organisations and individuals dedicated to the protection and restoration of aquatic flies, which form an integral part of the food chain in water. The RP's River Monitoring Initiative runs courses to teach anglers and other interested parties how to identify eight families of invertebrates, and then supports them in forming groups which regularly monitor their local rivers and, therefore, keep a watching brief on water quality. River flies are sensitive to pollution and so a sudden drop in numbers invariably signals a water quality problem, which can then be quickly addressed by the EA, a major partner and funder of the RP.

- continuing to support scientific projects in universities and other organisations, funding projects whose outcomes will help inform policies and management advice that support fish populations and the ecosystems on which they depend.

- expanding our learning programme, aimed at all ages and focussing on explaining the problems within our water environment and the solutions. Of special importance is encouraging volunteers to become involved on behalf of S&TA with local issues, interacting with statutory agencies where necessary and working alongside partner organisations, such as Rivers and Wildlife Trusts.

- S&TA also runs an extensive education programme which concentrates both on teaching people, particularly the young, how to fish, but also the importance of healthy rivers to communities. A recent pilot scheme in three Cumbrian primary schools was so successful that the Association is currently looking to fund a major roll-out of a similar scheme across the UK.

So, S&TA has a varied brief within its charitable objectives, all aimed at protecting fish stocks and the aquatic environment, supporting policies with environmental law and high quality science, and educating the next generation as to the vital importance of this work. No other sector of society invests so much time and funding in managing and conserving our rivers and stillwaters than do anglers and fishery managers, and the Association therefore believes its activities have public interest at heart, far beyond the interests merely of its members, regardless of the fact that they will benefit from its successes. That is truly enlightened self interest at work!

Why not Join S&TA?

Find out more at www.salmon-trout.org

South West branches

Devon Branch
Chairman and Treasurer: Mr S Phelps
Email: s.phelps127@btinternet.com
Website: www.sta-devon.org.uk
Secretary: Mr D Williams
Email: dvwilliams@btinternet.com

Bristol & West Branch
Chairman: Mr A Pope
Contact: Mr R Buckland
Email: roy@buckland-1.wanadoo.co.uk
Website: www.bristolsta.co.uk

Hampshire Branch
Chairman: Mr A Richards
Website: www.salmon-trout-hampshire.org

Wessex Branch
Chairman: Martin Small
Contact: Martin Small
Email: martinsmall948@btinternet.com

Membership from just £3.34 per month!
For further S&TA information
Tel: 0207 283 5838
Email: hq@salmon-trout.org

DEVON

@gethookedguide

RIVER FISHING

STILLWATER COARSE

STILLWATER TROUT

WHERE TO STAY

ADVERTISER LOCATION MAP

Map No	Advertiser	Sat Nav	Phone	Advert Page
	Game Fishing			
33	Arundell Arms Hotel	PL16 0AA	01566 784666	49 & 160
34	Avon Dam	TQ10 9ED	01822 855700	Back Cover
35	Bellbrook Valley Trout Fishery	EX16 9EX	01398 351292	80
36	Blakewell Fishery	EX31 4ET	01271 344533	77
37	Buckfastleigh River Fishing	TQ11 0	01566 771930	Back Cover
38	Burrator	PL20 6PE	01822 855700	Back Cover
39	Fernworthy	TQ13 8EA	01647 277587	Back Cover
40	Fox & Hounds Hotel	EX18 7JZ	01769 580345	81
41	Kennick	EX6 7NZ	01647 252898	Back Cover
42	Meldon	EX20 4LU	01409 211507	Back Cover
43	Newhouse Fishery	TQ9 7JS	01548 821426	80
44	Old Mill House	EX37 9DB	01598 763514	50
45	Prince Hall Hotel	PL20 6SA	01822 890403	44
46	Rising Sun Inn	EX37 9DU	01769 560447	51
47	Roadford	PL16 0JL	01409 211507	Back Cover
48	Venford	TQ13 7SS	01822 855700	Back Cover
49	Westcountry Angling Passport (Game & Coarse)		01579 372140	19
50	Wistlandpound	EX31 4SJ	01398 371116	Back Cover
	Coarse Fishing			
51	Anglers Paradise (Game & Coarse)	EX21 5XT	01409 221559	56
52	Bickerton Farm Fishery	TQ7 2EU	01548 511220	67
53	Bideford & District Angling Club	EX39 4QE	012374 77996	57
54	Bulworthy Forest Lodges		0844 8471356	81
55	Cofton Country Holidays	EX6 8RP	0800 085 8649 or 01626 89011	82
56	Coombe Fisheries	PL20 6HR	01822 616624 or 07899 958493	76
57	Coombe Water Fisheries	TQ7 4AD	01540 052030 or 07971 077980	67
58	Coombelands Coarse Fishery	EX15 1PT	01884 32320	61
59	Courtmoor Farm	EX14 9QA	01404 861565	66
60	Creedy Lakes	EX17 4AB	01363 772684	59
61	Culm Valley Fishery	EX15 3QZ	01823 330705 or 07766 600037	60
62	Darracott	EX38 7HL	01288 361712	Back Cover
63	Digger Lakes	EX15 2PE	07733 223417	60
64	Exeter & District Angling Association		07970 483913	62
65	Golland Farm	EX37 9JP	07516 601585	76
66	Hazelwood Holiday Park	EX7 0PF	01626 865005	81
67	Highampton Coarse Lakes	EX21 5LU	01409 231216	65
68	Jennetts	EX39 5JH	01288 321712	Back Cover
69	Kingslake Fishing Holidays	EX21 5JS	01409 231401	81
70	Lakeside Fishery	EX20 4NL	07900 198113	69
71	Little Comfort Farm	EX33 2NJ	01271 812414	58
72	Lower Hollacombe Fishery	EX17 5BW	01363 84331	59
73	Lower Slade	EX34 8NA	01288 321712	Back Cover
74	Luccombes Coarse Fishery	EX6 8AY	01823 284990 or 07510 545283	63
75	M & B Eastmoore Farm Fishery	TQ9 7PE	07739 082888	75
76	Melbury	EX39 5PW	01288 321712	Back Cover
77	Milemead Fisheries	PL19 8NP	01822 610888	73
78	Minnows Touring Caravan Park	EX16 7EN	01884 821770	74
79	Moorhead Farm & Country Holidays	EX39 5RG	01237 431461	56

Map No	Advertiser	Sat Nav	Phone	Advert Page
80	Oaktree Carp Farm & Fishery	EX36 3PU	01398 341568	72
81	Otter Falls	EX14 9QD	01404 861634	82
82	Park Mill Farm (Game & Coarse)	EX18 7EA	01769 580068	81
83	Pound Farm	EX15 1PH	01884 855208	82
84	Riverside Caravan & Camping Park	EX36 3HQ	01769 579269	73
85	Riverton Lakes & Holiday Cottages	EX32 0QX	01271 830009	54
86	Salmonhutch Fishery	EX17 3QL	01363 772749	60
87	South Farm Holiday Cottages & Fishery	EX15 2JE	01823 681078	82
88	South View Farm Fishery	EX2 9UP	01392 832278	64
89	Springfield Meadows	EX21 5UF	01409 221657	56
90	Squabmoor	EX9 7AS	01647 252898	Back Cover
91	Stafford Moor Country Park	EX19 8PP	01805 804360	76
92	Stenhill Fishery	EX15 2RH	01884 33707	61
93	Sunridge Fishery	PL8 2LN	01752 216645	71
94	Town Parks Coarse Fishing Centre	TQ4 7PY	01803 523133	70
95	Trenchford	TQ13 9PD	01647 252898	Back Cover
96	Upham Farm Carp Ponds	EX5 2JA	01395 232247	65
97	Week Farm	EX20 4HZ	01837 861221	69
98	Westcott Barton	EX31 4EF	01271 812842	54
99	Whitechapel Cottages (Coarse & Game)	EX36 3EG	01769 572529	74 & 82
100	Yeomadon Lakes	EX22 6SH	01409 253378	66

ADVERTISER LOCATION MAP

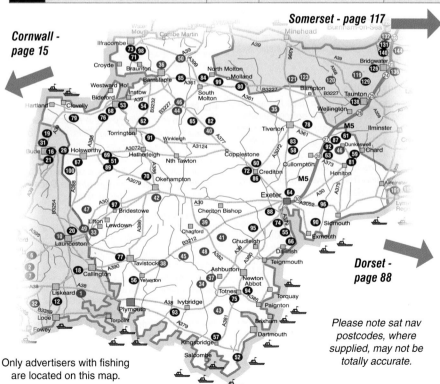

Somerset - page 117

Cornwall - page 15

Dorset - page 88

Please note sat nav postcodes, where supplied, may not be totally accurate.

Only advertisers with fishing are located on this map.

Devon
River Fishing

AVON

South Devon stream not to be confused with Hampshire Avon or Bristol Avon. Rises on Dartmoor and enters the sea at Bigbury. Expect to catch Brown Trout, Sea Trout and Salmon.

Avon Fishing Association
Contact: Mr Brian Dent, Aunebank, Avonwick, South Brent. *Water:* River Avon. *Species:* Salmon 11lb, Sea Trout 7lb 12oz and Brown Trout to 13 inches. *Permits:* Weekly, fortnightly and monthly tickets from Loddiswell Post Offices. *Charges:* £60 weekly, £76 fortnightly, £95 monthly. Day tickets through Westcountry Passport Scheme Tel: 01579 372140. *Season:* Brown Trout 15 March to 30 September. Salmon and Sea Trout 15 April to 30 September. *Methods:* Fly only.

Newhouse Fishery (River Avon)
Contact: Mrs Pam Cook, Newhouse Farm, Moreleigh, Totnes. *Sat Nav:* TQ9 7JS. *Tel:* 01548 821426. *Water:* 0.25 mile on the River Avon (also see entry under Stillwater Trout, Totnes, Devon). *Species:* Brown Trout, Sea Trout and Salmon. *Permits:* Newhouse Fishery. *Charges:* Various tickets available. *Season:* As current E.A. Byelaws. *Methods:* As current E.A. Byelaws.

AXE AND TRIBUTARIES

This quiet meandering stream rises in the hills of west Dorset, runs along the boundary with Somerset before flowing past Axminster to the sea at Seaton. The Axe is a fertile river with good Trout fishing and a run of Salmon and Sea Trout. The two main tributaries, the Coly and Yarty, are also Trout streams and the Yarty has a good run of Sea Trout.

Axmouth Fishing
Contact: Chris Chappell, Seaton Tackle Shop, The Harbour, Axmouth. *Tel:* 01297 625511. *Mobile:* 07930 398313. *Water:* Axmouth from lower end pool below Coly-Axe confluence to Axmouth Bridge. *Species:* Mullet, Bass, Sea Trout. *Permits:* Seaton Tackle Shop. *Charges:* Day ticket £5 adult, £2.50 child. Week £25 adult, £12.50 child. *Methods:* Fishing from east bank of estuary only.

Stillwaters (River Axe)
Contact: Michael Ford, Lower Moorhayne Farm, Yarcombe, Honiton. *Tel:* 01404 861284. *Water:* One Sea Trout rod on River Axe. Approx. one mile including sea pool. Also 1 acre lake, see entry under Stillwater Trout, Honiton. *Charges:* £35 per Day. *Methods:* Fly only.

Taunton Fly Fishing Club (Axe)
Contact: John Connolly, 35 Manor Road, Taunton, Somerset. *Tel:* 01823 274272. *Water:* Seven beats on the River Axe. *Species:* Brown Trout, Sea Trout, some Salmon. *Permits:* No day tickets - members only. *Charges:* Full member £90 (plus £90 joining fee). Junior £15. Joint members £120 (plus £120 joining fee). Prices may change for 2014. *Season:* Brown Trout 15 March to 30 Sept. Sea Trout 15 April to 31 October. *Methods:* Fly only.

Weycroft Bridge Fishery
Contact: Allan Howlings, Stretford Cottage, Chard Road, Weycroft, Axminster. *Sat Nav:* EX13 7LN. *Tel:* 01297 32095. *Mobile:* 07960 229726. *Water:* 0.25 mile on River Axe between Weycroft bridge and the railway bridge down stream. *Species:* Brown Trout, Sea Trout and occasional Salmon. *Permits:* Day permits are to be booked in advance and not available on bank side. *Charges:* £15. *Season:* April 15th - October 31st. *Methods:* Fly fishing and spinning only. Barbless hooks must be used. Catch and release only. Parking and toilets on site.

BRAY

One of the larger tributaries of the river Taw rising on Exmoor, the Bray offers good wild Trout fishing along with Salmon and Sea Trout fishing.

Little Bray House
Contact: Mr and Mrs C. Hartnoll, Little Bray House, Brayford, Barnstaple. *Sat Nav:* EX32 7QG. *Tel:* 01598 710295. *Water:* One mile on the River Bray. *Species:* Small Brown Trout. *Charges:* £3 per day. *Methods:* Fly only.

CULM

The Culm is a tributary of the river Exe and issues from the Blackdown Hills. In its upper reaches it is a typical dry fly Trout stream, with good hatches of fly and free-rising fish. From Cullompton until it joins the Exe, the Culm becomes a coarse fishery, with the Dace in particular of good average size.

Crediton Fly Fishing Club (Culm)
Contact: Mike Willis, 20 Powderham Road, Newton Abbot. *Tel:* 01626 364577. *Mobile:* 07973 525227. *Water:* 3 miles of river fishing on the Culm for Season permit holders only. See also Rivers Taw, Yeo and Creedy. *Species:* Brown Trout. *Permits:* Fly Fishing Tackle, 2 Parliament St., Crediton EX17 1AB. Tel: 01363 777783. Also from Mike Willis as above but please allow minimum 1 week notice. *Charges:* Day £15, Mid Week (5 days) £30, Season £90, Youth (under 18) £10. Over 65 £70. Two day weekend (Sat-Sun) £30. Joining fee £35 (First full season only). *Season:* EA Season. *Methods:* Fly only. Barbless and catch and release encouraged. Chest waders recommended.

Wild Brown Trout, 'river tiger'
Pic - The Editor

Westcountry Angling Passport (Culm)
Contact: Westcountry Rivers Trust, Rain-Charm House, Kyl Cober Parc, Stoke Climsland, Callington, Cornwall. *Tel:* 01579 372140. *Water:* 1900m double bank at Champerhaies. 1600m mixed single and double bank at the Upper Culm Fly Fishing Club. *Species:* Brown Trout, Chub, Dace, Roach and Pike at Champerhaies. Brown Trout at Upper Culm Fly Fishing Club. *Permits:* From: Snowbee UK, Plymouth, PL7 5JY - 01752 334933. Tamar Field and Stream, Lifton, PL16 0AA - 01566 780512. Devil's Stone Inn, Beaworthy, EX21 5RU - 01409 281210. Homeleigh Garden Centre, Launceston, PL15 9SP - 01566 771878. Blisland Inn, Bodmin, PL30 4JK - 01208 850739. Fly Fishing Tackle co uk, Crediton, EX17 2AW - 01363 777783. Hart Flyshop, Exebridge, TA22 9AY - 01398 323008. Lance Nicholson, Dulverton, TA22 9HB - 01398 323409. Tolley's of Tavistock, Tavistock, PL19 0HE - 01822 617186. *Charges:* £5 to £10 per rod per day. *Season:* Champerhaies - Trout - 1 April to 30 September. Coarse - 16 June to 31 December. U.C.F.F.C - 15 March to 30 September. *Methods:* Individual beat methods available from above. Champerhaies - all methods, U.C.F.F.C - Catch and release.

DART AND TRIBUTARIES

Deep in the heart of lonely Dartmoor rise the East and West Dart. Between their separate sources and Dartmeet, where they join, these two streams and their tributaries are mainly owned by the Duchy of Cornwall and provide many miles of Salmon, Sea Trout and Trout fishing for visitors. The scenery is on the grand scale and the sense of freedom enjoyed when you can fish away over miles and miles of river is seldom realised on this crowded island. This is a moorland fishery - swift flowing, boulder strewn, usually crystal clear.

Below Dartmeet the river rushes through a spectacular wooded valley before breaking out of the moor near Buckfastleigh and flowing on to its estuary at Totnes. Although there are Brown Trout throughout the river, these middle and lower reaches are primarily Salmon and Sea Trout waters.

Buckfastleigh
Contact: South West Lakes Trust, Lidn Park, Quarry Crescent, Pennygillam, Launceston, Cornwall. *Tel:* 01566 771930. *Water:* 0.25 miles on River Dart. Austins Bridge to Nursery Pool. *Species:* Salmon & Sea Trout. *Permits:* Summerlands Tackle (01237 471291). Fishing is also available via the Westcountry Rivers Trust Passport Scheme Tel: 01579 372140. *Charges:* Season - £90. *Season:* Salmon 1 Feb - 30 September. Trout 15 March - 30 September.

Dart Angling Association
Contact: Philip Prowse, 2 School Cottages, Stoke-in-Teignhead, Newton Abbot. *Tel:* 01626 872434. *Water:* 9 miles on River Dart. (3.9 miles of main river open to visitors plus the tidal Totnes weir pool). *Species:* Salmon, Sea Trout, Brown Trout. *Permits:* All permits - Sea Trout Inn, Staverton Tel: 01803 762274. *Charges:* Membership details from secretary. Totnes weir pool £25 per day (only 1 day Salmon, 1 night Sea Trout ticket available). Buckfast (Austin's Bridge) - Littlehempston (left bank) only 2 per day (unless resident at the Sea Trout Inn). *Season:* Salmon 1 February - 30 September. Sea/Brown Trout 15 March - 30 September. *Methods:* Fly (some stretches fly only), spinning, prawn (below Staverton) see club regulations i.e. conservation measures in force.

Hannaford Fishery
Contact: Simon Cooper, Fishing Breaks, The Mill, Heathman Street, Nether Wallop, Stockbridge, Hampshire. *Tel:* 01264 781988. *Species:* Brown Trout. *Permits:* By phone or e-mail from Fishing Breaks. *Charges:* March 14th - Sept 30th: £47/one, £70/two. May 23rd - July 31st: £47/one, £70/two. *Season:* March - September. *Methods:* Wet Fly.

Hatchlands Trout Farm &
Contact: Malcolm Davies, Greyshoot Lane, Rattery, South Brent. *Sat Nav:* TQ10 9LN. *Tel:* 01364 73500. *Mobile:* 07967 010136. *Water:* 600 yards, both banks of the River Harbourne (tributary of the Dart). *Species:* Brown Trout. *Permits:* EA Licence required. *Charges:* On application. *Season:* See current E.A. Byelaws. *Methods:* Barbless hooks only.

Prince Hall Hotel
Contact: Fi & Chris Daly, Nr. Two Bridges, Dartmoor. *Sat Nav:* PL20 6SA. *Tel:* 01822 890403. *Water:* Access to all Duchy water. *Species:* Wild Brown Trout 1.5lb, Sea Trout 6lb, Salmon 11lb. *Charges:* Brown Trout day £10, week £30. Salmon/Sea Trout day ticket £30, week £85. Salmon season £150. *Season:* March - September for Salmon and Sea Trout. March - October for Brown Trout. *Methods:* Fly only.

The Forest Inn
Contact: David Ellis, Hexworthy, Dartmoor. *Sat Nav:* PL20 6SD. *Tel:* 01364 631211. *Water:* East and West Dart. *Species:* Sea Trout, Brown Trout, Salmon. *Permits:* Day, Week, Season. *Charges:* On application. *Season:* 30 March - 30 September. *Methods:* Fly only.

Two Bridges Hotel
Contact: Two Bridges Hotel, Two Bridges, Dartmoor. *Sat Nav:* PL20 6SW. *Tel:* 01822 890581. *Water:* 600 yards double bank fishing. *Species:* Trout & Salmon. *Permits:* At hotel reception. *Charges:* On application. *Season:* E.A. Byelaws apply.

Westcountry Angling Passport (Dartmoor Fishery)
Contact: Westcountry Rivers Trust, Rain-Charm House, Kyl Cober Parc, Stoke Climsland, Callington, Cornwall. *Tel:* 01579 372140. *Water:* Over 25km of river fishing on the East & West Dart Rivers and tributaries. *Species:* Sea Trout and Salmon. *Permits:* Buckfast Post Office. Two Bridges Hotel, Princetown. Postbridge Post Office. Princetown Stores and Post Office. Prince Hall Hotel, Two Bridges, Princetown. The Arundell Arms, Lifton. James Bowden & Sons, The Square, Chagford. Badger's Holt Ltd., Dartmeet. Exeter Angling Centre, Smythen St, Exeter. The Forest Inn, Hexworthy. Ilsington Country House Hotel, Ilsington Village, Nr Newton Abbot. The White Hart Hotel, Moretonhampstead. *Charges:* Salmon & Sea Trout Season: £150, Week: £85, Day £30. Brown Trout Season: £70, Week £30, Day £10. *Season:* Salmon: 1 Feb to 30 Sept. Trout: 15 March to 30 Sept. *Methods:* Fly only.

EXE AND TRIBUTARIES
The Exe rises high on Exmoor and flows through open moorland until it plunges into a steep wooded valley near Winsford. By the time Tiverton is reached the valley has widened and from here to the sea the Exe meanders through a broad pastoral vale until it flows into the estuary near Exeter and finally into the sea between Exmouth and Dawlish Warren. It is the longest river in the south west.

Throughout most of its length the Exe is a good Trout stream, the fast flowing, rocky upper reaches abounding in fish of modest average size, which increases as the river becomes larger and slower in its middle and lower reaches, where fish approaching a pound feature regularly in the daily catch. The Exe has a good run of Salmon and can produce big catches when the grilse arrive in summer. In the deep slow waters around Exeter there is a variety of coarse fish, as there is in the Exeter Ship Canal which parallels the river from Exeter to the estuary at Topsham. The Exe only has a small run of Sea Trout, but Grayling are plentiful in the middle and lower reaches. The two main tributaries - the Barle and the Culm - could not be more different in character. The Barle is a swift upland stream which rises high on Exmoor not far from the source of the Exe, and runs a parallel course, first through open moor and then through a picturesque wooded valley, before joining the parent river near Dulverton. It has good Trout fishing throughout and Salmon fishing on the lower reaches.

The Culm issues from the Blackdown Hills and in its upper reaches is a typical dry fly Trout stream, with good hatches of fly and free-rising fish. From Cullompton until it joins the Exe, the Culm becomes a coarse fishery, with the Dace in particular of good average size.

RIVER FISHING

Bridge House Hotel
Contact: Brian Smith, Bridge House Hotel, Bampton. *Sat Nav:* EX16 9NF. *Tel:* 01398 331298. *Water:* 1 Mile on River Exe. 0.75 mile on Little Exe. 0.5 mile on Batherm. *Species:* Salmon, Trout and Grayling; (12.5lb Salmon, 3.75lb Brown Trout, 1.5lb Grayling)(Caught 15 Salmon in 2012). *Permits:* As above. *Charges:* Salmon from £35 per day, Trout £25 per day. *Season:* March 15th - Sept 30th. *Methods:* Fly, occasional spinner. Barbless until 16th June (Salmon). No Keepnets. Brown Trout catch and release under 1lb or 10 inches Barbless.

Exe Bolham Fishing Club
Contact: Glyn Howells, The Old Chapel, Chillaton. *Tel:* 01822 860279. *Water:* 1km on the Exe. *Species:* Salmon 16lb, Sea Trout 4lb, Grayling 2lb, Brown Trout 2lb. *Charges:* Club Membership £750 to £850 per rod per season. This entitles the holder to take a guest on their day. *Season:* As EA byelaws. *Methods:* Fly and spinner, barbless hooks preferred.

Exe Carnarvon Fishing Club
Contact: Glyn Howells, The Old Chapel, Chillaton. *Tel:* 01822 860279. *Water:* 1km on the Exe. *Species:* Salmon 16lb, Sea Trout 4lb, Grayling 2lb, Brown Trout 2lb. *Charges:* Club Membership £750 to £850 per rod per season. This entitles the holder to take a guest on their day. *Season:* As EA byelaws. *Methods:* Fly and spinner, barbless hooks preferred.

Exe Duck's Marsh (River Exe)
Contact: Exeter City Council, River & Canal Manager, Civic Centre, Exeter. *Tel:* 01392 274306. *Water:* River Exe, left bank 1 mile downstream Salmonpool weir. *Species:* Salmon and Trout. *Permits:* For Salmon day tickets contact River & Canal Office, Canal Basin, Haven Rd, Exeter. *Charges:* Day tickets only at £9.60. *Season:* EA byelaws apply. *Methods:* EA byelaws apply.

Exeter and District Angling Association (River Creedy)
Contact: Roly Palmer, PO Box 194, Exeter. *Mobile:* 07970 483913. *Water:* Cowley Bridge; just a short walk from the Exe. *Species:* Roach, Dace, Gudgeon, Carp, Pike. *Permits:* Exeter Angling Centre, Smythen Street (Off Market Street, Exeter). Exmouth Tackle & Sport, The Strand, Exmouth. Tackle Trader, Wharf Road, Newton Abbot. Exe Valley Angling, West Exe South, Tiverton. Tiverton Parkway Station (Cafe), Sampford Peverell. *Charges:* £40 Adults, £5 for Juniors (annual). £5 day. *Season:* Close season March 14th - June 16th. Details in association handbook or from agents. *Methods:* Stick/waggler with maggot, light groundbaiting. Details in association handbook.

Exeter and District Angling Association (River Culm)
Contact: Roly Palmer, PO Box 194, Exeter. *Mobile:* 07970 483913. *Water:* Paddleford Pool, Killerton and Beare Gate; Smaller faster flowing river. *Species:* Superb catches of Chub, Roach and Dace possible throughout. An excellent, yet relatively easy Pike water. Barbel now showing throughout.

RIVER FISHING

Permits: Exeter Angling Centre, Smythen Street (Off Market Street, Exeter). Exmouth Tackle & Sport, The Strand, Exmouth. Tackle Trader, Wharf Road, Newton Abbot. Exe Valley Angling, West Exe South, Tiverton. Tiverton Parkway Station (Cafe), Sampford Peverell. *Charges:* £40 Adults, £5 for Juniors (annual). £5 day. *Season:* Close Season March 14th - June 16th. Details in association handbook or from agents. *Methods:* Different restrictions on each water. Details in association handbook.

Exeter and District Angling Association (River Exe)
Contact: Roly Palmer, PO Box 194, Exeter. *Mobile:* 07970 483913. *Water:* Tidal stretch of Exe at Countess Wear; big catches of Mullet, Dace and Bream upstream. Non tidal stretch at Weirfield; big bags of Bream and Carp from 15 to 20lb. Shillhay runs nearly through the City centre; can produce big bags of Bream and Roach. Exwick is a faster flowing section adjacent to St David's railway section; good nets of quality Roach and Dace, fishes well in the autumn. Cowley Bridge is a relatively under fished stretch; good nets of Roach and Dace along the whole length. Oakhay Barton; fewer fish but good size and high quality fish. *Species:* Roach, Dace, Bream, Chub, Perch, Carp, Mullet. *Permits:* Exeter Angling Centre, Smythen Street (Off Market Street, Exeter). Exmouth Tackle & Sport, The Strand, Exmouth. Tackle Trader, Wharf Road, Newton Abbot. Exe Valley Angling, West Exe South, Tiverton. Tiverton Parkway Station (Cafe), Sampford Peverell. *Charges:* £40 Adults, £5 for Juniors (annual). £5 day. *Season:* Close Season March 14th - June 16th. Details in association handbook or from agents. *Methods:* Feeder or waggler/stick float, over heavy groundbaiting. Details in association handbook.

Kersdown Barton
Contact. John Dawson, 29 Bourchier Close, Bampton, Tiverton. *Tel:* 01398 331498. *Mobile:* 07816 453474. *Water:* 0.75 miles small stream fishing double bank on River Batherm. *Species:* Wild Brown Trout to 1.5lb. Grayling to 1lb. *Permits:* From John Dawson as above. *Charges:* £7.50 per rod per day. *Season:* 1st April to 31st September - Trout. Winter Grayling - October to beginning March. *Methods:* Fly fishing only. Barbless hooks. All fish to be returned. Max 2 rods per day.

River Exe (Exeter)
Contact: Exeter City Council, River & Canal Manager, Civic Centre, Exeter. *Tel:* 01392 274306. *Water:* River Exe, 13 beats between Head Weir & Countess Wear. *Species:* Salmon and Trout. *Permits:* From above. *Charges:* £84, limited annual permits. Day permit £9.60. *Season:* EA byelaws apply. *Methods:* EA byelaws apply.

Robert Jones Fly Fishing (Exe)
Contact: Valley Barn, Hawkerland, Colaton Raleigh, Sidmouth. *Tel:* 07020 902090. *Mobile:* 07970 797770. *Water:* River Exe. Private and Hotel water. Also fly fishing for Bass in saltwater. *Species:* Brown Trout and Salmon. *Permits:* Day permits. *Charges:* On application. *Season:* 15 March - 30 September. *Methods:* Fly and spinner.

Tiverton and District Angling Club (River Culm)
Contact: Exe Valley Angling, 19 Westexe South, Tiverton. *Tel:* 01884 242275. *Water:* 0.75 miles River Culm at Stoke Cannon. Various stretches on several rivers in Somerset. See also entry under Stillwater Coarse, Tiverton. *Species:* Roach, Dace, Chub, Perch, Pike and Eels. Salmon and Trout in season. *Permits:* Please ring Exe Valley for details. Also available from: Exeter Angling Centre, Enterprise Angling Taunton, Topp Tackle Taunton & Minnows Caravan Park - beside Grand Western Canal. *Charges:* Senior: Day £5, Annual £30. Conc: Junior £3 & OAP Day £5, Annual £15. Junior Annual £10. *Season:* Coarse: closed 15 March to 16 June. Trout: open from 15 March to 30 September. Salmon: open 14 February to 30 September. *Methods:* Canal Methods: Any. Restrictions: Fish from permanent pegs, no night fishing, no cars on bank, no digging of banks or excessive clearance of vegetation. Lakeside Methods: Any. Restrictions: No night fishing, no boilies, Trout pellets or nuts, one rod only, fishing from permanent pegs, no dogs, nets to be dipped. Ring Exe Valley Angling for full details.

Tiverton Fly Fishing Association
Contact: Exe Valley Angling, 19 Westexe South, Tiverton. *Tel:* 01884 242275. *Water:* 3.5 Miles on River Exe. *Species:* Trout & Grayling. *Permits:* Exe Valley Angling: 01884 242275. Fishing available to members and guests. Members must be in EX16 postcode area. *Charges:* Senior £20. Guests £15, OAP £5. *Season:* 15 March - 30 September. *Methods:* Fly only.

Westcountry Angling Passport (Batherm & Little Exe)
Contact: Westcountry Rivers Trust, Rain-Charm House, Kyl Cober Park, Stoke, Climsland, Callington, Cornwall. *Tel:* 01579 372140. *Water:* 700m double bank on the River Batherm at Westons. 900m of left hand single bank on the Little Exe at Week Bridge. *Species:* Brown Trout and Grayling. *Permits:* From: Snowbee UK, Plymouth, PL7 5JY - 01752 334933. Tamar Field and Stream, Lifton, PL16 0AA - 01566 780512. Devil's Stone Inn, Beaworthy, EX21 5RU - 01409 281210. Homeleigh Garden Centre, Launceston, PL15 9SP - 01566 771878. Blisland Inn, Bodmin, PL30 4JK - 01208 850739. Fly Fishing Tackle co uk, Crediton, EX17 2AW - 01363 777783. Hart Flyshop, Exebridge, TA22 9AY - 01398 323008. Lance Nicholson, Dulverton, TA22 9HB - 01398 323409. Tolley's of Tavistock, Tavistock, PL19 0HE - 01822 617186. *Charges:* £5 to £7.50 per rod per day. *Season:* Brown Trout: 15 March - 30 September. Grayling: 16 June - 14 March. *Methods:* Fly only.

An image of Autumn - Grayling from the Little Exe
Pic - Lance Nicholson

LYN

Chalk Water, Weir Water, Oare Water, Badgeworthy Water - these are the streams that tumble down from the romantic Doone Country of Exmoor and join to form the East Lyn, which cascades through the spectacular wooded ravine of the National Trust's Watersmeet Estate. The main river has good runs of Salmon and Sea Trout, and wild Brown Trout teem on the Lyn and the tributary streams.

Environment Agency - Watersmeet and Glenthorne

Tel: 08708 506506. *Water:* Salmon and Sea Trout - The Watersmeet and Glenthorne fishery remains closed until the end of the 2013 season to safeguard salmon and sea trout stocks. If you see any fish with signs of disease please report this on the Hotline phone number Tel: 0800 80 70 60. Brown Trout fishery remains open as usual as whilst the Environment Agency continue to monitor the situation. For up to date information please check www.gethooked.co.uk or the EA website.

The fishery is in two parts: The Watersmeet Fishery, leased by the Agency from the National Trust - Tors Road, Lynmouth to Woodside Bridge, right bank only; Woodside Bridge to Watersmeet both banks; upstream of Watersmeet right bank only to Rockford. The Glenthorne Fishery - right bank only upstream of Rockford to 300 yards downstream of Brendon Road Bridge. Half a mile of Trout fishing is available on the Hoaroak Water between Hillsford Bridge and Watersmeet; this is specifically for children, who only require a Trout rod licence when fishing this particular stretch if they are aged 12 years or over. WARNING: Anglers are advised that parts of the river are exceptionally steep and rocky and can be dangerous. *Species:* Salmon, Sea Trout, Brown Trout. *Permits:* Brendon House Hotel, Brendon. Tourist Information Centre, Town Hall, Lynton. Variety Sports, 23 Broad Street, Ilfracombe. Taunton Angling Centre, 63 Station Road, Taunton. Porlock Visitor Centre, West End, High Street, Porlock. Rockford Inn, Brendon, Lynton. The National Trust, Watersmeet House, Lynmouth. *Charges:* Salmon & Sea Trout, season withdrawn for conservation reasons, week £38, day £15, evening (8 pm to 2 am) £4.50; Brown Trout, season £30, week £11, day £3.50. Bag Limits: 2 Salmon, 4 Sea Trout, 8 Brown Trout per day. 2 Salmon week, 6 Salmon per season. *Season:* Salmon 1 March - 30 September; Sea Trout & Trout 15 March - 30 September. Fishing permitted 8 am to sunset, except from 1 June - 30 September when fishing by traditional fly fishing methods is permitted until 2 am between Tors Road & Rockford. *Methods:* Brown Trout, fly only. Salmon, no shrimp or prawn. Artificial fly or lure only before 16th June. Catch and release of all Salmon prior to 16th June. No weight may be used whilst fly fishing. The weight used for worm fishing and spinning must be lead free and not weigh more than 0.5 ounce and must be attached at least 18 inches from the hook. It is illegal to sell or offer for sale any rod caught Salmon and Sea Trout.

OTTER

The Otter springs to life in the Blackdown Hills and flows through a broad fertile valley to join the sea near the little resort of Budleigh Salterton. This is primarily a Brown Trout stream noted for its dry fly fishing for Trout of good average weight. There is also an improving run of Sea Trout.

Clinton Devon Estates

Rolle Estate, East Budleigh, Budleigh Salterton. *Tel:* 01395 443881. *Water:* 0.75 mile single bank fishing on the River

RIVER FISHING

Otter near Budleigh Salterton. Fishery starts at White Bridge (first road bridge over river) and ends at Clamour Bridge (first footbridge over river). *Species:* Brown Trout. *Charges:* Free to EA rod licence holders. *Season:* 1 April to 30 September.

Deer Park Hotel ♿
Contact: Reception, Buckerell Village, Weston, Honiton. *Sat Nav:* EX14 3PG. *Tel:* 01404 41266. *Water:* River Otter. 2.75 miles double bank. 0.75 miles single bank. *Species:* Brown Trout, Salmon, Sea Trout. *Permits:* From reception at Deer Park Hotel. *Charges:* £30 per rod per day, half day from 4pm £20. Limited season permits available. *Season:* Brown Trout 15 March - 30 September. Salmon - 15 March - 31 October. Sea Trout 15 March - 31 October. *Methods:* Dry & Wet Fly only. Max hook size 12, no bait or lure other than artificial wet fly.

River Otter Association
Contact: Andrew Luxton. *Mobile:* 07831 842004. *Water:* Comprises riparian owners, anglers and conservationists concerned with the preservation of the total ecology of the River Otter. *Species:* Brown Trout, Sea Trout and occasional Salmon. *Charges:* Fishing day tickets are not available through the River Otter Association.

Robert Jones Fly Fishing (Otter)
Contact: Valley Barn, Hawkerland, Colaton Raleigh, Sidmouth. *Tel:* 07020 902090. *Mobile:* 07970 797770. *Water:* River Otter. Private and Hotel water. Also fly fishing

for Bass in saltwater. *Species:* Brown Trout and Sea Trout. *Permits:* Day permits. *Charges:* On application. *Season:* 15 March - 30 September. *Methods:* Fly only.

PLYM
A short stream rising on Dartmoor and running into Plymouth Sound. Trout fishing on the Plym and its tributary the Meavy, some good Sea Trout fishing on the lower reaches and a late run of Salmon.

Plymouth and Dist Freshwater Angling Assoc. (Plym)
Contact: Mike Green. *Mobile:* 07866 315195. *Water:* 1 mile on River Plym, 1.5 miles on River Tavy. *Species:* Salmon, Sea Trout, Brown Trout. *Permits:* Please contact above for membership. *Charges:* To join the association contact secretary. Annual subscription is about £150. *Season:* Plym: March - 15 Dec; Tavy: March - 14 October. *Methods:* Artificial baits only.

Plymouth Command Angling Association (River)
Contact: Mr Vic Barnett Hon.Sec., 5 Weir Close, Mainstone, Plymouth. *Tel:* 01752 708206. *Mobile:* 07710 552910. *Water:* Fishing rights on the Plym, Tavy and Walkham plus a small private pond near Ivybridge. Access to rivers for serving members only. *Species:* Salmon, Sea Trout and Trout. *Permits:* Membership is open to all serving members of HM Forces. Associate membership is also open to ex-serving members, no matter when the time was served. *Charges:* Costs for full membership or associate membership available on application at the above contact. *Season:* Plym, Tavy and Walkham as per Environment Agency Byelaws.

Tavy, Walkham and Plym Fishing Club (Plym)
Contact: Roger Round, 7 Buena Vista Close, Glenholt, Plymouth. *Tel:* 01752 701945. *Water:* River Plym, approx.4 miles of bank fishing. Also water on Tavy and Walkham. See entry under Tavy. *Species:* Salmon, Sea Trout and Brown Trout. *Permits:* From: Osborne & Cragg, Barbican, Plymouth. Moorland Garage, Yelverton. Tolley's of Tavistock, 32 Brook Street, Tavistock. *Charges:* Season Tickets for Salmon, Sea Trout and Brown Trout. Day Tickets available. Sea Trout and Salmon - Season £140, Weekly £55, Day £20. Brown Trout - Season £60, Monthly £25, Weekly £15. Reduced prices for under 18 yrs. *Season:* As E.A. byelaws. No day tickets after 30 September. *Methods:* No worm, prawn or shrimp fishing. Complete rules are issued with permit. Full returns must be made to the club secretary as a condition of purchase.

TAMAR

The Tamar rises near the north coast, and for most of its course forms the boundary between Devon and Cornwall. It is always a lowland stream flowing through farmland and this fact is reflected in the size of its Trout which have a larger average size than the acid moorland streams. Around Launceston, the Tamar is joined by five tributaries - Ottery, Carey, Wolf, Thrushel and Lyd - which offer good Trout fishing, as does the Inny which enters a few miles downstream. There is a good run of Salmon and Sea Trout, the latter being particularly numerous on the Lyd. There are also Grayling in places.

Arundell Arms

Contact: Adam Fox-Edwards, The Arundell Arms, Lifton. *Sat Nav:* PL16 0AA. *Tel:* 01566 784666. *Water:* 20 miles of private fishing on Rivers Tamar, Lyd, Carey, Thrushel, Wolf, Ottery and Lew. Also 3 acre private lake stocked with Rainbow and Brown Trout (Residents only). *Species:* Rivers: Salmon, Sea Trout, Brown Trout & Grayling. Lake: Rainbow & Brown Trout. *Permits:* Arundell Arms. Cockpit Tackle Shop open 9-10am and 6.30-7.00pm daily in the season. Day permits available for non-residents on river beats. *Charges:* Trout/Sea Trout £30, Salmon £30-£40, Grayling (winter) £20.

Season: Salmon March 1st to October 14th. Trout March 15th to September 30th. Sea Trout March 3rd to September 30th. Grayling June 16th to March 14th. Lake open all year. *Methods:* Fly only on lake and rivers. Spinning (for Salmon only) permitted on River Tamar.

Endsleigh Fishing Club

Contact: John Dennis, The Coach House, Sydenham Damerel, Tavistock. *Tel:* 01822 870775. *Mobile:* 07816 219013. *Water:* 12 miles double bank River Tamar. *Species:* Salmon maximum 23lb & Sea Trout maximum 9lb. *Charges:* March and April £25. May 1st to the 15th June £35. June 16th to the 31st July £50. August 1st to the 31st August £60. September 1st to the 14th October £70. *Season:* March 1st - October 14th incl. *Methods:* Fly. Spinning only under certain conditions.

Hotel Endsleigh

Contact: Richard Dawson, Milton Abbot, Nr Tavistock. *Sat Nav:* PL19 0PQ. *Tel:* 01822 870000. *Water:* Eleven miles on the Tamar. *Species:* Salmon and Sea Trout. *Permits:* E.A. national rod licence required. *Charges:* Rod price per day £45 to £75. *Season:* March 15 to October 14 subject to availability. *Methods:* Fly only.

Westcountry Angling Passport (Tamar)

Contact: Westcountry Rivers Trust, Rain-Charm House, Kyl Cober Parc, Stoke Climsland, Callington, Cornwall. *Tel:* 01579 372140. *Water:* 19 beats on the Tamar, Inny, Lyd, Ottery, Carey, Kensey, Lew and Thrushel. Flexible token beats and bookable day ticket fishing for Brown Trout, Salmon, Sea Trout and Grayling. *Species:* Brown Trout, Sea Trout, Salmon and Grayling. *Permits:* From: Snowbee UK, Plymouth, PL7 5JY - 01752 334933. Tamar Field and Stream, Lifton, PL16 0AA - 01566 780512. Devil's Stone Inn, Beaworthy, EX21 5RU - 01409 281210. Homeleigh Garden Centre, Launceston, PL15 9SP - 01566 771878. Blisland Inn, Bodmin, PL30 4JK - 01208 850739. Fly Fishing Tackle co uk, Crediton, EX17 2AW - 01363 777783. Hart Flyshop, Exebridge, TA22 9AY - 01398 323008. Lance Nicholson, Dulverton, TA22 9HB - 01398 323409. Tolley's of Tavistock, Tavistock, PL19 0HE - 01822 617186. *Charges:* £17.50 per rod per day. *Season:* Brown Trout - 15 March to 30 September. Salmon - 1 March to 14 October. Grayling - 16 June to 14 March. Sea Trout - 3 March to 30 September. Please contact for individual beat seasons. *Methods:* Fly, Spinner and worm, depending on individual beats.

TAVY

A Salmon and Sea Trout river which rises high on Dartmoor and flows through Tavistock to its junction with the Tamar estuary north of Plymouth. There is moorland Brown Trout on the upper reaches and on the Walkham, its main tributary.

Plymouth and Dist Freshwater Angling Assoc. (Tavy)

Contact: Mike Green. *Mobile:* 07866 315195. *Water:* River Tavy above Harford Bridge Tavistock. *Species:* Salmon, Sea Trout and Brown Trout. *Permits:* Please contact above for membership. *Charges:* Contact the secretary for details. See entry under River Plym. *Season:* 1 March to 14 October. *Methods:* Artificial baits only.

Tavy, Walkham and Plym Fishing Club (Tavy)

Contact: Roger Round, 7 Buena Vista Close, Glenholt, Plymouth. *Tel:* 01752 701945. *Water:* Rivers Tavy, Walkham, Plym, Meavy. Approx. 15 miles of bank fishing. *Species:* Brown Trout, Salmon, Sea Trout. *Permits:* Only through Osborne & Cragg, Barbican, Plymouth. Moorland Garage, Yelverton. Tolley's of Tavistock, 32 Brook Street, Tavistock. *Charges:* Season Tickets for Salmon, Sea Trout and Brown Trout. Day Tickets available. Sea Trout and Salmon - Season £140, Weekly £55, Day £20. Brown Trout - Season £60, Monthly £25, Weekly £15. Reduced prices for under 18 yrs. *Season:* See Environment Agency season dates. Please note, no day tickets after 30 September. *Methods:* No worm, prawn, shrimp on club permit waters. Please note club rules on back of permit including the dates by which accurate returns must be made as a condition of taking a permit.

Westcountry Angling Passport (Tavy)

Contact: Westcountry Rivers Trust, Rain-Charm House, Kyl Cober Park, Stoke, Climsland, Callington, Cornwall. *Tel:* 01579 372140. *Water:* 800m of single bank fishing on the River Waltham at Leewood. *Species:* Brown Trout, Sea Trout and Salmon. *Charges:* £10 per rod per day. *Season:* Brown

Old Mill House

Located in a small hamlet of just a few houses, Old Mill house is set in grounds of about one acre. The cottage sleeps six and has been sympathetically converted.

The cottage is only a couple of minutes walk away from The River Taw - one of the best Salmon and Sea Trout rivers in the West Country. Day or evening tickets are available on our own 2.25 miles of double bank fishing and are payable locally. Catches have included Salmon up to 21lbs and Sea Trout to 15lbs.

Telephone: 01598 763514   Web: www.woolhanger.co.uk

Trout: 15 March - 30 September. Sea Trout: 3 March - 30 September. Salmon: 1 March - 30 September. *Methods:* Fly only.

TAW AND TRIBUTARIES

The Taw is a noted Salmon and Sea Trout river that rises high on Dartmoor and then flows through the rolling farmland of North Devon to its estuary at Barnstaple. Its main tributary, the Mole, also has good Salmon and Sea Trout fishing, and the Moles own tributary, the Bray, is a good little Trout stream.

Barnstaple and District Angling Association (River)

Contact: S.R. Toms (Secretary), Barnstaple & District Angling Association, Upcott Farm, Brayford. *Tel:* 01598 710857. *Water:* Approx. 3 miles on the River Taw. See also under Stillwater Coarse, Barnstaple. *Species:* Salmon, Sea Trout, and Brown Trout. *Permits:* No day tickets. Fishing by membership only. Details from the Secretary above. *Charges:* Membership £35, Juniors £10. *Season:* Current EA byelaws apply. *Methods:* Current EA byelaws apply.

Chenson Fishery

Contact: Chris Lynden, Chenson Farm Cottage, Chenson, Chulmleigh. *Sat Nav:* EX18 7LE. *Mobile:* 07961 848700. *Water:* 3 miles double and single bank on Rivers Taw and Yeo. 3 beats. *Species:* Salmon, Sea Trout, Brown Trout. *Charges:* Season day rods have priority. Some day rods may be available from season rods. 2 rods only per beat. £250 per season (named day rod). £20 per day. *Season:* March 1st - September 30th. *Methods:* Fly only except March when spinning is permitted.

Crediton Fly Fishing Club (Taw)

Contact: Mike Willis, 20 Powderham Road, Newton Abbot. *Tel:* 01626 364577. *Mobile:* 07973 525227. *Water:* 1.5 miles River Taw. 9 miles on Rivers Yeo, Creedy and Culm. (Season permit holders only on the Culm). *Species:* Brown Trout. *Permits:* Fly Fishing Tackle, 2 Parliament St., Crediton EX17 1AB. Tel: 01363 777783. Also from Mike Willis as above but please allow minimum 1 week notice. *Charges:* Day £15, Mid Week (5 days) £30, Season £90, Youth

(under 18) £10. Over 65 £70. Two day weekend (Sat-Sun) £30. Joining fee £35 (First full season only). *Season:* EA Seasons. *Methods:* Fly only. Barbless and catch and release encouraged. Chest waders recommended.

Fox & Hounds Hotel

Contact: Fox & Hounds Hotel, Eggesford, Chulmleigh. *Sat Nav:* EX18 7JZ. *Tel:* 01769 580345. *Water:* 5 miles private water on River Taw. *Species:* Prime Salmon to 14lb, Sea Trout 5lb & Brown Trout 2lb. *Permits:* Fox & Hounds. *Charges:* Brown Trout, Sea Trout and Salmon £25 per day, £15 eve. Season ticket, 1 day per week £350. Evening fishing 6pm-6am. *Season:* 1 March - 30 September. *Methods:* Spinning March only. Rest of season fly only.

Highbullen Hotel

Contact: Chris Taylor, Chittlehamholt, Umberleigh. *Sat Nav:* EX37 9HD. *Tel:* 01769 540561. *Water:* Access to beats on Mole, Taw and the Bray. *Species:* Salmon 24.5lb (2000), Sea Trout 12lb (1998) & Brown Trout 2lb (2002). *Permits:* From Highbullen Hotel. *Charges:* Prices on application. *Season:* Salmon 1 March - 30 September, Brown and Sea Trout 15 March - 30 September. *Methods:* Spinner March. Fly March - September. Local byelaw, August and September all Salmon over 70cm have to be returned.

Rising Sun Inn

Contact: Steve Tickner, Rising Sun Inn, Umberleigh, Nr Barnstaple. *Sat Nav:* EX37 9DU. *Tel:* 01769 560447. *Mobile:* 07564 236111. *Water:* Approx. 1.5 miles of River Taw fishing at Umberleigh. *Species:* Sea Trout 11.5lb, Brown Trout, Salmon 23lb. *Permits:* Post Office, Umberleigh for licence. *Charges:* Day tickets (3am - 3am) £40. Residents £25. *Season:* Salmon 1 March - 31 Sept, Sea/Brown Trout 15 March - 31 Sept. *Methods:* As per E.A. rules. Fly fishing only.

Taw Fishing Club

Contact: Mr N Payne, c/o The Mill, Taw Green, South Tawton, Okehampton. *Tel:* 01837 840442. *Water:* 3.25 miles on River Taw between Brushford and Hawkridge bridges. *Species:* Brown Trout, Sea Trout and Salmon. *Permits:* Fishing by membership of club only. Currently looking for new members. *Charges:* £60 season. *Season:* 15 March to 30 September. *Methods:* Fly only, barbless encouraged.

The Old Mill House

Contact: Ivan Huxtable. *Tel:* 01769 540835. *Mobile:* 07779 214909. *Water:* 2.25 miles double bank River Taw above Umberleigh bridge. *Species:* Salmon and Sea Trout. *Permits:* From Ivan Huxtable. *Charges:* £35 per day. £20 night fishing. Max. 6 rods. *Season:* 1 March to 30 September. *Methods:* Full rules with permit. Catch and release until 16 June.

The Rising Sun Fishing Club

Contact: Glyn Howells, The Rising Sun Inn, Umberleigh. *Tel:* 01822 860279. *Water:* 1.5 Miles of The River Taw. *Species:* Salmon, Sea Trout, Brown Trout. *Charges:* £40 for day tickets. *Season:* 1 March to the 31 September. *Methods:* Fly only.

Westcountry Angling Passport (Taw)

Contact: Westcountry Rivers Trust, Rain-Charm House, Kyl Cober Parc, Stoke Climsland, Callington, Cornwall. *Tel:* 01579 372140. *Water:* Seven beats on the Taw, Mole, Bray and Little Dart. *Species:* Brown Trout, Salmon and Sea Trout. *Permits:* From: Snowbee UK, Plymouth, PL7 5JY - 01752 334933. Tamar Field and Stream, Lifton, PL16 0AA - 01566 780512. Devil's Stone Inn, Beaworthy, EX21 5RU - 01409 281210. Homeleigh Garden Centre, Launceston, PL15 9SP - 01566 771878. Blisland Inn, Bodmin, PL30 4JK - 01208 850739. Fly Fishing Tackle co uk, Crediton, EX17 2AW - 01363 777783. Hart Flyshop, Exebridge, TA22 9AY - 01398 323008. Lance Nicholson, Dulverton, TA22 9HB - 01398 323409. Tolley's of Tavistock, Tavistock, PL19 0HE - 01822 617186. *Charges:* £7.50 to £60 per rod per day. *Season:* Brown and Sea Trout - 15 March to 30 September. Salmon - 1 March to 30 September. *Methods:* Fly only.

TEIGN

The Teign has two sources high up on Dartmoor which form the North and South Teign but the two branches of the Teign quickly leave the moor to join west of Chagford while still very small streams. Between Chagford and Steps Bridge the river runs through a dramatic wooded gorge which is at its most spectacular at Fingle Bridge, a popular beauty spot. All along the Teign the Spring fisherman is greeted by myriads of daffodils, which are at their most numerous around Clifford Bridge. The upper Teign offers good fishing for wild Trout and Sea Trout, with Salmon fishing in suitable conditions from April to the end of the season. Much of the upper river is controlled by the Upper Teign Fishing Association. From just south of the Moretonhampstead - Exeter road to the estuary at Newton Abbot the Teign is mostly controlled by the Lower Teign Fishing Association. This water has plenty of Brown Trout but is essentially a Sea Trout and Salmon fishery.

RIVER FISHING

Lower Teign Fishing Association

Contact: Dr. M. Megee, Box Tree Cottage, 2, Rattle Street, Trusham, Newton Abbot. *Tel:* 01626 853725. *Mobile:* 07581 485174. *Water:* 14 miles River Teign. *Species:* Salmon, Sea Trout, Brown Trout. *Permits:* 3 Beats with 3 tickets on each (beat 3 only available between 1st May and 31st August). One junior ticket per beat per day available. *Charges:* £20 per day (24 hour period - night Sea Trout fishing). Available from Tackle Trader, Newton Abbot. 01626 331613. 24hr bag limit (4 Sea Trout). From 1st February to end of season Salmon catch and release only (returned to river unharmed). Junior max 3 a day, tickets £5 each. *Season:* Salmon: 1 February - 30 September. Sea Trout: 15 March - 30 September. *Methods:* Spinning, fly (fly only at night), no worming or maggots.

Mill End Hotel

Contact: Mike Coombes, Sandy Park, Chagford. *Sat Nav:* TQ13 8JN. *Tel:* 01647 432282. *Water:* 3 miles plus access to a further 8 miles. *Species:* Brown Trout, Salmon and Sea Trout. *Permits:* At Hotel. *Charges:* £12.50 Adult Brown per day. £5 Juvenile Brown per day. *Season:* Brown 15th March - 30th September. Sea Trout 15th March - 30th September. Salmon 1st February - 30th September.

Robert Jones Fly Fishing (Teign)

Contact: Valley Barn, Hawkerland, Colaton Raleigh, Sidmouth. *Tel:* 07020 902090. *Mobile:* 07970 797770. *Water:* River Teign. Private and Hotel water. Also fly fishing for Bass in saltwater. *Species:* Brown Trout, Sea Trout and Salmon. *Permits:* Day permits. *Charges:* On application. *Season:* 15 March - 30 September. *Methods:* Fly and spinner.

Teign Fisheries Association

Contact: Neil Yeandle, 26 Belle Vue Road, Exmouth. *Tel:* 01395 276241. *Water:* Riparian Owners Association representing interest of owners of fishing waters on River Teign. *Species:* Salmon to 18lb, Sea Trout to 11lb and Brown Trout to 3lb. *Permits:* No day tickets available through the Association. Lower Teign Fishing Association tickets available from Tackle Trader, Newton Abbot. Upper Teign Fishing Association tickets available from Chagford Inn or Fingle Bridge Inn. Local Association rules apply. Details at time of purchase or by enquiry. *Season:* 1st February to 30th September. *Methods:* Salmon caught before 16 June to be returned. Limit of one Salmon per season per rod.

Upper Teign Fishing Association

Contact: Chris Hall (Membership sec.). *Water:* Approx. 8 miles on upper Teign from above Chagford to Steps Bridge, double and single bank. *Species:* Brown Trout, Sea Trout, Salmon. *Permits:* Fingle Bridge Inn, Drewsteignton. Drewsteignton Post Office. Bowdens, Chagford. Dunsford Post Office. Exeter Angling Centre, Smythen St, Exeter. Orvis, 18 Cathedral Yard, Exeter. Cheriton Bishop Post Office. Mill End Hotel, Nr Chagford. Fishing is also available via the Westcountry Rivers Trust Passport Scheme, Tel: 01579 372140. *Charges:* 2013 prices: Brown Trout (whole fishery) Adult £12.50 per day. £45 week. Junior £5 day, £10 week. Salmon & Sea Trout (above Fingle Bridge) £20 per

day. Annual full membership (waiting list) £190 plus joining fee. Brown Trout membership (open) £85 plus joining fee. *Season:* Brown Trout and Sea Trout: March 15 - September 30. Salmon: February 1 - September 30. *Methods:* Only one Salmon per season, per angler may be killed. No bait fishing for Salmon in September. Catch and release for Brown Trout.

TORRIDGE

Throughout its length the Torridge flows through the rolling farmland of North Devon. It rises close to the coast near the Cornish border and swings in a great arc before flowing into the estuary that it shares with the Taw. The middle and lower reaches are best known for their Salmon and Sea Trout, but can offer surprisingly good Trout fishing.

The upper reaches and its tributaries, the Waldon and Lew, offer plenty of opportunities for Brown Trout fishing.

Bradford Manor Fishing

Contact: Nigel Manners, Bradford Manor, Bradford, Holsworthy. *Sat Nav:* EX22 7AW. *Tel:* 01409 281544. *Mobile:* 07984 406025. *Water:* Rare opportunity to enjoy this water in a quiet fielded valley, meandering river frontage, grass banks, walkable shallows and deep pools. Approx. 800 yards beat of the famous fly fishing River Torridge. *Species:* Wild and Brown Trout and Salmon. *Charges:* Three rods available for day ticket or only £35 each. Interested syndicates for season call for details. *Season:* Mid March to end September. *Methods:* Fly fishing with correct Salmon hooks as regs. Salmon catch and release.

Gortleigh Fishing

Contact: Gill and Richard Trace, Gortleigh Farm, Sheepwash, Beaworthy. *Tel:* 01409 231291. *Mobile:* 07968 020254. *Water:* 1.5 miles double bank fishing. *Species:* Brown Trout, Sea Trout and occasional Salmon. *Permits:* From Farmhouse by prior arrangement - please phone first. You can fish this beat with Westcountry Angling Passport tokens. *Charges:* £10 per person per day. *Season:* E.A. Byelaws apply. *Methods:* No dogs.

Half Moon Inn

Contact: Half Moon Inn, Sheepwash, Beaworthy. *Sat Nav:* EX21 5NE. *Tel:* 01409 231376. *Water:* 10 miles River Torridge. *Species:* Sea, Brown & Wild Brown Trout, Salmon. *Permits:* Day tickets for residents & non residents. *Charges:* Non residents: Sea Trout & Salmon £35, Brown Trout £15. Residents Sea/Salmon £30 per day. *Season:* 1st March - 30 September. *Methods:* Dry & Wet Fly only.

Little Warham Fishery

Contact: Thesera Norton-Smith, Little Warham House, Beaford, Winkleigh. *Tel:* 01805 603317. *Water:* Nearly 2 miles of River Torridge. *Species:* Salmon, Sea Trout. *Permits:* As above. *Season:* 1 March - 30 September. *Methods:* Fly only.

Parsonage Farm

Contact: Mr and Mrs Ward, Parsonage Farm, Iddesleigh. *Sat Nav:* EX19 8SN. *Tel:* 01837 810318. *Water:* 400 metres on the River Torridge. *Species:* Wild Brown Trout, Sea Trout and Salmon. *Permits:* From Stafford Moor Fishery. *Charges:* £10 per rod per day. *Season:* Mid March to end September.

The Devil's Stone Inn

The Devil's Stone Inn, Shebbear, Beaworthy. *Tel:* 01409 281210. *Species:* Salmon, Sea Trout and Brown Trout. *Permits:* From the Inn. Night fishing available. *Season:* 1 March to 30 September. *Methods:* Fly and Coarse.

Torridge Fishery Association

Contact: Charles Inniss, Beeches, East Street, Sheepwash, Beaworthy. *Tel:* 01409 231237. *Water:* An association of riparian owners and Torridge fishermen, whose aim is to secure and maintain the well being of the river and its ecology. Several day permits available, please phone for details. *Species:* Salmon to 20lb. Sea Trout to 8lb. Brown Trout to 1lb. *Permits:* Half Moon Inn, Sheepwash, Beaworthy, Devon. Tel: 01409 231376. Mrs T Norton-Smith, Little Warham, Beaford, Winkleigh, Devon. Tel: 01805 603317. *Charges:* Salmon and Sea Trout from £25 to £35 daily. Brown Trout from £10 to £15 daily. *Season:* March 1st to September 30th. *Methods:* Fly Only.

Westcountry Angling Passport (Torridge)

Contact: Westcountry Rivers Trust, Rain-Charm House, Kyl Cober Parc, Stoke Climsland, Callington, Cornwall. *Tel:* 01579 372140. *Water:* Seven beats on the Torridge, Okement, Waldon and North Lew. Flexible token beats and bookable day fishing ticket for Brown Trout, Salmon and Sea Trout. *Species:* Brown Trout, Salmon and Sea Trout. *Permits:* From: Snowbee UK, Plymouth, PL7 5JY - 01752 334933. Tamar Field and Stream, Lifton, PL16 0AA - 01566 780512. Devil's Stone Inn, Beaworthy, EX21 5RU - 01409 281210. Homeleigh Garden Centre, Launceston, PL15 9SP - 01566 771878. Blisland Inn, Bodmin, PL30 4JK - 01208 850739. Fly Fishing Tackle co uk, Crediton, EX17 2AW - 01363 777783. Hart Flyshop, Exebridge, TA22 9AY - 01398 323008. Lance Nicholson, Dulverton, TA22 9HB - 01398 323409. Tolley's of Tavistock, Tavistock, PL19 0HE - 01822 617186. *Charges:* £5 to £20 per rod per day. *Season:* Salmon - 1 March to 30 September. Brown Trout and Sea Trout 15 March to 30 September. Please contact for individual beat seasons. *Methods:* Fly only.

YARTY

See Axe and tributaries.

Taunton Fly Fishing Club (Yarty)

Contact: John Connolly, 35 Manor Road, Taunton, Somerset. *Tel:* 01823 274272. *Water:* One mile on the River Yarty below Beckford Bridge. *Species:* Brown Trout, Sea Trout. *Permits:* No day tickets - members only. *Charges:* Full member £90 (plus £90 joining fee). Junior £15. Joint members £120 (plus £120 joining fee). Prices may change for 2014. *Season:* Brown Trout - 15 March to 30 Sept. Sea Trout - 15 April to 31 October. *Methods:* Fly only.

YEALM

The Yealm, (which is pronounced "Yam"), rises in the south of Dartmoor National Park, and runs into the picturesque Yealm Estuary. Brown Trout and Sea Trout fishing on the main River - a small late run of Salmon.

Upper Yealm Fishery

Contact: Snowbee U.K. Ltd., Drakes Court, Langage Business Park, Plymouth. *Tel:* 01752 334933. *Water:* 1 mile of single bank fishing split across two beats. *Species:* Sea Trout, Brown Trout, Salmon. *Permits:* Snowbee U.K. Ltd./West Country Rivers Trust - Passport scheme. (Bookable beats only). Please contact West Country Rivers Trust Tel: 01579 372140. *Charges:* Full season £125 unlimited visits. Daily rate £12.50. All bookings via Westcountry Rivers Trust (booking only) or contact Snowbee (UK) Ltd. for more details. To preserve the tranquillity of the fishery no more than 2 anglers on one beat at a time. *Season:* Brown Trout & Sea Trout 15 March - 30 Sept, Salmon 1 April - 15 December. *Methods:* Fly fishing (restricted spinning) in spate conditions only.

YEO

A tributary of the River Creedy which drains into the main Exe from the West close to Crediton. The Yeo has a good wild Brown Trout population.

Crediton Fly Fishing Club (Yeo)

Contact: Mike Willis, 20 Powderham Road, Newton Abbot. *Tel:* 01626 364577. *Mobile:* 07973 525227. *Water:* 9 miles Rivers Yeo, Creedy and Culm. 1.5 miles River Taw. Season permit holders only on the Culm. *Species:* Brown Trout. *Permits:* Fly Fishing Tackle, 2 Parliament St., Crediton EX17 1AB. Tel: 01363 777783. Also from Mike Willis as above but please allow minimum 1 week notice. *Charges:* Day £15, Mid Week (5 days) £30, Season £90, Youth (under 18) £10. Over 65 £70. Two day weekend (Sat-Sun) £30. Joining fee £35 (First full season only). *Season:* EA Season. *Methods:* Fly only. Barbless and catch and release encouraged. Chest waders recommended.

Stillwater Coarse

AXMINSTER

Summerleaze Pond
Contact: Summerleaze Farm, Kilmington, Axminster. *Sat Nav:* EX13 7RA. *Tel:* 01297 32390. *Water:* 1 coarse fishing lake. *Species:* Carp, Roach, Perch. Best Carp 20lbs. *Charges:* On site, £5 adults, £3 children under 16. *Season:* Open all year, dawn to dusk. *Methods:* Please ask at fishery.

BAMPTON

Four Ponds Fishery &
Contact: Phil & Geraldine Newton, Bowdens Lane, Shillingford, Nr Bampton. *Sat Nav:* EX16 9BU. *Tel:* 01398 331169. *Mobile:* 07864 697721. *Water:* 1.25 acre and 0.75 acre coarse lakes. 3 acre specimen Carp lake. *Species:* Carp 32lb, Tench 8lb, Perch 3lb, Roach 2.5lb, Bream 9lb, Rudd and Golden Rudd to 1lb. (verified) true Crucians to 3lb. *Charges:* Day tickets available on bankside or in tackle shop. Coarse day tickets £7 for 2 rods and £8 for 3 rods. Night ticket £8 for 2 rods, £9 for 3 rods. Specimen lake (6 swims) has to be booked, Price for 3 rods: day ticket £12, Night £14, 24hrs £22, 48hrs £40. *Season:* 1st March to 31st October. *Methods:* Coarse:- Strictly barbless hooks only, minimum 30" landing nets, no nut type baits to be used. No fish over 3lb in keepnets. Specimen lake:- nets, mats and slings provided, klin-ik must be used at all times. No sacking of fish, photos in kneeling position only, no nut baits.

BARNSTAPLE

Barnstaple and District A. A. (Coarse Ponds)
Contact: S.R. Toms (Secretary), Barnstaple & District Angling Association, Upcott Farm, Brayford. *Tel:* 01598 710857. *Water:* 2 mixed coarse fishing ponds in the Barnstaple area ranging from 0.5 acres to 2 acres. *Species:* Roach, Rudd, Carp, Perch, Bream, Tench and Eels. *Permits:* Members only. Details from the secretary. *Charges:* £35 per year adult. Children (18 and under) £10 per year. *Season:* All year, dawn to dusk. *Methods:* Full rules in the membership book. Barbless hooks only.

Harepie Coarse Fishery &
Contact: Jack Anderton, Bracken, 1 Style Close, Barnstaple. *Mobile:* 07813 625173. *Water:* Two ponds, 16 pegs and 5 pegs. 3 miles from Barnstaple. *Species:* Carp 22lb, Tench 6lb, Chub 3lb, Bream 5lb, Roach 2lb, Rudd 2lb, Crucian 1lb. *Permits:* Booking by phone only (use mobile no.). Site is kept locked. Anglers who have booked will be met at site to allow access. *Charges:* £5 per person. *Season:* Open all year. *Methods:* Barbless hooks. No keepnets except in competitions. No dog biscuits. Disabled anglers please telephone before travelling for more information.

Riverton Lakes & Holiday Cottages &
Contact: Carl and Jackie Robinson, Riverton House & Lakes, Swimbridge, Barnstaple. *Sat Nav:* EX32 0QX. *Tel:* 01271 830009. *Water:* 3.5 acre specimen lake, plus half acre Tench and Crucian lake and 2.5 acre lake match/pleasure lake. *Species:* Carp to 30lb, Crucian Carp 2lb, Bream 7lb, Tench 8lb, Roach over 1lb, Barbel 3lb, Chub 1lb, Perch 3lb, Rudd 3lb & Eels 6lb. *Permits:* Specimen lake to be booked in advance. *Charges:* Adult day £8, Junior £6. Night fishing by appointment. Specimen lake £10 for 12 hours 2 rods only. *Season:* Open all year. *Methods:* Barbless hooks, care and consideration. No keepnets at all. Float fishing only on Tench and Crucian lake.

George & Mark with a couple
of beauties from Kingslake

Westcott Barton

Contact: Howard, Westcott Barton, Middle Marwood, Barnstaple. *Sat Nav:* EX31 4EF. *Tel:* 01271 812842. *Mobile:* 07786 076940. *Water:* 1.5 acre lake and 2 small ponds. *Species:* Common and Mirror Carp, Roach, Rudd, Crucians and Tench. *Permits:* Tickets must be pre booked by phone. *Charges:* Pay on site. Adult £6. Junior £3 (Jnr's age under 14 years). OAP £3. No children under 14 unaccompanied by an adult. *Season:* All year. *Methods:* Barbless hooks only, no keepnets, no dogs, no radio's, no alcohol. Please take home all litter. Unhooking mats must be used over 5lb in weight. No nut type baits. No boilies. Full rules on site. Environment Agency rod licence will be checked.

BEAWORTHY

Anglers Eldorado

Contact: Zyg, The Gables, Winsford, Halwill, Beaworthy. *Sat Nav:* EX21 5XT. *Tel:* 01409 221559. *Water:* Four lakes from 1 acre to 4 acres. *Species:* Carp to 25lb, Grass Carp to 20lb, Wels Catfish to over 30lbs, Golden Tench to 5lb, Golden Orfe to 6lb, Blue Orfe to 5lb, Golden Rudd to 2lb, Koi to 10lb. *Permits:* Also from Halwill Shop. *Charges:* £5 per day per rod. £5 excess if found fishing without a permit. Max 2 rods. *Season:* All year, 8am-9pm or dusk (which ever is earlier). No night fishing. *Methods:* Barbless hooks, No keepnets or sacks. Landing nets must be used.

Anglers Shangrila

Contact: Mr Zyg Gregorek, The Gables, Winsford, Halwill, Beaworthy. *Sat Nav:* EX21 5XT. *Tel:* 01409 221559. *Water:* Two match only lakes, 200 pegs. *Species:* Carp, Golden Tench, Golden Orfe, Golden Rudd. Top weights of 100lbs possible. *Permits:* From Zyg only. *Charges:* You can book the whole lake, charges depend on how many people. Minimum up to £50 for 10 anglers, then £5 per angler after that. *Methods:* Barbless hooks.

Fatboys (Specimen) Carp Lake

Contact: Mr Zyg Gregorek, Anglers Nirvana, The Gables, Winsford, Halwill. *Sat Nav:* EX21 5XT. *Tel:* 01409 221559. *Water:* 2 acres. *Species:* Carp to over 20lbs. *Permits:* Only at Anglers Paradise. Pre booking advisable. *Charges:* £10 day (2 rods). £10 night. No night fishing without booking a day first. *Season:* All year. 8am to 9pm or dusk (which ever is earlier). *Methods:* Barbless hooks, no keepnets, no braided main line, minimum 8lb line, no particle baits except sweetcorn and hemp. Anglers Paradise rules and regulations apply. Minimum landing net size of 36".

Kraking Karp (Specimen) Carp Lake

Contact: Mr Zyg Gregorek, Anglers Nirvana, The Gables, Winsford, Halwill. *Sat Nav:* EX21 5XT. *Tel:* 01409 221559. *Water:* 2 acres. *Species:* Carp to over 40lbs. *Permits:* Only at Anglers Paradise. Pre booking advisable. Max 5 anglers per session. *Charges:* £20 day (2 rods). £10 night. No night fishing without booking day first. *Season:* All year. 8am to

9pm or dusk (which ever is earlier). *Methods:* Barbless hooks, no keepnets, no braided main line, minimum 10lb line, no particle baits except sweetcorn and hemp. Anglers Paradise rules and regulations apply. Minimum landing net size of 42".

SC Devon Catfish and Carp Lakes

Contact: Lee Bryan, Southcott, Halwill, Beaworthy. *Sat Nav:* EX21 5UX. *Tel:* 01409 220203. *Mobile:* 07886 935900. *Water:* One 0.5 acre lake. A Catfish and large Carp Lake. *Species:* Catfish Lake: Cats 43lb, Carp 27lb, Perch 4lb and some smaller match fish. *Charges:* Catfish lake only 24hr tickets £20 each or all 4 swims £75 - max four fishing. *Season:* Open all year. *Methods:* No keepnets unless previously agreed.

Specimen Catfish Lake

Contact: Mr Zyg Gregorek, Anglers Nirvana, The Gables, Winsford, Halwill. *Sat Nav:* EX21 5XT. *Tel:* 01409 221559. *Water:* 2 acres. *Species:* 12 Wels Catfish average size 35lbs. *Permits:* Only at Anglers Paradise. Pre booking advisable. *Charges:* £10 per day (2 rods). £10 per night. *Season:* All year. 8am to 9pm or dusk (Which ever is earlier). *Methods:* Barbless hooks, no keepnets, no braided main line, minimum 10lb line, deadbaits permissible provided they are bought at Anglers Paradise tackle shop. Anglers Paradise rules and regulations apply. Minimum landing net size of 42".

Xanadu

Contact: Mr Zyg Gregorek, Anglers Nirvana, The Gables, Winsford Lane, Halwill. *Sat Nav:* EX21 5XT. *Tel:* 01409 221559. *Species:* Carp to over 20lbs. *Permits:* Only at Anglers Paradise. Pre booking advisable. *Charges:* £10 per day. £10 per night. No night fishing without booking day first. *Season:* All year 8am - 9pm or Dusk.(Which ever is earlier). *Methods:* Barbless hooks, no keepnets, no braided lines, minimum 10lb line. No nut or pulses. Minimum 42" net. Anglers Paradise rules apply.

BIDEFORD

Fosfelle Country House Hotel (Coarse)

Contact: Hilary and Peter Mcardell, Hartland, Bideford. *Sat Nav:* EX39 6EF. *Tel:* 01237 441273. *Water:* Approx. half acre lake. *Species:* Carp, Tench, Roach, Rudd. *Charges:* £7 per day. *Season:* Open all year. *Methods:* Displayed on site.

Jennetts

Contact: South West Lakes Trust. *Sat Nav:* EX39 5JH. *Tel:* 01288 321712. *Water:* Reservoir 8 acres. *Species:* Common and Mirror Carp to 32lb. Tench to 9lb, Bream to 7lb, Perch to 4lb. *Permits:* Summerlands Tackle, Westward Ho! (01237 471291), Bideford TIC (01237 477676), Whiskers Pet Centre, Torrington (01805 622859), Barley Grove Service Station, Torrington (01805 623340), Exe Valley Angling, Tiverton (01884 242275), Barnstaple TIC (01271 375000), Barton Torrs Stores (01237 472977). Fishing is also available via the Westcountry Rivers Trust Passport Scheme, Tel: 01579 372140. *Charges:* Full day £6.50. Concession/child (12 -16 years) £5. *Season:* Open all year, strictly 6.30am - 10pm. *Methods:* Quality bags of smaller Carp, Roach and Tench to pole and float. Known as a runs water but good for surface fishing for Carp in summer and off the bottom all year. Method feeder on pegs 4 to 8 for larger Tench and Bream.

Little Weach Fishery

1 Weach Cottage, Westleigh, Bideford. *Sat Nav:* EX39 4NG. *Tel:* 01237 479303. *Water:* 2 lakes totalling approx. 1 acre.

Species: Crucian, Common, Mirror and Koi Carp to 16lb, Tench 7lb, Roach 1.5lb, Rudd, Bream, Goldfish 1lb. *Charges:* £6 per day, £3 Children. Under 12's must be accompanied by an adult. *Season:* Open all year dawn to dusk. *Methods:* No keepnets or boilies.

Melbury
Contact: South West Lakes Trust. *Sat Nav:* EX39 5PW. *Tel:* 01288 321712. *Water:* Reservoir 12 acres. *Species:* Mirror and Common Carp to 31lb. Perch 5lb 11oz, Tench 4lb, Bream 6lb, Roach 2lb, Eels. *Permits:* From Summerlands (01237 471291), Bideford TIC (01237 477676), Exe Valley Angling, Tiverton (01884 242275), Barnstaple TIC (01271 375000), Barton Torrs Stores (01237 472977) or online from our website. Fishing is also available via the Westcountry Rivers Trust Passport Scheme, Tel: 01579 372140. *Charges:* Full day £6.50. Concession/child (12 -16 years) £5. Season tickets available from Summerlands Tackle (01237 471291) - additional fisheries £35 each. *Season:* Open all year from 6.30am to 10pm. *Methods:* Good mixed bags of Roach, Rudd and quality Bream to pole, float and feeder. Carp on boilies year round from gravel bars and lily beds.

Tarka Swims &
Contact: Phil Vanstone, Bideford & District Angling & Social Club, Honestone Street, Bideford. *Sat Nav:* EX39 4QE. *Tel:* 01237 477996. *Water:* 1.5 acre lake at Gammaton. *Species:* Carp to 18lb 6oz, Tench 2lb, Roach 2lb, Rudd 0.5, Bream 4lb, Perch to 3lb 3oz. *Permits:* Day tickets from: Summerlands, Westward Ho!. Angler's Heaven, Bideford. Club Headquarters. *Charges:* Lake membership available one payment £40 joining fee (life membership) then £20 per year. Junior £2. Concession £12. *Season:* Open all year. *Methods:* Disabled toilets on site plus access to 26 disabled friendly pegs. Barbless hooks only. No Keepnets for Carp. No boilies. Under 16's must be accompanied by an adult.

BOVEY TRACEY

Bradley Pond
Contact: Newton Abbot Fishing Association, P.O. Box 229, Totnes. *Water:* See entry under Newton Abbot Fishing Association. Full members only. 4 acre former clay pit. *Species:* Popular match and Carp venue with Roach to 2lb, Perch to 5lb, Tench, Skimmers, Carp to 28lb and large Trout.

> Remember a & means the fishery has disabled facilities - contact them direct for further details

BRAUNTON

Little Comfort Farm
Contact: Roger or Jackie Milsom, Little Comfort Farm, Braunton. *Sat Nav:* EX33 2NJ. *Tel:* 01271 812414. *Water:* 1.5 acre stream fed lake with island, with water lilies and deep pools. *Species:* Carp - 18lbs, Rudd, Roach, Bream. *Permits:* Self pay ticketing system in fisherman's refreshments room. *Charges:* £7 all day, 2 rods £6 half day, 2 rods £4 evening, 2 rods concessions £1 off all prices for OAP and under 14. Multiple tickets available at reduced rates. *Season:* Open from dawn to dusk, closed January and February to day tickets. *Methods:* Barbless hooks.

BUCKFASTLEIGH

Nurston Farm Fishery &
Contact: Mabin Family, Nurston Farm, Dean Prior, Buckfastleigh. *Sat Nav:* TQ11 0NA. *Tel:* 01364 642285. *Mobile:* 07821 652837. *Water:* 2.5 acre lake. *Species:* Roach to 3lb, Tench to 5lb, Rudd to 1lb, Bream to 6lb, Carp (different species) to 30lb. Perch to 3lb 14ozs. *Permits:* Must be carried by the person fishing. *Charges:* Dawn till dusk £6. Under 14s £5. 4pm till dusk £5. Under 14 to be accompanied by an adult at all times. *Season:* Dawn till dusk all the year. *Methods:* Barbless hooks, no keepnets, no boilies. Match bookings in advance. Toilet on site. Transport down to Lakes edge. Can fish from car.

CHUDLEIGH

Trenchford

Contact: South West Lakes Trust. *Sat Nav:* TQ13 9PD. *Tel:* 01647 252898. *Water:* 33 acre reservoir. *Species:* Pike up to 30lb. Re stocked with Pike in 2010. *Permits:* From Kennick self-service kiosk or online from our website. Fishing is also available via the Westcountry Rivers Trust Passport Scheme, Tel: 01579 372140. *Charges:* Full day £6.50. Concession/child (12 -16 years) £5. 24 hrs £12. Season tickets available from Summerlands Tackle 01237 471291 - additional fisheries £35 each. Boats available bookable 48hrs in advance. *Season:* Open all year, 24 hours a day. *Methods:* Spinner, plug, fly, dead bait (sea fish only). No live baiting.

COMBE MARTIN

Newberry Valley Coarse Fishing

Contact: Newberry Valley, Woodlands, Combe Martin. *Sat Nav:* EX34 0AT. *Tel:* 01271 882334. *Water:* 2 acre lake. *Species:* Carp to 25lb & Green Tench to 8lb, Roach, Rudd & Perch. *Permits:* From above address. Environment Agency rod licence required. Available from local Post Office or by 'Telesales' service on 0844 800 5386. *Charges:* £6/day, max 2 rods; evening permit £4. *Season:* Open 23rd March till end October 9am - 8pm, or dusk if earlier. *Methods:* Barbless hooks only. No ground bait or keepnets. Children under 16 must be accompanied by an adult over 18 years. No dogs.

CREDITON

Creedy Lakes ♿

Contact: Sandra Turner, Longbarn, Crediton. *Sat Nav:* EX17 4AB. *Tel:* 01363 772684. *Water:* 4.5 acre & 1.75 acre spring fed lakes. *Species:* Common to 31lb 3oz, Mirror to 29lb 14oz. Koi Carp plus Tench. *Permits:* Self service on site, in car park. *Charges:* Day ticket £9 (1-2 rods). £13 (3 rods). Evening ticket £5 (1-2 rods). £7 (3 rods). *Season:* March through to December. *Methods:* Barbless hooks, minimum line 8lbs, no keepnets, no hemp, seed or nut baits. No poles or beachcasters. Unhooking mats and 'klin-ik' antiseptic compulsory. No night fishing. No unaccompanied children under 16. No dogs allowed.

Lake View Fishery ♿

Contact: Mr and Mrs Barber, Morchard Road, Crediton. *Sat Nav:* EX17 5LS. *Tel:* 01363 85187. *Water:* 0.75 acre lake. *Species:* Carp, Rudd and Bream. *Charges:* £5 per day Adult and Junior. Under 16's to be accompanied by fishing adult. *Season:* All year. *Methods:* Barbless hooks only. Full rules at fishery.

Lower Hollacombe Fishery

Contact: Mr C. Guppy, Lower Hollacombe, Crediton. *Sat Nav:* EX17 5BW. *Tel:* 01363 84331. *Water:* Approximately 1 acre. *Species:* Common Carp, Koi Carp, Rudd, Tench, Mirror Carp, Crucian Carp, Roach, Perch. *Permits:* At bank side. *Charges:* £7 per day. £5 per day under 16. £5 per evening. Under 16 must be accompanied by adult. *Season:* All year round. *Methods:* Barbless hooks, no boilies or nut baits.

Salmonhutch Coarse Fishery &

Contact: Mrs Mortimer, Uton, Crediton. *Sat Nav:* EX17 3QL. *Tel:* 01363 772749. *Water:* Three 1 acre spring fed lakes. *Species:* Mirror Carp over 29lb and Commons to 24lbs. Rudd, Tench and Perch. *Permits:* From Warden. *Charges:* Day fishing 7.00am to 8.00pm, Adults £5, Children/Disabled/OAP £3.50. Evening 5pm-8pm £3; Night Fishing 8pm-7am £5; 24 hour fish from arrival £10. No access after 8pm. Age restrictions: Anglers under 18 must not fish Island Pond and must be accompanied by an adult angler for night fishing. Children under 13 must be accompanied by an adult angler at all times. *Season:* All year. *Methods:* Barbless hooks. Min 8lb line for Carp, 4lb for general fishing. No bait boats. No Carp in keepnets. Unhooking mats must be used. Full rules from the fishery.

Hard to imagine a more perfect specimen than this 21lb 5oz Common landed by Mark Owen at Creedy.

STILLWATER COARSE

07733 223417. *Water:* 3 ponds, largest 0.25 acres. *Species:* Roach, Rudd, Gudgeon, Perch, Tench and Carp. *Charges:* £6 Dawn - Dusk. Please phone before travelling. *Season:* Open all year. *Methods:* No night fishing.

Digger Lakes
Verbeer Manor, Willand. *Sat Nav:* EX15 2PE. *Mobile:* 07733 223417. *Water:* Snails Lake: 5 acres. Persey's Pool: 3.8 acre. *Species:* Snails Lake contains 150 carp with 3 x 30's to 34.4lb. Persey's Pool contains 400 fish to 20lb. *Permits:* Snails Lake and Persey's Pool day and night tickets from Esso Garage at entrance. *Charges:* Snails Lake and Persey's Pool £10 per 12 hours. £20 for 48 hours. Week £100. *Season:* Open all year. *Methods:* Full rules on site.

Exeter and District A.A. (Kia Ora)
Contact: Roly Palmer, PO Box 194, Exeter. *Mobile:* 07970 483913. *Water:* A recently built Association water and now the clubs premier water offering big nets of Carp, Tench, Bream, Crucian, Roach. Pleasure Fishing often produces 25lb fish. *Species:* Heavily stocked with mixed species coarse fish. *Permits:* Exeter Angling Centre, Smythen Street (Off Market Street, Exeter). Exmouth Tackle & Sport, The Strand, Exmouth. Tackle Trader, Wharf Road, Newton Abbot. Exe Valley Angling, West Exe South, Tiverton. Tiverton Parkway Station (Cafe), Sampford Peverell. *Charges:* £40 Adults, £5 for Juniors (annual). £5 day. *Season:* No Close Season. Details in association handbook or from agents. *Methods:* Different restrictions on each water. Details in association handbook.

CULLOMPTON

Coombelands Coarse Fishery &
Contact: Mr & Mrs Berry, Higher Coombelands, Bunneford Cross, Knowle, Cullompton. *Sat Nav:* EX15 1PT. *Tel:* 01884 32320. *Water:* 3 Lakes totalling approx. 3 acres. *Species:* Mixed coarse ponds with Carp in excess of 20lb. *Charges:* From £7 per day or £18 for 24 hours. Evening and season tickets available. Night fishing £12 (Pre Book). *Season:* Open all year. *Methods:* Barbless hooks only, no keep nets, no boilies, night fishing with prior permission only, no dogs.

Culm Valley Fishery &
Contact: Mr Peter Newport, Styche House, Madford, Cullompton. *Sat Nav:* EX15 3QZ. *Tel:* 01823 330705 *Mobile:*

Goodiford Mill Fishery (Coarse Lakes) ♿
Contact: David & Anne Wheeler, Goodiford Mill, Kentisbeare, Cullompton. *Sat Nav:* EX15 2AS. *Tel:* 01884 266233. *Water:* 7 acre Match Coarse lake. Match record 482lb 11oz in 5 hours. *Species:* Carp: Common, Mirror, Crucian, Leather and Ghost. Tench, Roach, Rudd, Bream, Perch Gudgeon, Eels, Trout. *Permits:* At Lodge. *Charges:* £7 day ticket (1 rod). £5 concession. £2 for second rod. Children under 14 must be accompanied by an adult (1 rod). *Season:* All year 6am - dusk. *Methods:* Full rules on application, no keepnets unless silvers, barbless hooks, nets must be dipped, no Carp in keepnets, no nuts or pulses.

Goodiford Mill Fishery (Silver Lake) ♿
Contact: David & Anne Wheeler, Goodiford Mill, Kentisbeare, Cullompton. *Sat Nav:* EX15 2AS. *Tel:* 01884 266233. *Water:* One 0.5 acre Silver fish venue. *Species:* Roach, Rudd and Bream. *Permits:* Rod licence required. *Charges:* £8 1 rod. *Season:* All year.

Goodiford Mill Fishery (Specimen Carp) ♿
Contact: David & Anne Wheeler, Goodiford Mill, Kentisbeare, Cullompton. *Sat Nav:* EX15 2AS. *Tel:* 01884 266233. *Water:* 4 acre lake, (specimen). *Species:* Ghost, Mirror, Leathers and Common Carp. Best fish 30lb. *Permits:* At Lodge. Rod Licence required. *Charges:* £10 for 2 rods. No concessions. Under 16 years must be accompanied. Night fishing by arrangement £25. *Season:* Open all year. 6am - dusk. *Methods:* Full rules on application, barbless hooks only. Frozen boilies only.

Knapp Farm Lakes ♿
Contact: Mr Simon Connor, Knapp Farm Lakes, Clayhidon, Cullompton. *Sat Nav:* EX15 3TH. *Mobile:* 07931 358887. *Water:* Knapp Farm Lakes will be closed until further notice. Three lakes covering approx. 3 acres. *Species:* Common and Ghost Carp to 12lb. Roach, Rudd and Tench to 3lb. *Permits:* Pay on site. Self service or pay Warden. *Charges:* Please phone for prices. *Season:* Open all year. *Methods:* No boilies. No keepnets for fish over 3lb. Barbless hooks only. Under 16s must be accompanied by an adult.

Millhayes Fishery ♿
Contact: Mr Tony Howe, Millhayes, Kentisbeare, Cullompton. *Sat Nav:* EX15 2AF. *Tel:* 01884 266412. *Water:* 2 acre spring fed lake, 0.5 acre Crucian and Bream lake. *Species:* Carp 31lb, Tench 5lb, Roach, Rudd to 2lb. *Charges:* £6 Adults, £4 Under 16, £4 Evenings. *Season:* 1 March - 31 December. *Methods:* Barbless hooks only, no night fishing, no Carp over 1lb in nets, nets to be dipped, no dogs. Absolutely no fish to be removed from site. Please note opening and closing times clearly marked on entrance gate.

Newcourt Ponds
Contact: Andy Hitt, Newcourt Barton, Langford, Cullompton. *Sat Nav:* EX15 1SE. *Tel:* 01884 277326. *Water:* Four lakes totalling 1.5 acres. *Species:* Carp, Tench, Bream, Golden Orfe, Rudd, Golden Tench. *Permits:* Collected on bank. *Charges:* Adults £5 two rods. Under 14 £4 one rod. Extra rods £1. *Season:* Open all year dawn to dusk. No night fishing. *Methods:* No Boilies. Barbless Hooks. No Carp over 2lb in nets. No dogs.

STILLWATER COARSE

Padbrook Park &
Contact: Garry Scargill, Padbrook Park, Cullompton. *Sat Nav:* EX15 1RU. *Tel:* 01884 836100. *Water:* 3 acre lake. *Species:* Many Carp up to 20lb. *Charges:* £5 Day. *Season:* Open all year. *Methods:* No keepnets.

Pound Farm &
Contact: Mrs A.M. Davey, Butterleigh, Cullompton. *Sat Nav:* EX15 1PH. *Tel:* 01884 855208. *Water:* Small spring fed pond. *Species:* Roach, Tench, Perch, Rudd. *Charges:* £4 per rod per day. Children under ten £1.50. Under 16 £3. *Season:* All year - Dawn to dusk. *Methods:* Barbless hooks only. No Boilies. No keepnets. Good access and parking for disabled anglers.

South Farm
Contact: Gary Spencer, South Farm, Blackborough, Cullompton. *Tel:* 01823 681078. *Water:* 0.5 acre lake. *Species:* Carp, Chub, Perch, Roach. *Charges:* £7 per person (2 rods). *Season:* All year. *Methods:* Barbless hooks. No keepnets.

DAWLISH

Ashcombe Fishery
Contact: Ashcombe Adventure Centre Ltd., Ashcombe, Dawlish. *Sat Nav:* EX7 0QD. *Tel:* 01626 866766. *Water:* 3 Lakes approx. 3 acres. Just off B3192 at Colley Lane. *Species:* Carp 18lb, Tench 4lb, Roach 2lb, Rudd, Golden Rudd, Perch. *Permits:* Day tickets/permits available from reception (fishing inspector). EA licence required. Season tickets also available. *Charges:* Adults £4.50, Junior / OAP £3.50. *Season:* Open all year 09.00 - 17.00 Monday to Saturday, except 24/25/26 December and 1st January. Closed Sunday 13.00. *Methods:* Barbless hooks, No large Carp to be kept in keepnets, no boilies.

Hazelwood Holiday Park
Hazelwood Park, Warren Road, Dawlish Warren. *Sat Nav:* EX7 0PF. *Tel:* 01626 865005. *Water:* Three lakes totalling approx. 2.5 acres. *Species:* Carp, Roach and Tench. *Permits:* Day permits for non-residents available during quiet periods. *Charges:* £5 per day. Under 14 £4. *Season:* Closed from 1 to 15 Feb. *Methods:* Barbless hooks only. No night fishing.

Three Elms Angling Club
Contact: Graham Lockheart, Flat 27B, New Road, Brixham. *Tel:* 01803 852557. *Water:* Pathfield pond - approx. 0.5 acre. *Species:* Carp, Roach, Rudd, Perch, Bream, Skimmers, Crucian and Tench. *Permits:* Phone for details. *Charges:* Members only no day tickets, membership enquiries to Graham at above address. *Season:* Dawn to dusk. *Methods:* Barbless Hooks.

EXETER

Broadclyst Pond
Contact: Mr T Hammet, Jarvis Hayes, Broadclyst, Exeter. *Sat Nav:* EX5 3AR. *Tel:* 01392 461268. *Water:* One half acre lake. *Species:* Carp to 20lb plus, Tench 3.5lb, Perch 1.5lb, Rudd 12oz. *Permits:* On site - contact for details. *Charges:* £5 per day. *Season:* Open all year. No night fishing. *Methods:* No keepnets, barbless hooks only.

Bussells Farm
Contact: Lucy or Andy Hines, Bussells Farm, Huxham, Exeter. *Sat Nav:* EX5 4EN. *Tel:* 01392 841238. *Mobile:* 07802 435934. *Water:* Three lakes covering 2.5 acres. *Species:* Carp to 25lb, Bream to 7lb, Tench, Roach, Eels, Pike. *Charges:* £5 per day, £3 after 2pm. *Season:* Open all year. *Methods:* Barbless hooks only. No night fishing. No boilies.

Darts Farm Fishing Lakes
Contact: Morgan Wilkinson, Darts Farm, Clyst St George, Topsham, Nr Exeter. *Sat Nav:* EX3 0QH. *Tel:* 01392 878209. *Water:* 2 acres lakes. *Species:* Carp max 27lb, Bream max 8-10lb, Roach. *Permits:* Available from Darts farm shop. E.A. licence required. *Charges:* Max two rods. Adult £6 per day and £10 for 24 hours. Concessions £4 a day and £8 for 24 hours. *Season:* All year round; Night fishing by arrangement. *Methods:* Barbless hooks, disinfectant tanks for dipping tackle, no Carp in keepnets.

Exeter and District A.A. (Feneck Ponds) &
Contact: Roly Palmer, PO Box 194, Exeter. *Mobile:* 07970 483913. *Water:* Two very prolific ponds. Small but set in a beautiful, quiet environment, solitude fishing at its best. *Species:* Tench, Carp, Crucians, Roach and Rudd. *Permits:* Exeter Angling Centre, Smythen Street (Off Market Street, Exeter). Exmouth Tackle & Sport, The Strand, Exmouth. Tackle Trader, Wharf Road, Newton Abbot. Exe Valley Angling, West Exe South, Tiverton. Tiverton Parkway Station (Cafe), Sampford Peverell. *Charges:* £40 Adults, £5 for Juniors (annual). £5 day. *Season:* Different on each water. Details in association handbook or from agents. *Methods:* Different restrictions on each water. Details in association handbook. Family friendly toilets on site.

Exeter and District A.A. (Sampford Peverall Ponds) &
Contact: Roly Palmer, PO Box 194, Exeter. *Mobile:* 07970 483913. *Water:* Two small ponds adjacent to railway line, relatively easy fishing. *Species:* All coarse fish present with Carp to 20lb. *Permits:* Exeter Angling Centre, Smythen Street (Off Market Street, Exeter). Exmouth Tackle & Sport, The Strand, Exmouth. Tackle Trader, Wharf Road, Newton

Wendi Postma with a 47lb Wels Catfish from the Specimen Cat Lake at Anglers Paradise

Abbot. Exe Valley Angling, West Exe South, Tiverton. Tiverton Parkway Station (Cafe), Sampford Peverell. *Charges:* £40 Adults, £5 for Juniors (annual). £5 day. *Season:* No close season. Details in association handbook or from agents. *Methods:* Different restrictions on each water. Details in association handbook.

Exeter and District A.A. (Exeter Canal) &
Contact: Roly Palmer, PO Box 194, Exeter. *Mobile:* 07970 483913. *Water:* This very old waterway is approximately 12ft deep, throughout its six mile length. *Species:* Carp to 40lb, Tench, Chub, Roach and specimen Pike to 30lb. *Permits:* Exeter Angling Centre, Smythen Street (Off Market Street, Exeter). Exmouth Tackle & Sport, The Strand, Exmouth. Tackle Trader, Wharf Road, Newton Abbot. Exe Valley Angling, West Exe South, Tiverton. Tiverton Parkway Station (Cafe), Sampford Peverell. *Charges:* £40 Adults, £5 for Juniors (annual). £5 day. *Season:* No close season on canal. Details in association handbook or from agents. *Methods:* Different restrictions on each water. Details in association handbook.

Exeter Ship Canal
Contact: Exeter City Council, River & Canal Manager, Civic Centre, Exeter. *Sat Nav:* EX1 1RQ. *Tel:* 01392 274306. *Water:* 5.25 miles of canal, both banks; upper 1.5 miles free permits. *Species:* Roach, Bream, Tench, Carp, Pike & Eels. *Permits:* Free permits from - River & Canal Office, Canal Basin, Haven Rd, Exeter and Exeter City Council, Civic Centre, Customer First Reception, Paris Street. *Charges:* Free permits with proof of identity and E.A. licence. Lower level 3.25 miles on Exeter & District A.A. permit. *Season:* Open all year. *Methods:* No live or dead bait coarse fish.

Hogsbrook Lakes
Contact: Desmond & Maureen Pearson, Russett Cottage, Greendale Barton, Woodbury Salterton, Exeter. *Sat Nav:* EX5 1EW. *Tel:* 01395 233340. *Mobile:* 07952 913859. *Water:* One 1.5 acre and one 2 acre lake. *Species:* Bream, Tench, Roach, Rudd, Golden Rudd, Carp. *Charges:* Private club membership £275 per year, max 100 members. Day tickets available. Prior arrangement - please ring. *Season:* Open all year. *Methods:* Members rules: Barbless hooks, keepnets

by arrangement, no Carp in nets or sacks, all Carp anglers must have unhooking mats. No alcohol. Take all rubbish home. Night fishing by prior arrangement for members only.

Home Farm Fishery &
Contact: Mr F Williams, Red Cedars, Mamhead, Kenton, Exeter. *Sat Nav:* EX6 8HP. *Tel:* 01626 866259. *Mobile:* 07779 811386. *Water:* 1 lake approx. one acre. *Species:* Carp 24lb plus, Roach to 2lb, Tench to 4lb, Rudd to 12oz, Koi. *Permits:* From the cabin by the lake. *Charges:* 1 rod - £6.50, 2 rods - £7, weekly ticket £30 max two rods, concessions for children. Night fishing by arrangement. *Season:* Open all year. *Methods:* No groundbaiting with boilies, no tiger nuts. Ladies and Gents Toilets. (Suitable disabled fishing).

Luccombes Coarse Fishery &
Contact: Richard Davis, Luccombes Fishery, Towsington Lane, Exminster, Exeter. *Sat Nav:* EX6 8AY. *Tel:* 01823 284990. *Mobile:* 07510 545283. *Water:* 3 acres of five mature ponds with lilies, rushes and fishing platforms accommodating some 30 pegs. *Species:* Common and Mirror Carp to 25lb. Koi to 17lb, Ghost to 8.5lb. Perch 4lb, Bream 2.5lb, Tench 5lb, Roach and Rudd. *Permits:* On site, payable on arrival. *Charges:* Adult day £6 two rods. Under 16 (must be accompanied by an adult) £4.50. Evening after 4pm £4. Season tickets - £150 12 months, £90 6 months. 3 day ticket £16, 7 day ticket £30, 24 hour ticket £12. *Season:* Open all year from 7.30am to 30 mins before dark. *Methods:* Nets to be dipped. Barbless hooks only. No nuts, no fixed feeders. Please use unhooking mats and handle all fish with care.

South View Farm
Contact: Wilf and Dorothy Turner, Shillingford St George, Exeter. *Sat Nav:* EX2 9UP. *Tel:* 01392 832278. *Water:* 3 lakes totalling 3 acres. *Species:* Mirror, Common up to 30lb & Ghost Carp 22lb, Roach 2.5lb, Rudd 2.5lb, Perch 4lb, Bream, Green & Gold Tench to 3.5lb. *Permits:* Tickets on the bank. *Charges:* £6 for two rods, £5 Juniors (under 16, must be accompanied). Evening ticket after 5pm £4 adult, £4 junior. *Season:* Open all year round. 6 am until dusk. *Methods:* Barbless hooks, no keepnets, nets must be dipped, unhooking mats are essential. Boilies only allowed as hookbait. Parking and toilet facilities.

Upham Farm Ponds &

Contact: S.J.Willcocks, Upham Farm, Farringdon, Exeter. *Sat Nav:* EX5 2JA. *Tel:* 01395 232247. *Mobile:* 07971 827552. *Water:* Specimen Carp lake plus 6 well stocked ponds. *Species:* Carp 32lb 4oz, Tench 8lb 8oz and Bream. *Permits:* Day tickets on bank. Telephone for night fishing tickets. *Charges:* £7 per day (concessions for OAP, Junior). £9 per day on specimen lake. *Methods:* Barbless hooks, no keepnets, no trout pellets, no nuts. Unhooking mats to be used.

EXMOUTH

Squabmoor

Contact: South West Lakes Trust. *Sat Nav:* EX9 7AS. *Tel:* 01647 252898. *Water:* Reservoir 4 acres. *Species:* Good head of Carp to 35lb. Roach to 3lb, Tench, Bream and Rudd. *Permits:* Exmouth Tackle (01395 274918), Exeter Angling Centre (01392 436404), and Budleigh News (01395 443272). Exe Valley Angling, Tiverton (01884 242275), or online from our website. Fishing is also available via the Westcountry Rivers Trust Passport Scheme, Tel: 01579 372140. *Charges:* Full day £6.50, conc. £5, 24 hour £12, Season tickets available from Summerlands Tackle (01237 471291) - additional fisheries £35 each. *Season:* Open all year, 24 hours a day.

HALWILL JUNCTION

Springfield Meadows

Contact: Bob Langford, Springfield Meadows, Halwill Junction, Beaworthy. *Sat Nav:* EX21 5UF. *Tel:* 01409 221657. *Water:* Three lakes: 2.5, 2 and 0.5 acres. Two mixed and one Carp. *Species:* Carp 32lb, Tench 13lb, Bream 11lb 4oz, Perch 5lb, Roach 2lb 8oz, Rudd 3lb 8oz and Crucian 3lb 2oz. *Permits:* From bungalow on site. Please ring before arriving. *Charges:* £10 one rod. £15 two rods. Please phone before travelling. *Season:* Open all year. *Methods:* No keepnets. Barbless hooks only. No peanuts, tiger nuts, chick peas or kidney beans.

HATHERLEIGH

Highampton Lakes (Coarse Lake)

Contact: Greenacre Farm, Highampton, Beaworthy. *Sat Nav:* EX21 5LU. *Tel:* 01409 231216. *Water:* Two acre Coarse lake. *Species:* Carp to 26lb plus Tench, Roach, Rudd, Bream and Crucian Carp. *Permits:* Day tickets from lake car park. Available for competitions by prior arrangement. *Charges:* Coarse fishing £7, OAP £4. *Season:* Open all year. *Methods:* Barbless hooks only.

Legge Farm Coarse Fishery &

Contact: Rik Alder, Church Road, Highampton, Beaworthy. *Sat Nav:* EX21 5LF. *Tel:* 01409 231464. *Mobile:* 07815 420297. *Water:* 0.75 acre lake and 4 other ponds. *Species:*

Carp (common to 20lb plus), Tench, Perch to 4.3lb, Roach, Rudd, Crucians, Grass Carp, Bream. *Charges:* Adults £6 a day, OAP £4, Children £3.50. After 4 pm Adults £3.50. *Season:* All year 7am - dusk. *Methods:* Barbless hooks. No radios or plastic bait, no boilies. Children must be accompanied by adults.

HOLSWORTHY

Clawford Vineyard &
Clawford Vineyard, Clawton. *Sat Nav:* EX22 6PN. *Tel:* 01409 254177. *Mobile:* 07554 124700. *Water:* 17 lakes totalling over 45 acres of water. *Species:* Common, Mirror, Crucian, Ghost & Grass Carp, Tench, Roach, Rudd, Orfe, Barbel, Golden Tench, Blue Tench, Golden/Pink Orfe, Green Rudd, Gold Carp, Goldfish, Ide, Chub, Gudgeon. *Permits:* Please note there are currently only three silver fish lakes available for day ticket anglers. All the other lakes are for residents only. *Charges:* On application. *Season:* Open all year. *Methods:* No live or deadbait. No particles or nuts except hemp or sweetcorn. Barbless hooks only. No Carp whatsoever in keepnets. Full rules at the fishery.

Higher Shorston Lakes and Lodges &
Contact: Mr & Mrs R. Fursdon, Staddon Road, Holsworthy. *Sat Nav:* EX22 6NH. *Tel:* 01409 253657. *Mobile:* 07971 260584. *Water:* Two Coarse lakes, each lake in excess of one acre. *Species:* Common, Mirror, Ghost Carp, Roach, Rudd. Carp to over 25lb. *Charges:* Day Tickets Self Service £7. Concessions 2 rods. *Season:* Open all year dawn until dusk. *Methods:* Barbless hooks, no Carp in keepnets, no rigs or fixed leads, no beans or nuts. Other particles to be properly prepared. Unhooking mats to be used for Carp.

Mill Farm Fishery
Bradworthy. *Sat Nav:* EX22 7RX. *Tel:* 01409 241047. *Water:* One large lake. *Species:* Carp, Ghost Carp, Tench, Perch and Bream. *Charges:* £6 per day from farmhouse. *Season:* Open all year, dawn till dusk. *Methods:* Please read full rules on side of lodge before fishing.

Simpson Valley Fishery
Contact: Andrew Moores or Paul Cozens, Simpson Barton, Holsworthy. *Sat Nav:* EX22 6JW. *Tel:* 07855 413672. *Mobile:*

07881 764655. *Water:* 6 Lakes offering Coarse and Stillwater Trout Fishing: Upper Fuzzy 1.5 acre, Lower Fuzzy 1.25 acre, Martins 1 acre, Skylark 1 acre and Jenny Wren 1.25 acre Troutmaster Water. (See Stillwater Trout listing). *Species:* Mirror, Common & Ghost Carp to 25lb, Bream to 6lb, Roach 2lb, Rudd 2lb, Crucians 2lb, Tench 6lb, Perch 4lb, Chub 7lb. *Permits:* Self serving ticket office in house conservatory. Trout Fishing by appointment only. *Charges:* Adult Coarse £5 one rod, 2nd rod £2. Under 16/OAP £3 one rod, 2nd rod £2. *Season:* All year. *Methods:* Barbless hooks only. No Carp in keepnets. No keepnets except organised matches. No Carp sacks. No open fires. Take litter home. All fish to be returned alive as quickly as possible. No bent hook rigs.

Wooda Lakes Holiday Homes
Wooda Lakes, Pancrasweek, Holsworthy. *Sat Nav:* EX22 7JN. *Tel:* 01409 241934. *Water:* Four lakes from 0.75 to 1.5 acres. *Species:* Carp, Tench, Roach, Bream. *Permits:* On the bank. *Charges:* £6 per day. £4 junior/OAP. *Season:* Open all year, dawn to dusk. *Methods:* Barbless hooks only.

Woodacott Holiday Park
Woodacott, Thornbury, Holsworthy. *Sat Nav:* EX22 7BT. *Tel:* 01409 261162. *Water:* Two lakes, 1.25 acre and 1 acre. *Species:* Carp 30lb, Tench 8lb, Bream 5lb, Rudd 2lb, Roach 2lb. *Charges:* Adult Day 2 Rods £6, Juniors: 2 Rods £3. *Season:* All year. *Methods:* Barbless hooks, no keepnets, no boilies or peanuts, no surface fishing.

STILLWATER COARSE

Yeomadon Lakes

Contact: Robert Moore, Yeomadon, Pyworthy, Holsworthy. *Sat Nav:* EX22 6SH. *Tel:* 01409 253378. *Water:* Three 0.5 acre lakes and one acre lake. *Species:* Carp to 20lb, Roach 1.5lb, Bream 1lb, Crucians, Tench 3lb. *Charges:* 2 rods £5. OAP and under 16 £4. *Season:* Open all year dawn to dusk. *Methods:* Barbless hooks only. No keepnets. Groundbait in moderation. No peanuts or particle baits.

Youldon Waters &

Contact: Mick Brook, Youldon Waters, Chilsworthy, Holsworthy. *Sat Nav:* EX22 7JL. *Tel:* 01409 241097. *Mobile:* 07717 313294. *Water:* Two lakes: 1 Acre Carp Lake, relatively unfished. 1 Acre Mixed Species Lake. *Species:* Common, Mirror and Ghost Carp 20lbs plus. Roach 2lb 10oz, Rudd 2lb, Tench 4lb, Bream 4lb, Crucian 2.2lb, Perch 3lb 14oz. *Permits:* From owners on site by prior arrangement as permits are limited for the benefit of all concerned. *Charges:* £5 adults. £4 OAP and accompanied under 16s. *Season:* Open all year. Excellent winter Roach and Perch Fishery. *Methods:* Permits must be booked prior to arrival. Under 16s must be accompanied by an adult. Fishing from marked pegs only. Peg 1 must be vacated if booked by a disabled angler. No keepnets, nuts or seed baits. Groundbait in feeders only. Barbless hooks only. Minimum 8lb line in Carp lake, unhooking mats must be used. All visitors enter at their own risk.

HONITON

Hartsmoor Fisheries &

Contact: John Griss, Bolham Water, Clayhidon, Cullompton. *Sat Nav:* EX15 3QB. *Tel:* 01823 680460. *Water:* Two day ticket lakes - 2 acres and 1.25 acres, One syndicate lake - 3.5 acres, plus 5 acre lake. *Species:* Roach 3lb 10oz, Rudd to 2lb 8oz, Tench 6lb, Bream 7lb, Perch 4lb 3oz, Crucians 3.5lb (not hybrids!), Carp 26.5lb (syndicate 35lb) Gudgeon 4oz. *Permits:* Day tickets on the bank, Syndicate - get your name on the waiting list. *Charges:* £6 per day. £6 per night by arrangement. *Season:* Day tickets dawn to dusk all year round. *Methods:* Barbless hooks plus micro barb for Carp. No nuts of any kind. No Carp over 2lb in keepnets. Loose feed and groundbait is permitted. No braid except marker rods.

Lakeview Manor

Contact: Martin Hyde, Martin Hyde, Dunkeswell, Honiton. *Sat Nav:* EX14 4SH. *Tel:* 01404 891358. *Water:* 2 Lakes each over 1 acre. *Species:* Carp to 25lb, Rudd, Roach and Tench. *Charges:* Membership, annual or short term on application. *Season:* Open all year dawn to dusk. *Methods:* Barbless hooks, no keepnets.

Milton Farm Ponds

Contact: Brian Cook, Milton Farm, Payhembury, Honiton. *Sat Nav:* EX14 3HE. *Tel:* 01404 850236. *Mobile:* 07977 940443. *Water:* 5 lakes approx. 2 acres. *Species:* Carp to 27lb, Tench 8lb, Roach 2lb, Bream, Rudd. *Permits:* Collected on bank. *Charges:* £6 per person per day - no charge for extra rods, £3.50 children 15 or under. Evening £3.50 adults, £2 children. Night fishing by arrangement. *Season:* Open all year round. *Methods:* No groundbaiting with boilies.

ILFRACOMBE

Lower Slade

Contact: South West Lakes Trust. *Sat Nav:* EX34 8NA. *Tel:* 01288 321712. *Water:* Reservoir 6 acres. *Species:* Mirror & Common Carp to 27lb. Bream to 8lb. Perch to 4lb, Roach, Rudd, Gudgeon and Pike to 27lb (no livebaiting). *Permits:* From: Variety Sports (01271 862039), Summerlands (01237 471291) Barnstaple TIC (01271 375000), Richardsons Newsagents (01271 864 668) or online from our website. Fishing is also available via the Westcountry Rivers Trust Passport Scheme, Tel: 01579 372140. *Charges:* Full day £6.50, Conc/Child (12-16 years) £5, 24 hour £12. Season tickets available from Summerlands Tackle (01237 471291) - additional fisheries £35 each. *Season:* Open all year, 24 hours a day. *Methods:* Carp can be caught year round in all areas. Larger Pike on deadbaits, smaller Pike on spinners and plugs. Recently re-stocked with Carp.

Mill Park Coarse Fishing Lake

Contact: Stephen Hill, Mill Park, Mill Lane, Berrynarbor, Ilfracombe. *Sat Nav:* EX34 9SH. *Tel:* 01271 882647. *Water:* 1.5 acre lake between Ilfracombe and Combe Martin. *Species:* Bream, Carp, Roach, Tench, Golden Orfe, Golden Tench, Chub. *Permits:* Day tickets from reception on site. *Charges:* Adult £6.50, Junior £4. All juniors (under 16) must

be accompanied by adult. Evening ticket available - 4pm to 9pm or dusk £4. Evening Junior £.2.50. Residents £2.50 - day, £15 - week. Weekly visitor £39 (non residents). *Season:* Open all year. *Methods:* Barbless hooks only, dip all nets, no night fishing. No landing nets, only in competitions.

KINGSBRIDGE

Bickerton Farm Fishery &
Contact: Mr Graham Tolchard, Bickerton Farm, Hallsands, Kingsbridge. *Sat Nav:* TQ7 2EU. *Tel:* 01548 511220. *Water:* 3 ponds - 0.3 acre, 0.75 acre and 0.5 acre. *Species:* Carp 15lb, Roach, Rudd, Perch, Tench, Bream. *Charges:* £5 per rod Adults/Children. *Methods:* Barbless hooks. No keepnets unless fishing match. No night fishing. Parking very close to pond with level access for disabled. Please phone for further info.

Coombe Water Fisheries &
Contact: J.W. Robinson, Coombe Farm, Kingsbridge. *Sat Nav:* TQ7 4AB. *Tel:* 01548 852038. *Mobile:* 07971 077980. *Water:* 3 Lakes. *Species:* Carp to 25lb, Bream to 4lb, Roach to 2.5lb. *Permits:* No E.A. licence required. Lakes are covered by general E.A. licence. *Charges:* £7 day ticket, £4 Under 16. 1/2 day ticket £5. OAP £5. *Season:* All year dawn to dusk. Night fishing by arrangement only. *Methods:* Barbless hooks, no ground bait, no Carp over 1lb in keepnets.

Emperor Lakes &
Contact: David Lidstone, Blackdown Cross, Loddiswell, Kingsbridge. *Sat Nav:* TQ7 4EA. *Tel:* 01548 821680. *Mobile:* 07814 060147. *Water:* 4.5 acre, 7 acre, and 3.5 acre lakes plus 2 coaching pools. *Species:* Carp over 40lb. Pike over 30lb. Catfish over 70lb. Tench to 12lb. *Charges:* 4.5 acre lake £25 per 24 hours. 3.5 acre lake £17.50 for 24 hours. Booking Line: 07814 060147. *Season:* All year.

Slapton Ley National Nature Reserve
Contact: Nick Binnie, Slapton Ley Field Centre, Slapton, Kingsbridge. *Tel:* 01548 580685. *Water:* Please note all fishing suspended to 2015.

Valley Springs &
Contact: John Bishop, Sherford, Nr Kingsbridge. *Sat Nav:* TQ7 2BG. *Tel:* 01548 531574. *Water:* Coarse lake. *Species:* Common, Mirror, Crucian and Leather Carp. *Permits:*

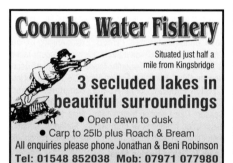
Booking advised. *Charges:* £10 per day. *Season:* Open April - October. *Methods:* Barbless hooks, no keepnets, unhooking mats to be used. All nets to be dipped before fishing.

LAUNCESTON

Westcountry Angling Passport (Downacarey)
Contact: Westcountry Rivers Trust, Rain-Charm House, Kyl Cober Parc, Stoke Climsland, Callington, Cornwall. *Tel:* 01579 372140. *Water:* 1.5 acre lake near St. Giles - On - The - Heath. *Species:* Mixed coarse with Carp, Tench, Bream, Roach and Perch. *Permits:* From: Snowbee UK, Plymouth, PL7 5JY - 01752 334933. Tamar Field and Stream, Lifton, PL16 0AA - 01566 780512. Devil's Stone Inn, Beaworthy, EX21 5RU - 01409 281210. Homeleigh Garden Centre, Launceston, PL15 9SP - 01566 771878. Blisland Inn, Bodmin, PL30 4JK - 01208 850739. Fly Fishing Tackle co uk, Crediton, EX17 2AW - 01363 777783. Hart Flyshop, Exebridge, TA22 9AY - 01398 323008. Lance Nicholson, Dulverton, TA22 9HB - 01398 323409. Tolley's of Tavistock, Tavistock, PL19 0HE - 01822 617186. *Charges:* £5 per rod per day. *Season:* All year.

LEWDOWN

Alder Lake
Contact: Mr Bob Westlake, Alder, Lewdown, Okehampton. *Sat Nav:* EX20 4PJ. *Tel:* 01566 783444. *Water:* 4 acre Lake. *Species:* Perch, Carp to 25lb, Bream to 8.25lb, Specimen

Roach and Tench. Plus natural stock of Trout. *Charges:* £5 per rod per day. *Season:* No closed season. Please phone first as school uses lakes on activity days. *Methods:* No restrictions. Night fishing allowed.

NEWTON ABBOT

Decoy Lake
Contact: Simon Cunningham. *Sat Nav:* TQ12 1EA. *Tel:* 01626 215773. *Water:* 11 acre lake. *Species:* Tench, Roach, Rudd. *Charges:* On application. From above or kiosk on site. *Season:* Open all year. *Methods:* Full rules on site.

Exeter and District A.A. (Abrook Pond) &
Contact: Roly Palmer, PO Box 194, Exeter. *Mobile:* 07970 483913. *Water:* Good looking pond with rustic bridges and plenty of lily pads. Relatively easy fishing for the pleasure or specimen Carp angler. *Species:* Tench, Beam, Roach and Carp to mid twenties. *Permits:* Exeter Angling Centre, Smythen Street (Off Market Street, Exeter). Exmouth Tackle & Sport, The Strand, Exmouth. Tackle Trader, Wharf Road, Newton Abbot. Exe Valley Angling, West Exe South, Tiverton. Tiverton Parkway Station (Cafe), Sampford Peverell. *Charges:* £40 Adults, £5 for Juniors (annual). £5 day. *Season:* Close season March 14th - June 16th. Details in association handbook or from agents. *Methods:* Different restrictions on each water. Details in association handbook.

Learn To Fish In Newton Abbot &
Contact: Paul Power, 103 Broadlands Ave., Newton Abbot. *Tel:* 01626 205941. *Mobile:* 07814 060147. *Water:* Open to all who would like to learn to fish in Newton Abbot area. Angling Trust qualified Coach, coarse and sea angling covered. Tuition free of charge. *Species:* Carp 33lb, Tench 11lb, Bream 9.5lb, Perch 5lb, Roach 2.5lb, Rudd 2lb and Pike 20lb. *Permits:* Tackle Trader, Newton Abbot - 01626 331613. Tidal Tackle Ltd, Torquay. Take the Bait, Teignmouth. Oakford Service Station, Kingsteignton. *Charges:* Dawn - Dusk £6, 24hr ticket £10. *Methods:* Barbless hooks. No nut baits, club rules apply.

Newton Abbot Fishing Association (Coarse Ponds)
Contact: Ian Donaldson (Hon. Secretary), PO Box 229, Totnes. *Water:* 17 coarse ponds in the Newton Abbot area. Also member of S.L.A.C. (Somerset Levels Association of Clubs) with stretches of the Parrett, Brue and Isle. *Species:* Carp to 36lb, Tench to 10lb, Bream to 8lb, Roach to 2lb, Perch to 5lb, Rudd to 1.5lb. *Permits:* From Tackle Trader, Newton Abbot. Oakford Filling Station, Kingsteignton. Torbay Angling, Paignton and Exeter Angling, Exeter, Newton Tackle and Gun, Newton Abbot. *Charges:* Day Tickets: £6 senior, £2 junior, 24 hour ticket £10. Associate licence £50 senior (1 year fishing majority of waters). Full member £75 adult. £15 junior, £30 OAP/Conc. (must live within 20 miles of Newton Abbot). Association key for gates £2. *Season:* Ponds and lakes are open 24 hours a day, 365 days a year. Rivers are controlled by the national close season for coarse fish; Rocombe Ponds and Wapperwell Ponds open from dawn to dusk. *Methods:* Barbless or crushed barbs. 2 rods 1st

Nice 'Ghostie' from Oaktree Fishery

April to 30th September. 3 rods 1st October to 31st March. No lead shot. No nut baits. No fires. No dogs. No keepnets at Rocombe.

Preston Ponds
Contact: Newton Abbot Fishing Association, PO Box 229, Totnes. *Water:* See entry under Newton Abbot Fishing Association. Three ponds at Kingsteignton. Key Transport: Popular match water (full members only). Eddison Pond: small water. Sawmills: about 3 acres coloured by run off from local clay works but don't be put off. *Species:* Key Transport: Skimmers, Bream, big Roach, Rudd, Perch, Tench and Crucians to over a pound. Eddison Pond: Most species with Tench, Crucians and mid-double Carp. Sawmills: Skimmers, Bream, Perch, Tench Carp and Roach to over 1lb with odd Perch to 3lb, Carp to 20lb.

Rackerhayes Complex &
Contact: Newton Abbot Fishing Association, PO Box 229, Totnes. *Tel:* 01626 834032. *Water:* See entry under Newton Abbot Fishing Association. 6 waters just outside Newton Abbot. Island Pond 5 acres, First Pond 2 acres, Dores Pond 9 acres (full members only), Linhay Pond 3 acres, Weedy Pond (just under 1 acre) and Wheel Pond (juniors have preference). Disabled toilet facilities at Rackerhayes. *Species:* Island Pond: most species, Tench over 10lb. Good sized Roach, Rudd, Pike, Bream and Eels. First Pond: Good head of Carp to 20lb, Tench, Roach, Bream etc. and a large number of Jack Pike. Wheel Pond: Carp to 14lb, Roach, Rudd, Perch, Golden Orfe, Tench and occasional small Pike. Linhay Pond: Most coarse species with some excellent Bream. Dores Pond:

Very large head of Carp to 30lb, superb Tench averaging 6lb and up to 11lb 15oz. Weedy Pond: Most coarse fish including good Tench and some large Carp. *Permits:* See main entry. Tench 8lb, Bream 8lb. Weedy Pond - Carp 15lb, Tench 6lb, lots of silver fish. Dores Pond - Full members only - Carp 36lb, Tench 10lb, Pike 20lb, Bream 10lb.

Wapperwell Pond
Contact: Newton Abbot Fishing Association, Ian Donaldson (Hon. Secretary), PO Box 229, Totnes. *Water:* A small secluded pool, good for evening or morning sessions. Now open to juniors if accompanied by over 21 year old. *Species:* Crucians 1lb and Tench 2 to 3lb, Carp 4lb, plenty of Skimmers and Roach.

West Golds
Contact: Newton Abbot Fishing Association, PO Box 229, Totnes. *Water:* A tidal water that is incorporated in the local flood defence system. Extreme care should be taken as flash tidal flooding is common. *Species:* Dace, Roach, Skimmers, Mullet and Carp to over 20lb. Stock changes with flow of higher tides.

NORTH TAWTON
North Tawton Angling Specimen Group
Contact: Mr J.D. Mansfield, 4 Taw Vale Close, North Tawton. *Tel:* 01837 880048. *Mobile:* 07828 324566. *Water:* Fishing waters in Avon, Somerset, Devon & Cornwall. Lake, River & Sea fishing from shore only. *Species:* Any species listed in the British records. *Charges:* Membership: £10 per year adult. £5 under 16 and OAP. Membership starts at 12 years of age. *Season:* June 1st - May 31st. *Methods:* Abide by regulations laid out on lake or river that the group are fishing.

Spires Lakes
Contact: Barry Ware, Riverside, Fore Street, North Tawton. *Sat Nav:* EX20 2ED. *Tel:* 01837 82499. *Water:* Two lakes, 25 peg match lake and 2 acre lake. *Species:* Carp 30lb, Tench 5lb, Roach 1lb 8oz, Rudd 1lb, Bream 3.5lb, Perch 4.6lb, Orfe 6lb, Ghost Carp 1lb, Crucian Carp 2lbs 8oz. *Permits:* On site kiosk, self service. *Charges:* £6 Day, £5 Eve, £5 Junior & OAP. *Season:* Dawn to dusk. All year. *Methods:* Barbless hooks, no boilies, no tiger or peanuts.

OKEHAMPTON
Lakeside Fishery &
Contact: Ian Langbridge, Lower Maddaford, Southcott, Okehampton. *Sat Nav:* EX20 4NL. *Mobile:* 07900 198113. *Water:* Two lakes, 4 acres and 2 acres. *Species:* Mixed Carp (Common, Mirror, Koi, Leather, Crucian, Ghost), Tench, Rudd, Roach, Perch, Bream. *Permits:* On site or from Okehampton Post Office. *Charges:* £5 per day, £2 per extra rod. Night fishing by prior arrangement. £5 a night. *Season:* Open all year. *Methods:* Barbless hooks only. All nets must be dipped. Unhooking mats to be used for Carp. No beans or nuts, other particles to be properly prepared. Fishing dawn to dusk only. EA licence required.

Week Farm &
Contact: John & Grenville Hockridge, Bridestowe, Okehampton. *Sat Nav:* EX20 4HZ. *Tel:* 01837 861221. *Mobile:* 07866 854121. *Water:* Two 0.5 acre lakes & one 0.25 acre lake. *Species:* Mixed Carp (Common, Mirror, Crucian), Bream in 0.25 acre, Roach, Rudd & Green Tench. Prize given for largest catch of the year. *Charges:* £6 per day plus £1 extra rod, £2 eve. Children & OAP half price. *Season:* Open all year. *Methods:* Barbless hooks only, all nets to be dipped, night fishing by arrangement, dogs under control. EA rod licence required.

PAIGNTON
New Barn Angling Centre &
Contact: Yvonne Rogers, Newbarn Farm, Totnes Road, Paignton. *Sat Nav:* TQ4 7PT. *Tel:* 01803 553602. *Mobile:* 07850 907184. *Water:* 6 ponds up to 1.25 acre suitable for juniors (parent supervision), beginners, pleasure and specimen anglers. *Species:* Carp to 28lb, Ghost Carp to 23lb, Crucian Carp (8oz.) Tench to 7lb, Roach to 3lb 8oz, Bream to 9lb, Perch to 4lb 8oz, Rudd to 2lb 8oz. *Permits:* No EA rod licence required as can purchase on site. Purchase day tickets on arrival. *Charges:* To be Confirmed. *Season:* Open all year from 7am - 9pm. Night fishing by appointment only and must be paid in advance. 11 fishing shelters around main lake, first come first served or call to book. Reservations for all anglers. £5 advance booking fee to reserve per swim. *Methods:* Barbless hooks only, no nut baits. All baits

STILLWATER COARSE

4lb 2oz Perch from Hemerdon Lakes - Plymouth Command Angling Assn.

Night (6pm - 6am) £12.50, Evening (4pm - Dusk) £6.50, 24 hrs £17.50. Match lake - Full day £8.50, Night (6pm - 6am) £10.50, Evening (4pm - Dusk) £5.50, 24 hrs £15.50. *Season:* 24hrs, 365 day a year. Night fishing available. *Methods:* A full list of rules are posted on site.

PLYMOUTH

Plymouth and District Angling Club
Contact: Bill Cox, 17 Thetford Gardens, Eggbuckland, Plymouth. *Tel:* 01752 317329. *Water:* 4 lakes at Cadover Bridge, two at St. Germans. - ranging in size from 0.5 to 2 acres. *Species:* Carp to 29lb 8oz, Tench 7lb, Bream 11lb 8oz, Rudd 1lb 6oz, Roach 2lb 8oz and Crucians. *Charges:* Joining fee is £15. If renewed the following year this fee is removed. Full senior members- £40, OAP- £20, all junior- £5. *Season:* Open all year. St Germans and Cadover 24 hours. *Methods:* Barbless hooks. No Carp in keepnets. Unhooking mats for all Carp.

Plymouth and District Angling Club (Filham Lake) &
Contact: Bill Cox, 17 Thetford Gardens, Eggbuckland, Plymouth. *Tel:* 01752 317329. *Water:* Approx. 3 acre lake (Filham Lake). *Species:* Roach, Carp, Chub, Crucian, Bream and Tench. *Permits:* Membership packs from Watermark Centre in Ivybridge who also supply day tickets. *Charges:* £6.25 day ticket. *Season:* Open all year. *Methods:* Barbless Hook. Carp friendly nets to be used (nothing over 3lb in net).

effective. Sensible ground baiting allowed, float fishing and ledgering (ledger rigs will be checked to ensure safety), summer time good for floating baits. No artificial baits.

Town Parks Coarse Fishing Centre &
Contact: Mr J. Hewitt, Town Parks Farm, Totnes Road, Paignton. *Sat Nav:* TQ4 7PY. *Tel:* 01803 523133. *Water:* Specimen Carp lake 1.5 acres (max 16 anglers at any one time). Match lake 2 acres (21 pegs) available for club/block bookings, phone for details. *Species:* Carp lake - Mirror and Common Carp to 32lbs. Match lake - Carp 10lbs, Crucian Carp 3lbs, Tench 5lbs, Chub 4lbs, Bream 4lbs, Roach 2lbs, Rudd 1lb, Perch 4lbs, Catfish to 40lbs. *Permits:* No E.A. Rod licence required. *Charges:* Carp lake - Full day £10,

STILLWATER COARSE

Plymouth Command Angling Association (Ponds) &

Contact: Mr Vic Barnett Hon. Sec., 5 Weir Close, Mainstone, Plymouth. *Tel:* 01752 708206. *Mobile:* 07710 552910. *Water:* Two lakes of 0.75 and 1.25 acres for coarse fishing within ten minutes of Plymouth. Also member access to several associated waters in the south west. Qualified tuition available for newcomers to the sport. Friendly advice and tuition for family members. *Species:* Carp, Tench, Bream, Perch, Roach, Rudd, Crucians, Goldfish, Eels, Golden Carp and some Koi. *Permits:* Membership is open to all serving members of HM Forces. Associate membership is also open to ex-serving members of HM Forces, no matter when the time was served. Day tickets available from Trader Jacks, Manadon, Plymouth, Premier Angling and Tackle Barn, £5 per person, up to 8 per day in total. *Charges:* Costs for full or associate membership are available on application at the above contact. Carp society for the specimen angler - details on application. *Season:* No close season for coarse fish. *Methods:* Barbless hooks only at the coarse fishery. Knotless keepnets to be used as per E.A. guidelines, minimum 3 metres length. All spawning fish are to be returned to the water immediately. No Carp over 2lb in keepnets.

Sunridge Fishery &

Contact: D Hammett, Sunridge Nurseries, Worston, Yealmpton, Plymouth. *Sat Nav:* PL8 2LN. *Tel:* 01752 880438. *Mobile:* 07817 749091. *Water:* Approx. half acre private lake, which is 13 feet when full that can be reserved for exclusive use. Established 30 years. *Species:* Mirror and Common Carp up to 27lb. *Permits:* From the Nurseries. *Charges:* £10 adult day, £6 child/OAP. *Season:* Open all year dawn to dusk, night fishing by arrangement only. *Methods:* Barbless hooks only, no keepnets (except by prior arrangement).

Warleigh Barton Fishery

Contact: Andrew Kent, Tamerton Foliot, Plymouth. *Sat Nav:* PL5 4LG. *Tel:* 01752 771458. *Mobile:* 07811 339569. *Water:* 2 acre lake plus 0.25 acre pond. *Species:* Mirror and Common up to 30lbs. *Permits:* Day tickets. *Charges:* £10 per day, £15 for 24 hrs. *Season:* All year. *Methods:* Barbless hooks, no keep nets.

Remember a & means the fishery has disabled facilities - contact them direct for further details

SEATON

Horriford Fishing &

Contact: Mr Pady, Horriford Farm, Colyford, Colyton. *Sat Nav:* EX24 6HW. *Tel:* 01297 552316. *Water:* 2 ponds - 1 with access for disabled. *Species:* Bream 5lb, Roach 1lb, Tench 6lb, Carp 15lb, Perch 2lb, Rudd 1.5lb. *Permits:* From farmhouse or on bank. *Charges:* Day ticket £5. Half day ticket £3. Six month tickets £65 single, £80 family. *Season:* Open all year dawn to dusk. *Methods:* Barbless hooks only, no boilies.

SOUTH BRENT

Hatchlands Coarse Fishery &

Contact: Malcolm Davies, Greyshoot Lane, Rattery, South Brent. *Sat Nav:* TQ10 9LN. *Tel:* 01364 73500. *Mobile:* 07967 010136. *Water:* Two 2 acre lakes. *Species:* Carp to 22lb, Tench, Roach, Bream, Rudd and Gudgeon. *Permits:* E.A. licence required. *Charges:* £6 per person per day. *Season:* Open all year. *Methods:* Barbless hooks only. No large Carp in keepnets.

Little Allers Coarse Fishery

Contact: M & J Wakeham, Little Allers Farm, Avonwick, South Brent. *Sat Nav:* TQ10 9HA. *Tel:* 01364 72563. *Mobile:* 07855 427510. *Water:* 2 acre lake. *Species:* Carp, Bream, Tench, Roach, Rudd. *Charges:* £5 per day adults, £3 under 16, £3 evening ticket after 5pm. Payments at hut in car park (correct money). *Season:* Open all year dawn to dusk. *Methods:* Barbless hooks only, no Carp in keepnets. No dogs allowed. No bait boats.

SOUTH MOLTON

Furzebray Carp Lakes

Contact: MJ and TJ Kingdon, Furzebray Farm, George Nympton Road, South Molton. *Sat Nav:* EX36 4ER. *Tel:* 01769 572653. *Water:* 3 acre specimen lake. 2 acre Willow Lake. *Species:* Specimen Lake: Carp to over 39lb and Perch. Willow Lake: Carp. *Permits:* Bookings only on 01769 572653. *Charges:* Specimen Lake: Day £10, 24 hours £25. Willow Lake: Day £10, 24 hours £15. *Season:* Open all year.

STILLWATER COARSE

Oaktree Fishery &

Bottreaux Mill, West Anstey, South Molton. *Sat Nav:* EX36 3PU. *Tel:* 01398 341568. *Water:* Three 2 acre lakes. *Species:* Catfish to 56lb, Carp over 35lb, Tench to 8lb, Bream, Roach, Perch to over 5lb, Koi Carp. *Permits:* On site only from tackle and bait shop. *Charges:* Otter Lake/Oaktree Lake - 1 rod £7, 2 rods £8 - £1 less for concessions. Extra rods for Otter/Oaktree £3. Stags Lake £10 up to 2 rods - extra rods £5. 24 hour ticket £15. *Season:* Open all year 24hrs. *Methods:* Barbless hooks only. No nut type baits. See board at fishery.

Riverside Caravan and Camping Park &

Contact: Nicky Penfold, Marsh Lane, North Molton Road, South Molton. *Sat Nav:* EX36 3HQ. *Tel:* 01769 579269. *Water:* Three lakes covering approx. 5 acres. Also stretch of the River Mole. *Species:* Specimen lakes Carp to over 28lb. Beginners lake: Bream, Tench, Carp, Perch, Koi. *Charges:* Day tickets from £6. Extra rods £3. Also concession, weekly and evening tickets. Prices on application. River day ticket £5. Booking advisable. *Season:* Open all year. *Methods:* Full rules on site.

TAVISTOCK

Milemead Fisheries &

Contact: Andrew & Paul Evenden, Mill Hill, Tavistock. *Sat Nav:* PL19 8NP. *Tel:* 01822 610888. *Water:* Three lakes of 2 acres each comprising of : Specimen Carp lake exclusively stocked with quality Carp to 30lb plus. Carp lake - stocked with 11 coarse species with Carp to 20lb. Match lake - open matches are held throughout the year on alternate Sundays, together with our popular Summer Thursday evening matches which run between May and July. An 8 peg Canal and Canal Basin - 16 peg pleasure and mini match water. *Species:* Specimen Lake Carp to 30lb plus (average 15lb). Other lakes: Carp to 20lb. Tench to 4lb, Bream to 4.5lb, Roach to 2lb 10oz, Rudd to 1.5lb, Crucians to 1.5lb, Barbel 2lb & Chub stocked in match lake. *Permits:* Available from tackle and bait shop should be purchased prior to fishing. *Charges:* Adult - Day £8, Concession £7, Evening Adult £5, Concessions £4. Specimen Lake - pre booking is essential £11 day, £22 for 24hrs. All prices are for 2 rods per person. *Season:* All year excluding Christmas Day and Boxing Day, 7am to dusk. Night fishing only permitted on specimen lake. *Methods:* Barbless Hooks, keepnets only in official matches or on Canal and Basin. No fixed leads or fixed feeders allowed. Floating baits to be freelined only - no bubble floats or controllers. Please read the rule boards.

TIVERTON

Coombe Farm Fishponds

Contact: Mrs Curtis, Coombe Farm, Cadleigh, Tiverton. *Sat Nav:* EX16 8HW. *Tel:* 01884 855337. *Mobile:* 07855 416369. *Water:* 2 lakes totalling 0.5 acre. *Species:* Carp to 20lb, Roach, Tench to 4lb, Bream to 1.5lb. *Charges:* £3 per day. *Season:* Open all year. *Methods:* No boilies.

STILLWATER COARSE

Dart Raffe Fishery
Contact: Mr and Mrs G Manning. *Sat Nav:* EX16 8PX. *Tel:* 01884 560557. *Water:* 1.5 acre lake. *Species:* Carp, Tench, Roach, Rudd, Eels. *Permits:* From the above. *Charges:* Per person up to 3 rods £10. *Season:* Strictly by arrangement only.

Tiverton and District Angling Club &
Contact: Exe Valley Angling, 19 Westexe South, Tiverton. *Tel:* 01884 242275. *Water:* 11.5 Miles on Grand Western Canal, 1.25 acre mixed fishery lake at Exebridge. Various stretches on several rivers in Somerset. *Species:* Canal: Carp, Bream, Tench, Roach, Perch, Pike, Eels. Lakeside: Carp, Bream, Roach, Tench, Eels, Crucian Carp. *Permits:* Please ring Exe Valley for details. Also available from: Exeter Angling Centre, Enterprise Angling Taunton, Topp Tackle Taunton & Minnows Caravan Park - beside Grand Western Canal. *Charges:* Senior: Day £5, Annual £30. Junior (10 - 17): Day £3, Annual £10. OAP: Day £5, Annual £15. Under 10's Free. *Season:* Open all year. *Methods:* Canal Methods: Any. Restrictions: Fish from permanent pegs, no night fishing, no cars on bank, no digging of banks or excessive clearance of vegetation. Lakeside Methods: Any. Restrictions: No night fishing, no boilies, Trout pellets or nuts, one rod only, fishing from permanent pegs, no dogs, nets to be dipped. Ring Exe Valley Angling for full details.

West Pitt Farm Fishery &

Contact: Susanne Westgate, Whitnage, Nr. Tiverton. *Sat Nav:* EX16 7DU. *Tel:* 01884 820296. *Mobile:* 07855 582374. *Water:* 3 lakes up to 2.75 acres. *Species:* Common & Mirror Carp, Bream, Tench, Roach, Rudd, Crucians, Golden Tench, and Golden Orfe. *Permits:* Self service day tickets (correct money please!). *Charges:* £7 day, £4 evening. *Season:* Open dawn till dusk all year round. *Methods:* No boilies. Barbless hooks only, nets to be dipped, groundbait in moderation.

TORQUAY

Butterlake Fishing Club

Contact: John Palmer, 37 Allerbrake Road, Newton Abbot. *Water:* Freshwater Pond at Compton. *Species:* Tench, Carp, Perch, Crucian Carp. *Permits:* To apply and join the waiting list please apply in writing to John Palmer. *Charges:* Day tickets restricted to members and their families. *Season:* Open all year. *Methods:* Keepnets permitted.

TORRINGTON

Bakers Farm

Contact: Mr & Mrs Ridd, Bakers Farm, Moortown, Torrington. *Sat Nav:* EX38 7ES. *Tel:* 01805 623260. *Water:* 1 acre lake. *Species:* Mirror & Common Carp, Tench, Roach & Rudd. Carp 5lb - 20lb. *Charges:* £5 per rod per day. *Season:* Open all year. Dawn to dusk. *Methods:* Barbless Hooks, no large Carp in keepnets.

Darracott

Contact: South West Lakes Trust Fishery Assistant. *Sat Nav:* EX38 7HL. *Tel:* 01288 361712. *Water:* Reservoir 3 acres. *Species:* Roach up to 2lb. Mixed bags to 20lb plus of Roach, Rudd, Bream and Tench. Perch to 4lb. Carp to 25lb. *Permits:* From: Whiskers Pet Centre, Torrington (01805 622859), Summerlands, Westward Ho! (01237 471291), Bideford TIC (01237 477676), Barley Grove Service Station, Torrington (01805 623340), Exe Valley Angling, Tiverton (01884 242275), Barnstaple TIC (01271 375000), Barton Torrs Stores (01237 472977) or online from our website. Fishing is also available via the Westcountry Rivers Trust Passport Scheme, Tel: 01579 372140. *Charges:* Full day £6.50, Conc/Child (12-16 years) £5, 24 hour £12. Season tickets available from Summerlands Tackle (01237 471291) - additional fisheries £35 each. *Season:* Open all year 24 hours a day. *Methods:* Good surface fishing year round. Method feeder or pole for mixed bags using worm and corn hookbait.

Stevenstone Lakes

Contact: Rebecca Parnell, Deer Park, Stevenstone, Torrington. *Sat Nav:* EX38 7HY. *Tel:* 01805 622102. *Water:* Three lakes, total of four acres in a parkland setting. *Species:* Mirror Carp 26lb, Common 13lb, Tench 6lb, Rudd 1lb, Eels 3lb. *Permits:* Only at Deer Park. *Charges:* Day tickets £10 per person per day. *Season:* Open 7am to sunset all year around. *Methods:* Barbless hooks only, no boilies, no nut type baits, no fish over 2lb in keepnets, no dogs, no litter. Unhooking mats essential.

STILLWATER COARSE

TOTNES

M and B East Moore Farm Fishery &
Contact: John Lear, Diptford, Totnes. *Sat Nav:* TQ9 7PE. *Tel:* 01626 203460. *Mobile:* 07739 082888. *Water:* Two acre lake. *Species:* Carp to 20lb, Roach, Rudd, Bream, Tench and Perch. *Permits:* Rod licence required. *Charges:* On site, £5 OAP, £10 all other day tickets. £15 24 hours. *Season:* Dawn to dusk, April 1st to Oct 31st. Night fishing by arrangement. *Methods:* No keepnets, landing mats must be used, no boilies, barbless hooks only. Full rules at Fishery.

Wagland Lake
Contact: Rupert Cutcliffe, Wagland Farm, Halwell, Totnes. *Sat Nav:* TQ9 7LB. *Tel:* 01548 821293. *Mobile:* 07411 096908. *Water:* 1.75 acre specimen Carp & Coarse lake. *Species:* Carp to 31 lbs 8oz, Tench to 8lbs 2oz, Rudd to 3lbs 12oz, Roach to 2lbs 12oz, Perch to 3lbs 8oz and Pike to mid doubles. *Permits:* Day tickets, night fishing, 24 hour or longer, winter syndicate (runs 15th Oct-15th Mar). *Charges:* Day £12. Night £15. 24 hours £20. For longer sessions please enquire. Winter syndicate please enquire. *Season:* Fishing all year, 24 hours a day. *Methods:* Barbless hooks only, no keepnets, no braid mainline, no leadcore, no nuts, minimum 12lb line Carp, minimum 7lb line coarse, landing nets 36" for Carp/unhooking mats must be used, bivvies allowed and no bait boats.

UMBERLEIGH

Golland Farm
Contact: Claire Bryce, Golland Farm, Burrington, Umberleigh. *Sat Nav:* EX37 9JP. *Mobile:* 07516 601585. *Water:* 2 half acre lakes. Brook fishing for wild Brown Trout. *Species:* Hundreds of Carp, average 6lb, run to 15lb+ easy pleasure fishing, Tench and Roach. Quality hard fighting fish. *Permits:* Available from Farm House. *Charges:* Day tickets. £5 per person per day or night. *Season:* Lakes open all year, brook fishing seasonal. *Methods:* Barbless hooks only, no Carp in keepnets, no spinning.

WINKLEIGH

Stafford Moor Fishery &
Contact: Andy or Debbie Seery, Dolton, Winkleigh. *Sat Nav:* EX19 8PP. *Tel:* 01805 804360. *Water:* 8 acre specimen lake, 100 peg match fishery (bookings available); 100 peg pleasure lake. 4 acre Carp bagging water (3lb to 10lb fish). 3 acre lake with Tench, Crucians and Bream. *Species:* Carp 30lb, Tench 5lb, Bream 5lb, Roach 2lb, Rudd 1.5lb, Eels 5lb. 318lb match record. *Permits:* At lodge at Stafford Moor. Specimen lake pre-booking only. *Charges:* £7.50 pleasure/

Remember a & means the fishery has disabled facilities - contact them direct for further details

day, £6 conc./OAP/junior; £9 specimen/day (12 hrs) £9 night (12 hrs). *Season:* All year. *Methods:* The method is banned, barbless hooks (max. size 6), night fishing by arrangement.

YELVERTON

Coombe Fisheries &

Contact: Mr Stephen Horn, Yelverton, Plymouth. *Sat Nav:* PL20 6HR. *Tel:* 01822 855585. *Mobile:* 07899 958493. *Water:* Two 1 acre lakes. *Species:* Rudd, Roach, various Carp (28lb), Tench (8lb), Crucian, Eels, Wild Trout. *Charges:* £6 day, £4 evening. *Season:* No close season, dawn to dusk. Night fishing by arrangement. *Methods:* Barbless hooks, no peanuts.

Victoria is delighted with this 7.5lb Carp from Kingslake

Stillwater Trout

ASHBURTON

Venford

Contact: South West Lakes Trust. *Sat Nav:* TQ13 7SS. *Tel:* 01822 855700. *Water:* Reservoir 33 acres. *Species:* Wild Brown Trout. *Permits:* Fishing is also available via the Westcountry Rivers Trust Passport Scheme, Tel: 01579 372140. *Charges:* Free to holders of a valid Environment Agency Licence. Bag limit of 4 fish over seven inches. *Season:* 15 March - 12 October. *Methods:* Angling by spinning, fly or bait.

BARNSTAPLE

Blakewell Fishery &

Contact: Mr Richard & John Nickell, Blakewell Fishery, Muddiford, Barnstaple. *Sat Nav:* EX31 4ET. *Tel:* 01271 344533. *Water:* 5 acre lake. Disabled toilets and facilities. Wheelchair friendly. Parking close to lake. *Species:* Rainbow to 15lb 10oz. Brown to 12lb. *Permits:* On site. *Charges:* 10 Fish £60, 6 Fish £36, 5 Fish £34, 4 Fish £32, 3 Fish £30, 2 Fish £26. *Season:* All year. *Methods:* Fly Only. No catch and release.

Bratton Fly Fishery

Contact: Mike or Jan, Bratton Fishery, Loxhore Cross, Nr. Barnstaple. *Sat Nav:* EX31 4ST. *Tel:* 01271 850642. *Water:* Two acre site. *Species:* Rainbow and predominately Brown Trout. *Permits:* E.A. rod licence required. *Charges:* 2 fish £20. 3 fish £22. 4 fish £26. 5 fish £28. *Season:* Open all year, 9am to dusk. *Methods:* Fly only. Strictly no catch and release.

Southwood Fishery

Contact: Nigel Early, Bratton Fleming. *Sat Nav:* EX32 7JX. *Tel:* 01271 343608 or 01598 710787. *Mobile:* 07767 492800. *Water:* 2.5 acre lake, max 10 rods. *Species:* Rainbow to 20lbs plus. Brown to 10lb. *Permits:* Must be obtained in advance. Please phone numbers above. *Charges:* £25 for 4 fish and nothing stocked under 3lbs. *Season:* Open all year. *Methods:* Tickets must be pre-booked. Fly only, children under 16 must be accompanied by a fishing adult.

BEAWORTHY

Trout Lake

Contact: Mr Zyg Gregorek, Anglers Nirvana, The Gables, Winsford, Halwill. *Sat Nav:* EX21 5XT. *Tel:* 01409 221559. *Water:* 3 acres. *Species:* 5 different species of Trout. Blue, Rainbow, Tiger, Brown and Golden. Grass Carp, Golden Orfe and Golden Tench. *Permits:* Only at Anglers Paradise. Pre booking advisable. *Charges:* £20 per 8 hours. *Season:* All year. 8am to 9pm or dusk (which ever is earlier). No Night fishing. *Methods:* Catch and release only, fly only. Barbless hooks only. Landing nets must be used. Anglers Paradise rules and regulations apply. Please try and unhook in water.

BIDEFORD

Fosfelle Country House Hotel (Game)

Contact: Hilary and Peter Mcardell, Hartland, Bideford. *Sat Nav:* EX39 6EF. *Tel:* 01237 441273. *Water:* Approx. half acre Lake. *Species:* Rainbow & Golden Trout. *Charges:* £18 half day - 2 Trout, full day £23 - 3 fish. *Season:* Open all year. *Methods:* Displayed on site.

Haycroft Fishing Club

Contact: Mr John Irving. *Tel:* 01409 240026. *Water:* Two lakes totalling 3 acres. *Species:* Rainbow Trout to 3lb. *Permits:* Annual membership only. *Charges:* Annual membership costs £200. *Season:* All year during daylight hours. *Methods:* Fly fishing only.

Torridge Fly Fishing Club

Contact: Michael Ball, 111 Morwenna Park Road, Northam, Bideford. *Tel:* 01237 700205. *Mobile:* 07899 742757. *Water:* Fishing Gammaton 2 x 4 acre reservoirs situated 2 miles east of Bideford. *Species:* Stocked Rainbow Trout from 2 - 4lb. Natural Browns to 5lb. *Permits:* 2 day tickets allowed each day. *Charges:* Day tickets: from Summerlands Fishing Tackle, Westward Ho!, Tel. 01237 471291. £20 per day (3 fish limit) Season tickets: £150 (waiting list, membership limited to 30). *Season:* 1st April - end of November for Rainbow Trout, 1st April - 30 September for Brown Trout. Sunrise - Sunset. *Methods:* Fishing rules on car park board. Fly only.

Stunning Brownie from Blakewell

STILLWATER TROUT

CHAGFORD

Fernworthy

Contact: South West Lakes Trust. *Sat Nav:* TQ13 8EA. *Tel:* 01647 277587. *Water:* Reservoir 78 acres. *Species:* Brown Trout. *Permits:* Self Service Kiosk on site or online from our website. Fishing is also available via the Westcountry Rivers Trust Passport Scheme, Tel: 01579 372140. *Charges:* Full day £14, Concession £12, Child £5. Season permits also available from Summerlands Tackle (01237 471291). *Season:* 1 April - 12 October. *Methods:* Catch & Release operates (barbless hooks must be used).

CHUDLEIGH

Kennick &

Contact: South West Lakes Trust. *Sat Nav:* EX6 7NZ. *Tel:* 01647 252898. *Water:* Reservoir 50 acres. *Species:* Rainbow fishery. Boats available including Wheelyboats. To guarantee boats please book at least 24hrs in advance via the ranger. Rod average 2012: 2.8 fish per rod per day. Fishery record 14lb 11oz. *Permits:* Self service at Kennick hut or online from our website. Fishing is also available via the Westcountry Rivers Trust Passport Scheme, Tel: 01579 372140. *Charges:* Full day £22.50, Concession £19, Evening £18. Catch and Release Tickets £14, Child £5. Boats £15 per day. Season permits also available from Summerlands Tackle (01237 471291). *Season:* 15 March - 31 October 2013. *Methods:* Catch and release available (barbless hooks must be used), fly fishing only.

Kennick Fly Fishers Association &

Contact: Mike Boston, 5 Shirburn Rd, Torquay. *Tel:* 01803 325722. *Water:* 45 acre reservoir. *Species:* Rainbow & wild Brown Trout. *Permits:* Club members able to obtain SWLT discounted tickets. *Charges:* Membership fee for club is £10 annual subscription. Under 16yrs free. *Methods:* I.A.W. SWLT byelaws.

HOLSWORTHY

Simpson Valley Fishery

Contact: Andrew Moores or Paul Cozens, Simpson Barton, Holsworthy. *Sat Nav:* EX22 6JW. *Tel:* 07855 413672. *Mobile:* 07881 764655. *Water:* Jenny Wren 1.5 acre Troutmaster Water plus Coarse Lakes. (See Stillwater Coarse listing). Skylark 1 acre Troutmaster. Mallard 2.5 acre. *Species:* Jenny Wren: Rainbow Trout 2-18lb, Browns to 7lb, Blues to 9lb, Tigers 6lb. Skylark: Rainbow from 1lb to 6lb, Browns 12oz-6lb. Mallard: Rainbow 1lb-6lb. *Permits:* Trout Fishing by appointment only. Self serving ticket office in house conservatory. *Charges:* Jenny Wren: 2 fish ticket £17, 3 fish ticket £22, 4 fish ticket £27. Skylark: 1 fish ticket £7, 2 fish ticket £10, 3 fish ticket £15, 4 fish ticket £20. *Season:* All year. *Methods:* Fly only. All Trout must be kept and recorded in the catch records, located in the Trout Hut - Jenny Wren - fly only. Skylark - fly, lure, catch and release from 1st Oct - 31st March. Mallard - lure and fly.

HONITON

Hollies Trout Farm ♿

Contact: Robert and Ginny Snaith, Sheldon, Honiton. *Sat Nav:* EX14 4QS. *Tel:* 01404 841428. *Water:* 2 Stream fed lakes totalling 2.5 acres and 1 small pool. *Species:* Rainbow & Brown Trout. Best Rainbow 22lb (July 2011). Best Brown 7lb 7oz (July 2010). *Permits:* Tickets available on site. *Charges:* 2 fish - £17, 3 fish - £20, 4 fish - £25, 5 fish - £30. Catch and release £15 half day, £20 full day. Concessions for under 12's. *Season:* Open all year dawn to dusk. *Methods:* Barbless hooks debarbed when fishing catch and release.

Stillwaters Lake ♿

Contact: Michael Ford, Lower Moorhayne Farm, Yarcombe, Honiton. *Sat Nav:* EX14 9BE. *Tel:* 01404 861284. *Water:* One acre lake for Brown and Rainbow fishing. Sea Trout fishing on the River Axe. *Species:* Trout up to 17lb 10oz in lake (2003) and 10lb 4oz in lake (2006). Best Sea Trout in 2006 3.5lbs. (2010) 6lb 12 oz Rainbow Trout in Lake. River Axe Sea Trout and a few Salmon. *Charges:* £25 per day. £15 for a morning, £15 afternoon. *Season:* March 1st - November 30th. *Methods:* Fly only. Catch and release, no keepnets.

LIFTON

Arundell Arms (Trout Lake)

Contact: Adam Fox-Edwards, The Arundell Arms, Lifton. *Sat Nav:* PL16 0AA. *Tel:* 01566 784666. *Water:* Three acre private lake for Hotel residents only. 20 miles of river fishing on Tamar, Lyd, Carey, Thrushel, Wolf, Ottery and Lew. Day permits available for non-residents on our river beats. *Species:* Rainbow & Brown Trout in lake. Salmon, Sea Trout, Brown Trout and Grayling on rivers. *Permits:* Arundell Arms. Cockpit Tackle Shop open 9-10am and 6.30-7.00pm daily in the season. *Charges:* Lake £38, residents only on lake. £30 Trout fishing on rivers, Salmon up to £40. *Season:* Open all year (lake). Rivers: Trout 15th March to 30th September. Sea Trout 3rd March to 30th September. Salmon 1st March to 14th October. Grayling 16th June to 14th March. *Methods:* Fly only on lake and rivers. Spinning (for Salmon only) permitted on River Tamar.

OKEHAMPTON

Meldon

Contact: South West Lakes Trust. *Sat Nav:* EX20 4LU. *Tel:* 01409 211507. *Water:* Reservoir 57 acres. *Species:* Wild Brown Trout. *Permits:* Fishing is also available via the Westcountry Rivers Trust Passport Scheme, Tel: 01579 372140. *Charges:* Free to holders of a valid Environment Agency Licence. Bag limit of 4 fish over seven inches. *Season:* 15 March to 12 October. *Methods:* Angling by spinning, fly or bait.

Roadford ♿

Contact: South West Lakes Trust, Angling & Watersports Centre. *Sat Nav:* PL16 0JL. *Tel:* 01409 211507. *Water:* Reservoir 738 acres. *Species:* Brown Trout. Boats available including a Wheelyboat. To guarantee boats please book at least 24hrs in advance. *Permits:* Angling & Watersports Centre at Lower Goodacre or online from our website. Fishing is also available via the Westcountry Rivers Trust Passport Scheme, Tel: 01579 372140. *Charges:* Full day £14, Concession £12, Child £5. Boats £15 per day. Season permits also available from Summerlands Tackle (01237 471291). *Season:* 15 March to 12 October. *Methods:* Fly fishing only, catch and release available. (barbless hooks must be used). Self launch for kayak and float tube fishing available, please enquire on site for further information.

SOUTH BRENT

Avon Dam

Contact: South West Lakes Trust. *Sat Nav:* TQ10 9ED. *Tel:* 01822 855700. *Water:* Reservoir 50 acres. *Species:* Wild Brown Trout. *Permits:* Fishing is also available via the Westcountry Rivers Trust Passport Scheme, Tel: 01579 372140. *Charges:* Free to holders of a valid Environment Agency Licence. Bag limit of 4 fish over seven inches. *Season:* 15 March to 12 October. *Methods:* Angling by spinning, fly or bait.

Hatchlands Trout Lakes ♿

Contact: Malcolm Davies, Greyshoot Lane, Rattery, South Brent. *Sat Nav:* TQ10 9LN. *Tel:* 01364 73500. *Mobile:* 07967 010136. *Water:* 6 acres. *Species:* Rainbow and Brown Trout. *Permits:* E.A. Licence required. *Charges:* Prices from £14 for 2 fish. Other prices on application. *Season:* Open all year.

SOUTH MOLTON

Wistlandpound ♿

Contact: South West Lakes Trust. *Sat Nav:* EX31 4SJ. *Tel:* 01398 371116. *Water:* Reservoir 41 acres. *Species:* Rainbow Trout. A Wheelyboat is available for disabled anglers via the Calvert Trust (01598 763221). *Permits:* Challacombe Post Office (01598 763229), Variety Sports (01271 862039), Calvert Trust (01598 763221). Barnstaple TIC (01271 375000), Richardsons Newsagents (01271 864668) or online from our website. Fishing is also available via the Westcountry Rivers Trust Passport Scheme, Tel: 01579 372140. *Charges:* Full day £16, conc. £13.50, evening £12. Catch and release £13, Child £5. Season permits also available from Summerlands Tackle (01237 471291). *Season:* 15 March - 31 October. *Methods:* Fly fishing only, catch and release available - barbless hooks must be used.

Wistlandpound Fly Fishing Club ♿

Contact: Nigel Bird, 9 Kingston Avenue, Combe Martin. *Tel:* 01271 883252. *Water:* Fishing regular monthly competitions at Wistlandpound and other waters. Regular social events. Juniors welcome. *Species:* Rainbow Trout 1.5 to 2lb. Brown Trout 8oz to 1lb. *Permits:* Permits to fish Wistlandpound available at a reduced rate - members only. *Charges:* Subscriptions (March to March): Adults £14, Under 16s 50p. Free tuition arranged. *Season:* Seasonal at Wistlandpound. Competitions all year round. *Methods:* Fly fishing only.

STILLWATER TROUT

TAVISTOCK

Tavistock Trout Farm & Fishery &

Contact: Abigail Underhill, Parkwood Road, Tavistock. *Sat Nav:* PL19 9JW. *Tel:* 01822 615441. *Mobile:* 07970 608890. *Water:* 5 lakes totalling approx. 4 acres. *Species:* Rainbow Trout (Osprey 3lb/Kingfisher & Heron 2lb to 14lb), Brown Trout. *Permits:* E.A Licences available and required. *Charges:* Osprey 3 fish £50. Kingfisher/Heron 4 fish £35. Please enquire for more permit prices. *Season:* Open all year 8am - dusk. Closed Christmas Day and Boxing Day. Fishery is closed on Mondays(except Bank Holidays). *Methods:* Max hook size 10.

TIVERTON

Bellbrook Valley Trout Fishery &

Contact: Mr Chris Atwell, Bellbrook Farm, Oakford, Tiverton. *Sat Nav:* EX16 9EX. *Tel:* 01398 351292. *Mobile:* 07967 335159. *Water:* 6 Lakes totalling 7.5 acres. *Species:* Rainbow Trout (25lb 12oz), Exmoor Blue (13lb 6oz) and Brown Trout (14lb 2oz). *Charges:* Half day prices: Three fish normal lakes £22, 2 fish specimen lake £25. Range of rover tickets allowing mix of normal and specimen from £26. Gift Certificates and season tickets available. *Season:* Open all year 8am to dusk (No later than 9.00pm). *Methods:* Fly only. Fishery has some disabled access.

TOTNES

Newhouse Fishery

Contact: Mrs Pam Cook, Newhouse Farm, Moreleigh, Totnes. *Sat Nav:* TQ9 7JS. *Tel:* 01548 821426. *Water:* 4 acre lake (also see entry under River Fishing, Avon, Devon). *Species:* Rainbow Trout, Brown Trout. *Charges:* Various tickets available. Bag limits may be made up in beginners lake. No EA Rod Licence required, lakes are covered by a general licence issued by the Environment Agency. *Season:* Open all year. 8am to 1hr after sunset. *Methods:* Fly only, barbed hooks.

Remember a & means the fishery has disabled facilities - contact them direct for further details

YELVERTON

Burrator

Contact: South West Lakes Trust. *Sat Nav:* PL20 6PE. *Tel:* 01822 855700. *Water:* Reservoir 150 acres. *Species:* Rainbow & Brown Trout (all Brown Trout must be returned). *Permits:* Yelverton Garage. Snowbee UK., (01752 334933) or online from our website. Fishing is also available via the Westcountry Rivers Trust Passport Scheme, Tel: 01579 372140. *Charges:* Full Day £17. Concession £14.50. Child £5, Eve £13. Season Permits from Summerlands Tackle (01237 471291), £260 adult, £50 junior. Concession £220. *Season:* 15th March to 31 October 2013. *Methods:* Fly fishing only, catch and release available - barbless hooks must be used.

Burrator Fly Fishers

Contact: Peter Macconnell, 6 Lyndhurst Road, Plymouth. *Tel:* 01752 560538. *Mobile:* 07738 378227. *Water:* Burrator Fly Fishers Association is a small club running competitions during the summer and winter, with fishing trips to local stillwaters. Regular monthly meetings all year. The club has 2 boats on Burrator Reservoir, one has been adapted for the disabled angler. *Species:* Stocked Rainbow and Brown Trout. *Permits:* Esso Garage, Yelverton. Snowbee Tackle, Langage Business Park, Plympton. Book online at South West Lakes Trust website. *Charges:* Club membership £12.50 per year, includes membership of club insurance scheme. *Season:* 1st March - 31 October. *Methods:* Fly only.

Where to Stay in Devon

Jaime with her first ever 2lb+ Koi from the Float Lake at Anglers Paradise

A Little Reflection

The Editor

We were sorting through some family photos at home the other day. Many of you will remember those boxes under the stairs, or on top of the wardrobe, stuffed full of prints and negatives. The sort of box you should not open casually because you know it's a whole afternoon gone as soon as you start browsing. One downside of digital cameras I suppose, no more shoe boxes of photos for children and grandchildren to rediscover.

Anyhow I found a picture of Josh (our first child) with his first carp. I then remembered the occasion and I had written an article for this very publication. A bit more digging and there it was, black and white and the 1995 edition, the second Get Hooked!

This just happened to coincide with Josh (now 23) returning from a six month army tour of Cyprus - time for some fishing, and a little reflection.

So what has changed? Well, in the Get Hooked world, we have gone from 44 black and white pages in issue one to a peak of 226 in full colour. What started as a project in 1994 grew into more than we hoped. Of course the publishing world has changed hugely. There really was no world wide web, certainly as far as the fishing community was concerned, back in 1994. In fact it is still an ongoing transition as the media munching public shifts from traditional paper to digital delivery. But we are on it, with a constantly developing web site and regular 'tweeting', 'facebooking', and 'blogging'. All terms so familiar in today's society but so very new to angling and the planet in general.

I do find this paper guide (ignore that if you are reading online or the ebook version) somehow reassuring in an analogue way. No batteries required, no wi-fi, no 3g, no service provider, I fear I may be sounding a little bit 'grumpy old man', I hope not, I love really useful gadgets but not technology for technology's sake.

Much like fishing really isn't it? I know tackle manufacturers re-invent the reel and rod every year and bait and tackle developments have been

1995

huge (boilies, hair rigs, bite alarms, fish finders, bait boats) but you don't actually NEED all of that paraphernalia.

Fishing has an essence, a quintessential anticipation of excitement. It can be a bite alarm sounding or a bit of silver paper flying off the line as a fish of unknown proportions makes off with the bait. It can be an expensive float suspended from a very expensive pole or a matchstick attached to a piece of line. The first glimpse of those barely discernible concentric ripples spreading from where that float peeks from the water will create much the same flutter of the heart and that little sip of breath.

Don't get me wrong, I can be a bit of a tackle slut as well. I have far more rods than I will ever need, I have reels that have yet to see any line on them and bargain dozen packs of flies of which two may see action, but I am still tempted by shiny 'bargains'. Was far less tempted before email newsletters and web site promotions though.

So presumably all this technology and wizardry is to make it easier to catch fish? It's a bit of a paradox really, in that if someone invented the ultimate bait, that would catch a fish every cast, all year round, fishing would surely become boring? We have previously seen 'boobies' banned (for those that don't know that is a type of fly - really), I have seen 'fish location devices' banned, I can even remember stories in the Angling Times of 'bloodworm and joker' being banned when I was in my teens.

Perhaps it is the fact we mainly 'sport fish' these days and rarely for the pot. The fact that many of our wild species are under pressure and in decline must also contribute to not making it too 'easy'.

I digress, we were going fishing! Venue was a coarse lake only five miles from home. I have not actually been coarse fishing for about five years (I know that's awful). Recently it's been brownies and grayling on the fly, back on the rivers of my youth - Ottery, Inny and Tamar.

So we needed some bait. A stop off at the handily 'en route' angling centre for some hemp, maggots and dendrobaena plus a crusty loaf from the supermarket and we are sorted.

Josh always uses a whip and I set up my usual float rod. The lake is quite narrow and 'L" shaped with some nice lily pads, obvious spots to fish. I met the owner while getting permits and he said someone had recently had some nice pound plus perch on luncheon meat, did not buy any luncheon meat, but likes the sound of some pound plus perch. There are also resident rudd and carp. I have a feeling they will be predominantly small fish though.

Josh was fishing first (one advantage of a whip setup), maggot over hemp and maggot loose feed. First cast, float shot away, yep - a small perch. They really are voracious to the point of stupidity, with a huge mouth that negates the use of a large bait to avoid them.

I was soon into fish as well, small rudd and perch. I moved a couple times and tried by the outlet to find some deeper water but the lake was pretty shallow overall. I struggled to find more than three feet. I also (as I always do) chucked out a dozen crusts around the margins and lilies to see if any of the resident carp might oblige but, although a few crusts were nosed enthusiastically, none were taken.

So we just stuck with the maggot or worm, or a combination, as hook bait and to be honest were more than happy to keep catching the rudd and perch, knowing that with a bed of hemp down there was a good chance of something a bit larger later on.

2013

About half an hour before dark it started to liven up in Josh's swim. I had been moving around but he had stayed put and fed two swims steadily with hemp. The one to his left was clouding beautifully as a carp or two got in on the feed. He hooked one which went off like a scalded cat, took the elastic to the brink and threw the hook and another which buried itself in the lilies. That's the problem with the whip, lack of control.

I was struggling to see as the light went so I passed my rod over in the hope of him hooking another. That did not happen but that swim was a fish every cast with them taking on the drop. He fished until we could not see the float clearly.

So, a bag of predominantly perch, one of a reasonable size, with a few rudd. We took a pic of the ones we bothered to put in the keep net and packed up as the light was really going.

Josh learning to fish, at a pretty basic level, all those years ago means he can pick up a rod and reel and catch fish anywhere. The principles are the same, fresh or saltwater. We both enjoy it as much now as we ever have. Memorable fish are the icing on the cake but, like this session, the cake is always sweet anyway.

Go on - teach somebody

South West Lakes Trust

South West Lakes Trust manages around 30 lakes as fisheries in the South West of England. The Trust was formed to provide, promote and enhance sustainable recreation, access and nature conservation at these lakes. One of the most popular activities for visitors is angling for both coarse and game fish.

Each of the lakes has its own unique character. Some lakes are found in wild and secluded settings, or you may choose to fish at locations which offer other amenities such as campsites with modern facilities, and cafes. The lakes are regularly re-stocked with good-sized fish, and regulars will be familiar with the legendary large fish landed at some of the coarse fishing sites. Day tickets may now be booked online through the Trust's website (www.swlakestrust.org.uk). In March 2013, Roadford Lake hosted a new attraction – The South West Fly Fair, organised jointly with the Westcountry Rivers Trust and the Angling Trust and funded by the Environment Agency from rod licence money. The event, which is set to become a regular feature in the trout fisherman's calendar in anticipation of the new season, included the opportunity to watch and learn from some of the greatest fly-tiers in the region, brush up on casting skills, see and try the latest tackle, and listen to a series of guest speakers.

Bank, boat and more

We aim to provide great fishing for both experienced anglers and beginners. The South West Fishing For Life scheme now has well established branches at Kennick, Siblyback, and Wimbleball, giving people living with breast cancer an opportunity to experience and enjoy fly fishing, which can aid their physical and emotional healing (all equipment is provided, and novices are welcomed).

In conjunction with a local instructor based at Wimbleball, we have introduced kayak fishing, and will be offering introductory experience days. There are now improved access facilities at Argal, Upper Tamar, Burrator, and Roadford, thanks to a partnership incentive with the Environment Agency.

Our successful training and family days are held regularly throughout the year. Juniors will be encouraged to fish for both coarse fish and trout with the parent/child ticket again being available allowing youngsters under 12 years to fish for free, sharing the parent bag limit (where applicable). Please note that children under 14 years should be accompanied by an adult over 18 at all times.

Tuition for beginners

Beginners' Days are held in conjunction with local qualified professional instructors and the Environment Agency. They include National Fishing Week family events at Siblyback and Stithians, as well as Beginners Days, Junior Days, Ladies' Days and Family Days at Kennick, Siblyback, Wimbleball and Stithians. For more details contact 01566 771930 or click on fishing at www.swlakestrust.org.uk

These events have been very successful over the past seasons, with many novices taking up the sport, including the formation of a Ladies' Club at Wimbleball. Equipment can be provided and a local professional instructor will share his knowledge and experience in the use of equipment and where to catch fish.

The Trust held a series of coarse fishing junior days during 2012 which attracted more than 125 youngsters and these will run again in 2013/14.

The tuition days are very popular, so prior booking is essential. Individual tuition can also be arranged with local, qualified instructors.

Access for all

Through its partnership with the Wheelyboat Trust, South West Lakes Trust is able to provide wheelyboats suitable for wheelchair access at Roadford, Upper Tamar, Wimbleball, Stithians, Siblyback and Kennick. These must be booked at least 48 hours in advance. There is also a Wheelyboat at Wistlandpound, which is operated by the Calvert Trust. We provide facilities for disabled anglers at some of our fisheries.

Competitions

The Trust holds three main trout fishing competitions each year: The Peninsula Classic bank competition at Kennick in early summer, supported by Fly Fishing Tackle, Crediton; the Snowbee Team bank competition at Siblyback in Spring; and the Wimbleball 2000 boat pairs competition in early autumn, supported by Orvis.

Dates and booking information are available from the Angling Centres at these lakes or click

on fishing at www.swlakestrust.org.uk

The Trust also holds its successful Carp Fishing weekend competitions at Upper Tamar. Details of these may be found on the website.

Porth and Upper Tamar are both popular coarse fishing large competition venues which may be booked in advance by contacting 01566 771930, as can other coarse fisheries. Details of all competitions at these sites and other Trust waters in the region may be found on our website on the Fishing Diary page. Fishing news and catch reports may also be found here – photos of your successful catches, or articles, are always welcome.

Season permits

In addition to pay-per-visit, you can also purchase a season ticket. These are available locally through the Trust's 'Outdoor And Active' Centres, or through Summerlands Tackle in Westward Ho!, either in person, over the phone on 01237 471291 or via their website:

www.summerlands-tackle.co.uk

You can spread the cost of your season ticket by paying using direct debit (please ring the Trust's Head office – 01566 771930, or ask at your local fishery for more detail).

Westcountry Angling Passport tokens, which are available through the Westcountry Rivers Trust and other outlets, may be used as part-payment for fishing on the trout fisheries. This payment option may be used at self-service lodges and at ticket agents.

What's going on?

If you would like to receive a copy of the Trust's Coarse or Trout Fisheries Newsletter, please email: info@swlakestrust.org.uk or phone 01566 771930 to be included on the mailing list.

The Trust is committed to angling and creating the best possible experience for its visitors. So any comments are welcome to help us provide what you, the angler, really wants.

For information on sites, facilities, instruction and competitions please contact:

Ben Smeeth on 01566 771930

bsmeeth@swlakestrust.org.uk

or visit **www.swlakestrust.org.uk**

DORSET

DORSET

RIVER FISHING

STILLWATER COARSE

STILLWATER TROUT

WHERE TO STAY

ADVERTISER LOCATION MAP

Map No	Advertiser	Sat Nav	Phone	Advert Page
	Game Fishing			
101	Amherst Lodge	DT7 3XH	01297 442773 or 07753 640737	100 & 161
102	Flowers Farm Lakes	DT2 7BE	01300 341351	100
	Coarse Fishing			
103	Christchurch Angling Club (Game & Coarse)		01202 480009	90
104	Coking Farm Fishery	SP8 5SF	01747 839879	96
105	Dorchester & District Angling Society		01305 835283	91
106	Gold Oak Country Cabins	BH21 5QT	01725 517654	95
107	Highway Farm	DT6 6AE	01308 424321	94
108	Lyons Gate Fishing Lakes	DT2 7AZ	01300 345260	95
109	Mangerton Valley Coarse Fishing	DT6 3SF	01308 422884	94
110	Martin's Farm Fishery	BH21 8LY	01202 823631 or 07717 887357	95
111	Ringwood & District Anglers Association		01202 659393	97
112	Rosewall Camping (Wally's Lake)	DT3 6HA	01305 832248	99
113	Sturminster & Hinton Angling Association		01258 472068 or 07770 891669	91
114	Todber Manor Fisheries	DT10 1JB	01258 820384	101
115	Wood Farm Caravan & Camping Park	DT6 6BT	01297 560697	101

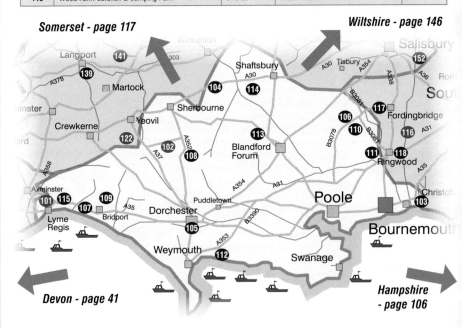

Somerset - page 117

Wiltshire - page 146

Devon - page 41

Hampshire - page 106

Only advertisers with fishing are located on this map. Their listings within this guide are highlighted in blue.

Please note sat nav postcodes, where supplied, may not be totally accurate.

Dorset River Fishing

ALLEN

The River Allen is a pure chalk stream that runs through the finest countryside in Dorset. With a total length of thirteen miles, the Allen is a tributary of the Stour, the two rivers coming together just outside Wimborne Minster.

Wimborne St Giles

Contact: Simon Cooper, Fishing Breaks, The Mill, Heathman Street, Nether Wallop, Stockbridge, Hampshire. *Tel:* 01264 781988. *Water:* One mile on the village water. Single rod. *Species:* Brown Trout. *Permits:* By phone or e-mail from Fishing Breaks. *Charges:* Fishing 1 to 2 rods. River Allen: May 1st - June 15th is £150. June 16th - September 30th is £115. *Season:* May to September. *Methods:* Dry fly & Nymph only.

THE 'HAMPSHIRE' AVON

For detailed description of the Hampshire Avon and tributaries, see under Hampshire River fishing - page 106.

RIVER AVON PEWSEY - CHRISTCHURCH

Fisheries located between Pewsey and Salisbury are predominantly managed for Brown Trout fly fishing. A mixture of Coarse, Salmon and Trout fishing is available on the main river between Salisbury and Christchurch.

Winton Fishery

Contact: Christchurch Angling Club Office, Unit 6, Silver Business Park, Airfield Way, Christchurch. *Tel:* 01202 480009. *Water:* Christchurch Angling Club controlled stretch of the lower Avon above Christchurch. Approx. 3.5 miles double bank. *Species:* Barbel 12lb plus, Chub 7lb 7oz, Dace 1lb, Pike 25lb, Carp 26lb, Roach 3lb, Perch 3lb. *Permits:* From local tackle shops. *Charges:* Day ticket £6. £3 Conc/Junior. (2 rods per day, coarse only). *Season:* Coarse: 16 June to 14 March from one hour before sunrise to two hours after sunset. *Methods:* No spinning. Coarse fish only. No Barbel in keepnets. Any Salmon, Sea Trout or Salmon Parr caught accidentally should be returned immediately.

FROME

The Frome rises through chalk on the North Dorset Downs near Evershot, and flows south east through Dorchester, and finally Wareham, where it confluences with the River Piddle in Poole harbour.

Mark Sims and a fine 2lb 13oz Grayling caught from the Frome at Wool

The River Frome is well known for its excellent Salmon, Brown Trout and Grayling fishing. There are also good numbers of coarse fish in certain areas; although access is limited sport can be very rewarding. Salmon and Trout fishing is generally controlled by syndicates and local estates.

Dairy House Fishery

Contact: John Aplin, The Dairy House, West Stafford, Dorchester. *Sat Nav:* DT2 8AL. *Tel:* 01305 257490. *Mobile:* 07889 680464. *Water:* 1.5 miles on River Frome near Dorchester. *Species:* Wild Brown Trout to 7lb and Grayling to 4lb 2oz. *Permits:* Fishing is also available via the Westcountry Rivers Trust Passport Scheme Tel: 01579 372140. *Charges:* From £60 per rod per day. *Season:* Trout - April 1st to October 15th. Grayling June 16th to March 14th. *Methods:* Upstream dry fly and nymph only.

Dorchester Fishing Club

Contact: Mr R Miller (Hon. Secretary). *Water:* Approx. 6.5 miles of double bank on the Frome near Dorchester, Brown Trout fly fishing. *Species:* Brown Trout, Grayling. *Permits:* John Aplin, Dorchester. Tel: 01305 266500. Membership details by email only. *Charges:* Day tickets and membership available. Please telephone John Aplin for day tickets or email for membership details. *Season:* April 1st - October 14th. *Methods:* Dry fly and Nymph only. Barbless hooks are encouraged.

RIVER FISHING

East Burton Estate

Contact: Harry Warr, Cliff Cottage, Moreton, Dorchester. *Tel:* 01929 462270. *Water:* Fishing on two carriers of the River Frome near Wool. *Species:* Brown Trout and Grayling with occasional Sea Trout and Salmon. Pike in winter. *Permits:* From the above. *Charges:* On application. *Season:* Trout from 1 May to 1 October. EA byelaws apply.

River Frome (Town Section)

Contact: Purbeck Angling Centre / Deano or Barry, 28 South Street, Wareham. *Tel:* 01929 550770. *Water:* One mile stretch of the River Frome. *Species:* Roach, Dace, Grayling, Eels, Pike, Salmon, Trout, Sea Trout, Mullet, Bass, Flounder, Carp and Perch. *Permits:* Enquiries to Purbeck Angling Centre. *Charges:* Free fishing on public section. Enquiries to Purbeck Angling Centre. *Season:* Normal closed seasons apply. *Methods:* This stretch is run as a Coarse Fishery only. All Game and Saltwater fish are to be returned immediately.

Wareham and District Angling Society

Contact: Deano Watts, c/o Purbeck Angling Centre, 28 South Street, Wareham. *Tel:* 01929 550770. *Water:* River waters on Piddle and the Frome. 1 lake Wareham area plus 5 near Dorchester and 2 near Weymouth. *Species:* Coarse. Roach 3lb+, Pike 30lb+, Dace 1lb+, Grayling record. *Permits:* Purbeck Angling Centre Tel: 01929 550770. *Charges:* Senior £50, OAP £25, Junior £10. Membership runs from June 1st to May 31st. Winter ticket for rivers only £30. *Season:* Lakes open during Coarse closed season. *Methods:* Barbless, no litter, no cans, variations as per membership book.

Wessex Chalk Streams Ltd. (Frome)

Contact: Richard & Sally Slocock, Lawrences Farm, Southover, Tolpuddle, Dorchester. *Sat Nav:* DT2 7HF. *Tel:* 01305 848460. *Water:* Numerous beats above and below Dorchester. Wild Browns, Stocked Browns and Grayling in lower beats. *Species:* Brown Trout. Some beats with all wild fish, other beats with stocked browns to augment the wild fish. *Permits:* From the above address. *Charges:* From £45 to £85 max day. Generous discounts for large bookings. Season rods available £560. *Season:* 1 April - 15 October. *Methods:* Barbless hooks, catch and release.

Wrackleford Estate Fishery &

Contact: Oliver Pope, Wrackleford House, Dorchester. *Sat Nav:* DT2 9SN. *Tel:* 01305 267643. *Mobile:* 07980 694487. *Water:* Eight beats on 4 miles of Frome chalkstream, with a still water lake. *Species:* Mainly Brown Trout. *Permits:* From the above. *Charges:* On application. *Season:* April 1 to October 15. EA Byelaws apply. *Methods:* Dry fly only. Some beats suitable for disabled access, please phone first for further details.

PIDDLE AND WEST DORSET STREAMS

'West Dorset' streams include the River Brit, Asker, Bride and Char. These streams are relatively short, 'steep' water courses supporting populations of mainly Brown Trout and Sea Trout.

RIVER FISHING

large bookings. Season rods available. *Season:* 1 April - 15 October. *Methods:* Catch and release. Fly only.

STOUR

The River Stour in Dorset is well known by anglers across the country for the quality of its fishing. Over the years many British record captures have been made here, for example, the current Roach record stands at 4lb 3oz, taken from the Stour near Wimborne.

The Stour rises on the Greensand at St. Peters Pump in Stourhead Gardens and flows through Gillingham. Nearby it is joined by the Shreen Water and the River Lodden. The Stour stretches out for 96 km, passing through the Blackmoor Vale down to the sea at Christchurch; the total fall over this distance is approximately 230m. Other notable tributaries along its length include the River Tarrant confluencing near Spetisbury, the River Allen at Wimborne and the Moors River coming in near Christchurch. The Stour confluences with the River Avon at the 'Clay Pool' in Christchurch, before flowing into the harbour area and ultimately out into the English Channel.

Dorchester and District Angling Society
Contact: Steve Sudworth, 3 Buddleia Close, Weymouth. *Tel:* 01305 835283. *Mobile:* 07816 175579. *Water:* 7.5 miles on Dorset Stour, 1.5 miles Dorset Frome plus lakes at Weymouth, Kingcombe, Warmwell, Broadmayne and Buckland Newton. River Brue, Somerset plus water sharing agreements and Federation waters on Somerset Levels. *Species:* Roach, Dace, Chub, Pike, Gudgeon, Perch, Eels, Carp, Bream, Grayling. *Permits:* 'Reels & Deals', Weymouth. Surplus International, Dorchester. Wareham Angling, Wareham. *Charges:* Adult members £50. Reductions for OAP's, Disabled, Juniors & Partners. Members guest tickets, no day tickets, reduced price membership from November 1st. *Season:* June 16th - March 14th. Stillwater open all year. *Methods:* Various, specific to particular waters.

The River Piddle rises at four major springs near Alton St. Pancras, initially flowing south before turning east at Puddletown towards Poole Harbour, where it confluences with the River Frome. This small chalk stream offers excellent Brown Trout fishing, with Salmon, Sea Trout and coarse fish in the lower reaches. The Agency operates a salmon and sea trout rod fishery in this area. Other fish species can be found in the River Piddle including, Roach, Dace, Pike and Perch. Much of the fishing is controlled by local syndicates and estate waters.

Manor of Wareham
Contact: Lara Manningham-Buller, Manor of Wareham, Cow Lane, Wareham. *Sat Nav:* BH20 4RD. *Tel:* 01929 552666. *Water:* Stretch on River Piddle single bank fishing. *Species:* Brown Trout and Sea Trout. *Charges:* Season tickets and day tickets. Price on application. *Season:* E.A. Byelaws. *Methods:* E.A. Byelaws.

Wessex Chalk Streams Ltd. (Piddle)
Contact: Richard & Sally Slocock, Lawrences Farm, Southover, Tolpuddle, Dorchester. *Sat Nav:* DT2 7HF. *Tel:* 01305 848460. *Water:* Seven beats. *Species:* Brown Trout only. Wild and stocked. *Permits:* From the above address. *Charges:* From £40 to £85 day. Generous discounts for

RIVER FISHING

Gillingham and District A A (Stour)

Contact: Simon Hebditch (Hon. Secretary), 10 Pimpernel Court, Gillingham. *Tel:* 01747 821218. *Mobile:* 07990 690613. *Water:* 7 miles Upper Stour - Gillingham to Marnhull. Also Turners Paddock lake at Stourhead. Mappowder Court 4 lakes at Mappowder. *Species:* Roach 3lb, Chub 4lb 8oz, Barbel 6lb, Pike 21lb, Dace 1lb, Bream 6lb, Gudgeon 3oz, Perch 3lb 4oz, Tench 3lb, Carp 10lb, Eels 4lb. Trout, Grayling 2lb 8oz. *Permits:* Mr P Stone (Treasurer) The Timepiece, Newbury, Gillingham, Dorset, SP8 4HZ. Tel: 01747 823339. Mr J Candy, Todber Manor Fisheries Shop, Tel: 01258 820384. Crockers Hardwear, High Street, Gillingham, Tel: 01747 822900. *Charges:* £5 day ticket, £41 season ticket. £20.50 junior, OAP £31. *Season:* June 16th to March 14th. *Methods:* Best stick float with maggot casters and bread. Large lump of bread for Chub. Sweetcorn also very productive for Bream. Feeder for Bream.

Lower Stour / Christchurch Harbour &

Contact: Ringwood & District A.A.. *Tel:* 01202 659393. *Species:* Roach 2lb, Dace 1lb, Pike 20lb, Bream 7lb, Perch 3lb, Carp 30lb, Eels 5lb, Mullet 10lb. *Permits:* Available from local tackle shops and online. *Charges:* Adult £150, Junior £50, Concessions for OAP and disabled. *Season:* Coarse: 16 June to 14 March. *Methods:* See club rules for individual waters.

Muscliffe and Longham

Contact: Neil Cooke, 904 Wimborne Road, Moordown, Bournemouth. *Tel:* 01202 514345. *Water:* 1.5 miles River Stour at Muscliffe and 0.25 miles at Longham. *Species:* Chub, Barbel, Roach, Dace, Pike, Eels, Minnow, Gudgeon Carp and Perch. *Permits:* Free (owned by Bournemouth Council). *Charges:* Free. E.A. licence required. *Season:* 16 June to 14 March. *Methods:* No restrictions.

Ringwood and District A.A. (Stour)

Contact: J Sudworth. *Tel:* 01202 659393. *Water:* 11 stretches on Stour including total control of Throop fishery and various stretches upstream to Stourpaine. *Species:* Throop - Barbel to 16lb, Chub 8lb. Middle regions good general Roach, Chub, Bream, Pike 30lb plus, Perch, some Trout, Grayling and Carp. *Permits:* Ringwood Tackle. Tel: 01425 475155. Christchurch Angling Centre Tel: 01202 480520. *Charges:* Adult £150, Junior £50, Concessions for OAP and Disabled; Throop day tickets £10. Concessions, OAP, Disabled and Junior available from local tackle dealers. Weekly £55. *Season:* As per coarse season. *Methods:* Details in permit or reverse of ticket.

Ringwood and District Angling Club (Throop Fisheries)

Contact: J Sudworth. *Tel:* 01202 659393. *Water:* Northern edge of Bournemouth. 10 miles of river bank on Dorset Stour & Stillwater Mill Pool. *Species:* Barbel to 16lb 2oz, Chub to 8lb 10oz, Carp 32lb, Roach 3lb, Tench 8lb, Perch 3lb, Dace 10oz, Pike 32lb, Bream 9lb. *Permits:* Ringwood Tackle - Tel. 01425 475155, Bournemouth Fishing Lodge - Tel. 01202 514345. Christchurch Angling Centre - Tel: 01202 480520. Davis Tackle - Tel. 01202 458169. *Charges:* Day tickets £10, to be obtained before fishing. *Season:* 16 June - 14 March inclusive. *Methods:* See reverse of tickets.

John Aplin with a 3lb 14oz Grayling

Stalbridge Angling Association (Stour)

Contact: Bernie Ackland. *Tel:* 01935 474284. *Water:* 2.5 miles Stour. *Species:* Bream, Tench, Roach, Dace, Pike, Chub, Rudd. *Permits:* C.C. Moores Ltd (animal foods), Stalbridge, 01963 362234. Bernie Ackland, 01935 474284. *Charges:* Senior Annual £25 no joining fee, Junior (under 17 years) £10 & Concessions (Reg. Disabled & OAP) £14 no joining fee. Husband and wife ticket £35. Day Tickets £5 senior, £2.50 junior. *Season:* Normal river closed season.

Sturminster and Hinton A.A &

Contact: Mr D Rigby (Secretary), Penny Gates, Penny St, Sturminster Newton. *Tel:* 01258 472068. *Mobile:* 07770 891669. *Water:* 14 miles river Dorset Stour; joint fisheries at Lodden Lakes, Gillingham and full members may also fish Revels fishery near Dorchester. *Species:* Roach 3lb 2.5oz, Chub 6lb 3oz, Tench 7lb 3.5oz, Bream 9lb, Perch 3lb 6oz, Carp 20lb 10oz, Pike 32lb 3oz, Dace 11.5oz. *Permits:* Candy's Newsagents, The Square, Sturminster Newton. Marsh's Electrical, The Square, Sturminster Newton. Todber Manor fisheries, Todber, Nr Sturminster Newton. Membership Sec. (Full Season and Lakes). The Bull Tavern, The Bridge, Sturminster Newton. Conyers, Blandford. *Charges:* £5 day, £15 Week, £40 Season. *Season:* Closed March 15th - June 15th inclusive on river. *Methods:* No dogs, radios, no live baiting. One rod, second rod only for Pike. Barbless hooks at lakes. No night fishing. Always carry your membership permit. 2 disabled angler friendly platforms on river and lakes. Please enquire for more details.

Wimborne and District Angling Club (Stour)

Contact: Mr Rob Doyle, WDAC PO Box 6632, Poole. *Mobile:* 07740 675788. *Water:* 10 miles River Stour and 16 miles. *Species:* Trout & Coarse Fisheries. *Charges:* Membership: £110, Junior £27, under 12 accompanied by an adult free. *Season:* Coarse - all year round. Sea Trout - 15 April to 31 Oct. Salmon - 1 Feb to 31 Aug. 3 x Trout Lakes - 1 Mar - 31 Oct. Winterbourne Zelston - 365 days a year. *Methods:* Rules in fishing permit.

Stillwater Coarse

BEAMINSTER

Bakers Mill Farm
Mosterton, Beaminster. *Sat Nav:* DT8 3JD. *Tel:* 01872 261525. *Mobile:* 02380 293353. *Water:* Two spring fed lakes totalling 1.5 acres. *Species:* Carp to double figures, Bream, Tench, Roach. *Charges:* £5 per day. *Season:* Open dawn to dusk. *Methods:* No boilies, nuts or beans. No night fishing. All fish to be returned.

Higher Kingcombe Lodge ♿
Contact: Mr Crocker, Higher Kingcombe, Dorchester. *Sat Nav:* DT2 0EH. *Tel:* 01300 320537. *Mobile:* 07967 968846. *Water:* 7 lakes - approx. 5 acres of water in total. *Species:* Carp (Mirror, Common & Ghost), Perch, Roach, Rudd, Bream, Tench. Specimen lake - Carp to 31lb. *Charges:* Day ticket £5, Evening (after 6pm) £3, Night Fishing £10, Juniors (16 and under) £2.50 per day. *Season:* Open all year. *Methods:* Max 2 rods per person, barbless hooks only, under 14's must be accompanied by an adult.

BLANDFORD

Dairy House Farm Fisheries
Contact: Derek Cooper, Dairy House Farm, Woolland, Blandford Forum. *Sat Nav:* DT11 0EY. *Tel:* 01258 817501. *Mobile:* 07966 308998. *Water:* 3 lakes totalling 4.5 acres. *Species:* Carp, Rudd, Tench, Bream, Commons and Mirror Carp. *Charges:* £7 per person for 2 rods per day. £10 per day per person for over two rods. *Season:* Open all year. No night fishing. *Methods:* No keepnets, Barbless hooks only, Children under 16 must be accompanied by an adult.

Milton Abbas Lakes
Contact: Wayne Little, Milton Abbas, Blandford. *Sat Nav:* DT11 0BW. *Tel:* 01258 880919. *Mobile:* 07780 966117. *Water:* Three acre day ticket lake. Please note lake is adjacent to 8 acre syndicate lake - no fishing permitted for day ticket anglers. *Species:* Carp 10lbs up to 18lbs, Grass Carp to 16lbs, Tench to 6lbs, Roach to 2lbs, Crucian Carp, Bream, Tench, Perch & Eels and Pike to 20lb. *Permits:* Maximum of 10 anglers per day. Tickets on the bank. *Charges:* Adult £10 per day. Juniors £5 per day (Must be under 16 and accompanied by an adult). *Season:* No close season. Fishing times 7am until Sunset. *Methods:* No keep nets or Carp sacks, 2 rods only. No peas, nuts or beans, a suitable landing net and unhooking mat if Carp fishing, no dogs, fires, swimming or bait boats.

BOURNEMOUTH

East Moors Lake ♿
Contact: Mr Nicolas Hoare, East Moors Farm, East Moors Lane, St. Leonards, Ferndown, Bournemouth. *Sat Nav:* BH24 2SB. *Tel:* 01202 872302. *Water:* 1.5 acre lake. *Species:* Mainly Carp, Tench and Roach. *Charges:* Please

Nice Tench from Lyons Gate

telephone for details. *Methods:* Barbless hooks only, no boilies, no keepnets, no dogs. Children under 14 must be accompanied by adult.

Throop Fisheries (Coarse Lake)
Contact: Ringwood & District Angling Club. *Tel:* 01202 659393. *Water:* Stillwater Mill Pool. Also 10 miles on Dorset Stour. *Species:* Barbel, Chub, Carp, Roach, Tench, Perch, Dace, Pike. *Permits:* Bournemouth Fishing Lodge - Tel. 01202 514345. Christchurch Angling Centre - Tel: 01202 480520. Davis Tackle - Tel. 01202 458169. *Charges:* Day tickets £10, to be obtained before fishing. *Season:* 16 June - 14 March (Open every day between these dates). *Methods:* No night fishing.

BRIDPORT

Golden Cap Holiday Park
Contact: Reception, Seatown, Chideock. *Sat Nav:* DT6 6JX. *Tel:* 01308 426912. *Water:* Half acre lake. *Species:* Carp, Roach, Rudd Silver fish and Eels. *Permits:* Available from Park reception during opening hours. *Charges:* £4.50 per day plus £5 peg deposit. *Season:* Third week in March till first week in November. *Methods:* No barbless hooks, keepnets or toxic shot weights.

Highway Farm
Contact: John & Pauline Bale, West Road, Bridport. *Sat Nav:* DT6 6AE. *Tel:* 01308 424321. *Water:* 2 small lakes in quiet, secluded valley. *Species:* Carp, Roach, Rudd. *Permits:* From the Post Office, Bridport. *Charges:* £7 day. Under 16 £5. Evening from 5pm £5, under 16 £3. *Season:* Open all year, dawn to dusk. No night fishing. *Methods:* No boilies or keepnets. Barbless hooks only. No dogs.

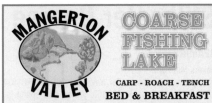
STILLWATER COARSE

Mangerton Valley Coarse Fishing Lake
Contact: Clive & Jane Greening, New House Farm, Mangerton Lane, Bradpole, Bridport. *Sat Nav:* DT6 3SF. *Tel:* 01308 422884. *Water:* 1.6 acre lake. *Species:* Carp to 30lb (Common and Mirror), Roach, Tench. *Permits:* From Post Office. *Charges:* £7 day, £4 half day, £3 evening. *Methods:* Barbless hooks. No nuts, no dogs. All children under 12 to be accompanied by an adult. Check closing times when paying. No night fishing. Landing and unhooking mats for Carp. No keepnets. Toilet in the Summer and parking close to lake.

Washingpool Farm Fishing
Washingpool Farm, North Allington, Bridport. *Sat Nav:* DT6 5HP. *Tel:* 01308 459549. *Water:* 3 lakes. (1 acre, 0.5 and 0.25). *Species:* Carp to 22lb, Mirror, Common, Crucian, Ghost 15lb, Wild Carp, Tench, Roach, Rudd & Bream. *Charges:* Tickets from Farm. £5 per day. £3 half day. *Season:* Open all year dawn to dusk. *Methods:* No boilies.

CHRISTCHURCH

Avon Tyrrell Lakes
Contact: Dave Clarke, Avon Tyrrell House, Bransgore, Christchurch. *Sat Nav:* BH23 8EE. *Tel:* 01425 672347. *Water:* Two lakes totalling approx. 2.5 acres. *Species:* Carp, Tench, Roach, Bream, Perch and Rudd. *Permits:* On site from reception. *Charges:* £8 Day Tickets Adults. £5 Juniors(Under 16). Season Tickets also available, please note Night Fishing only available on a season ticket. *Season:* Open mid June to mid March - 08.30 to 17.00hrs on day ticket. *Methods:* Barbless hooks, No keepnets, No nut baits. See rules on site.

Hordle Lakes &
Contact: Jim and Richard Seeds, Hordle Lakes, Golden Hill, Ashley Lane, Hordle, Nr New Milton, Hampshire. *Sat Nav:* SO41 0GA. *Tel:* 01590 683767. *Mobile:* 07709 853353. *Water:* Seven spring fed lakes set in 11 acres. *Species:* Double figure Carp, Tench, Roach, Rudd, Bream and Perch. *Permits:* From the fishery. Can also issue EA rod licences on site. *Charges:* Adults £10 per day. OAP £7. Children £6. *Season:* Open all year 7am to dusk. Night fishing by arrangement. *Methods:* All fish to be returned immediately. Loose feeding only. Barbless hooks only, no larger than size 6. No nut baits. Full rules at the fishery. Un hooking mats compulsory.

Mudeford Wood Angling Club
Contact: John Scott. *Tel:* 01202 478764. *Water:* Small Lake. *Species:* Roach, Tench, Carp, Bream. *Permits:* From Christchurch Angling Centre, Tel: 01202 480520. *Charges:* £7 per day. £30 season. *Season:* Open all year. *Methods:* No boilies, nuts or Trout pellets.

Whirlwind Lake
Contact: Mr & Mrs Pillinger, Whirlwind Rise, Dudmore Lane, Christchurch. *Sat Nav:* BH23 6BQ. *Tel:* 01202 475255. *Water:* Secluded lake. *Species:* Common, Crucian and Mirror Carp, Roach, Rudd, Tench, Chub etc. *Permits:* On site and local fishing tackle shops. Advanced booking advisable, limited number available. *Charges:* Adults £8.50 day ticket. £5 half day (limited places). Children (must be accompanied) £5 day. *Season:* Open all year. *Methods:* Barbless hooks only, no keepnets, no boilies.

CORFE

Arfleet Mill Lakes
Contact: Mr B Charron, Dairy Cottage, Knitson, Corfe Castle. *Sat Nav:* BH20 5JG. *Tel:* 01929 427421. *Water:* 1 acre spring fed lake and 1 acre deep water lake. Situated off the B3351 near Corfe Castle. *Species:* Carp to 29lb 3oz, Roach 2lb, Rudd, Tench, Perch and Eel. *Permits:* Purbeck Angling in Wareham or Clealls Stores in Corfe Castle. *Charges:* £7 day. £3.50 Evening (5pm - sunset). Night fishing by appointment at £10. *Season:* Open early April until mid October. *Methods:* No Trout pellets, no keepnets, barbless hooks only, no ground bait.

CRANBORNE

Martins Farm Fishery
Contact: Mary and Jonathan Stephens, Martins Farm, Woodlands, Verwood. *Sat Nav:* BH21 8LY. *Tel:* 01202 823631. *Mobile:* 07717 887357. *Water:* 2.5 acre spring fed lake. *Species:* Carp to 30lb, Tench to 6lb, Perch, Roach, Rudd. *Charges:* £10 Adult day, £5 after 4pm. Junior (12 and under) half price. *Methods:* No keepnets, barbless hooks, no hemp. Boilies in moderation. Toilets on site.

Wimborne and District Angling Club
Contact: Mr Rob Doyle, WDAC PO Box 6632, Poole.
Mobile: 07740 675788. *Water:* 2 acre lake. *Species:* Mixed coarse. *Charges:* Membership: £110, Junior £27, under 12 accompanied by an adult free.

DORCHESTER

Dorchester & District Angling Society (Coarse Lake) &
Contact: Steve Sudworth, 3 Buddleia Close, Weymouth. *Tel:* 01305 835283. *Mobile:* 07816 175579. *Water:* See entry under Stour. Coarse lakes 1.5 acre - Luckfield lake. 2.5 acre at Kingcombe - all access platform (BDAA approved). 4 acre at Warmwell. Free fishing at Revels. Sharnhill Green - 2 carp lakes - night fishing available. Weymouth 2 coarse lakes. Concessions at some local commercial Fisheries. *Species:* Carp, Tench, Perch, Bream and Roach. *Permits:* Reels and Deals, Weymouth, Surplus International, Dorchester. *Charges:* £50 Adult. Reductions for OAP's, Disabled, Juniors and Partners. *Season:* Lakes open all year. *Methods:* Barbless hooks only. No boilies or bivvies on lakes. No keepnets.

Gillingham and District A.A. (Mappowder Court)
Contact: Simon Hebditch (Hon. Secretary), 10 Pimpernel Court, Gillingham. *Tel:* 01747 821218. *Mobile:* 07990 690613. *Water:* Mappowder Court Fishing Complex (4 lakes), Mappowder Nr Dorchester. (See also entry under river fishing Stour). *Species:* Crucian/Crucian cross 2lb, Carp 22lb, Tench 4lb, Eels 3lb, Roach 2lb, Rudd 1lb, Gudgeon, Perch 2lb, Bream 3lb, Barbel 1lb, Grass Carp 8lb. *Permits:* Mr P Stone (Treasurer), The Timepiece, Newbury, Gillingham, Dorset, SP8 4HZ. Tel: 01747 823339. Mr J Candy, Todber Manor Fisheries Shop, Tel: 01258 820384. Kings Stag Garage, Kings Stag, Nr Hazelbury Bryan. *Charges:* £5 day ticket, £41 season ticket. £20.50 junior and OAP £31. *Season:* Open all year. *Methods:* Barbless hooks. Mainly pole fishing. Big baits for double figure Carp on Pheasant lake. Pole on Spring lake for mixed bags.

Litton Lakes
Contact: Andrew Romans, Charity Farm, Litton Lane, Litton Cheney. *Tel:* 01308 482574. *Water:* 1.5 acre lake. *Species:* Carp, Roach, Rudd, Bream, Tench, Perch, Trout. *Charges:* Dawn to dusk: Adult £6. Under 16 years £4.50. *Season:*

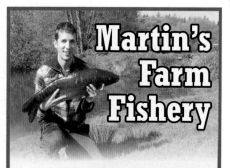
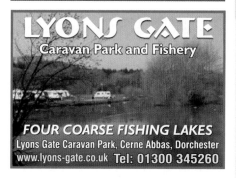
Open all year. 24 hour fishing. *Methods:* Barbless hooks, no keepnets, landing nets to be disinfected, maximum 2 rods per person, juniors to be accompanied by an adult. Well behaved dogs allowed. No fires, no litter.

Lyons Gate Fishing Lakes
Contact: Stuart Jones, Lyons Gate, Nr Cerne Abbas, Dorchester. *Sat Nav:* DT2 7AZ. *Tel:* 01300 345260. *Water:* Four lakes totalling approximately 3.5 acres. *Species:* Carp over 40lb, Tench to 11lb, Chub, Barbel, Bream, Golden Orfe, Roach, Rudd and Perch. *Permits:* On bankside. *Charges:* £5 p/day (2 rods), night fishing can be arranged. *Season:* Open all year dawn to dusk. *Methods:* Barbless hooks only. Full details at the fishery.

STILLWATER COARSE

Coking Farm Fishery and Touring Caravan Park

Coking Farm, West Stour, Gillingham, Dorset SP8 5SF

20 Acres of water on 5 Lakes Specimen Carp and Catfish to 36lbs
Mixed Match Lakes with variety of fish and some superb Tench

Shower and Toilet facilities

Extensively Stocked Bait and Tackle Shop for the Carp and Match Angler

30 hard-standing touring pitches with electric hook-ups and water

Tel: 01747 839879
Mobile: 07789 003044

email: info@cokingfarmfishery.co.uk
www.cokingfarmfishery.co.uk

West Compton Manor Lakes
Contact: Mrs Oonagh Stewart, West Compton Manor, West Compton, Dorchester. *Sat Nav:* DT2 0EY. *Tel:* 01300 320400. *Mobile:* 07958 968798. *Water:* 2 acre Lake. *Species:* Mirror and Common Carp, Roach and Rudd. *Charges:* £75 per year. *Season:* Open all year. *Methods:* Members only. Night fishing by appointment. No disabled access. Barbless hooks only. No keepnets. Max 2 rods per person. Children of 16 and under must be accompanied by an adult.

GILLINGHAM

Culvers Farm Fishery
Contact: V.J. Pitman, Culvers Farm, Gillingham. *Sat Nav:* SP8 5DS. *Tel:* 01747 822466. *Water:* One 1.5 acre lake. One 3 acre lake. *Species:* Carp, Bream, Roach, Chub and Tench. *Charges:* Syndicate with waiting list. Please contact the above for more info. *Season:* Open all year. *Methods:* Barbless hooks only. No Boilies. No keepnets allowed.

Gillingham and District A.A. (Lodden Lakes) ♿
Contact: Simon Hebditch (Hon. Secretary), 10 Pimpernel Court, Gillingham. *Tel:* 01747 821218. *Mobile:* 07990 690613. *Water:* 2 lakes (5 acres and 3 acres). *Species:* Carp to 27lb, Pike to 25lb, Crucians to 4lb, Tench to 7lb, Eels to

7lb, Roach to 2lb, Bream to 9lb, Grass Carp to 18lb. *Permits:* As River Stour. *Charges:* As River Stour to join club. Guest Tickets - £4. Season Ticket - £12 day, £32 day/night, Junior £8. Must be a member of either Gillingham or Sturminster. *Season:* Open all year. *Methods:* Large Carp favour boilies, Pike on deadbaits, Bream on pole or feeder with worm, pellet and groundbait, Tench from margins on worm/caster.

LYME REGIS

Wood Farm Caravan Park
Contact: Jane Bremner, Axminster Road, Charmouth. *Sat Nav:* DT6 6BT. *Tel:* 01297 560697. *Water:* 2 ponds totalling approx. 1 acre. *Species:* Carp, Rudd, Roach, Tench & Perch. *Permits:* From local Post office. *Charges:* £5 day ticket. £20 week. £60 season. *Season:* All year. *Methods:* No boilies, keepnets. Barbless hooks only.

POOLE

Bourne Valley Park
Contact: Borough of Poole Leisure Services, Alderney, Poole. *Tel:* 01202 265265. *Water:* Small fishing lake used as an introduction to angling for local people. *Species:* Rudd and Carp. *Charges:* Free of charge. *Season:* Open all year. *Methods:* Barbless hooks only. No boilies, no litter. Full rules on site. Parking in on street only.

Remember a ♿ means the fishery has disabled facilities - contact them direct for further details

STILLWATER COARSE

RINGWOOD

Cranebrook Lakes
Contact: Christchurch Angling Club Office, Unit 6, Silver Business Park, Airfield Way, Christchurch. *Tel:* 01202 480009. *Water:* Four small lakes at Verwood. *Species:* Roach, Rudd, Perch, Crucians and a few Carp. *Permits:* Christchurch A.C. membership. *Charges:* Annual CAC membership. *Season:* Open all year dawn to dusk.

Moors Valley Country Park &
Contact: The Rangers, Horton Road, Ashley Heath, Nr Ringwood. *Sat Nav:* BH24 2ET. *Tel:* 01425 470721. *Water:* The Moors Lake covers an area of 9 acres. Maximum depth 2 meters. *Species:* Tench to 6lb, Roach to 2lb, Perch to 2lb, Rudd 2lb, Pike to 20lb. Occasional Dace/Gudgeon/Chub. *Permits:* Fishing is from the bays marked by wooden posts on the west bank and has disabled access. Permits from visitor centre. *Charges:* Adults (17 - 65yrs) £4.20, season £30. Over 65yrs £3.70, season £24. Under 16 £3.50, season £20. Car park charges vary throughout the year, pay on foot system. *Season:* Moors lake from 16 June to 14 March. *Methods:* Rod licence required for over 12yrs. Fishing from 8-30am to dusk. No keepnets, no boilies, barbless hooks, float/ledger/feeder/dead bait for Pike. Max two rods per angler. All anglers must be in possession of a landing net and unhooking mat for larger species. Use of weed rake mat required. Toilets on site at visitor centre including disabled. One platform may be suitable for disabled angler.

SHAFTSBURY

Coking Farm Fishery
Contact: Chris Lyle, Coking Farm, West Stour, Nr Shaftsbury. *Sat Nav:* SP8 5SF. *Tel:* 01747 839879. *Mobile:* 07789 003044. *Water:* 5 lakes. Meadow Lake (match) 4.25 acres. Rush Lake (match) 3 acres. Oak Specimen Lake 4.5 acres. Long Lake 4.5 acres. Woodland Specimen Lake 3.5 acres. *Species:* Meadow Lake: Tench 8lb, Carp 15lb, Roach 3lb, Rudd 3lb, Crucians 2lb, Bream 8lb, Golden Tench 4lb, Golden Rudd 2lb. Rush Lake: Tench to 8lb, Carp 14lb, Roach 3lb, Rudd 3lb, Crucians 2lb, Bream 5lb, Golden Tench 5lb, Golden Rudd 2lb. Oak Specimen Lake: Huge head of 20lb plus Mirror and Common Carp. Long Lake: Massive head of Carp to

25lb, Catfish to 30lb. Woodland: Carp to 35lb, Catfish to 35lb. *Charges:* Meadow Lake £8, £15 for 24hrs. Rush Lake £8. Oak Lake £10, £20 for 24hrs. Long Lake £10, £20 for 24hrs. Woodlands Lake £10, £20 for 24hrs. *Season:* Open all year. *Methods:* Barbless hooks only. No keepnets. No Carp sacks. No nuts. Unhooking mats and suitable quality landing net must be used.

SHERBORNE

Yeovil & Sherborne Angling Association (Sherborne Lake)
Contact: Richard Cattle, 14 Millford Road, Yeovil, Somerset. *Tel:* 01935 473515. *Water:* Sherborne Castle Lake and all other association waters. Also see River Club Card entry under River Fishing, Somerset Frome. *Species:* Roach, Bream, Carp, Perch, Rudd, Tench. *Permits:* Membership details from above & local tackle shops. *Charges:* No day tickets. Lake Section licence £50 per year, covers all waters. Junior £25. Juniors must be accompanied by an adult. *Season:* Open all year.

STURMINSTER NEWTON

Gillingham and District A.A. (Whitepost Lakes)
Contact: Simon Hebditch (Hon. Secretary), 10 Pimpernel Court, Gillingham. *Tel:* 01747 821218. *Mobile:* 07990 690613. *Water:* Two 1 acre lakes. *Species:* Carp to 7lb, Crucians/Crucian cross to 1lb, Tench to 4lb, Roach, Rudd, Perch and Eels. *Permits:* As River Stour. *Charges:* As River Stour. *Season:* Open all year. *Methods:* Pole, waggler or feeder for Carp. Sweetcorn, pellet, maggots or meat good for Carp.

Sturminster and Hinton A.A (Coarse Lakes) &
Contact: Mr D Rigby (Secretary), Penny Gates, Penny Street, Sturminster Newton. *Tel:* 01258 472068. *Mobile:* 07770 891669. *Water:* 14 miles river Dorset Stour; joint fisheries at Lodden Lakes, Gillingham and Mappowder. Full members may also fish Revels fishery near Dorchester. *Species:* Carp and all coarse species. *Methods:* 2 disabled angler friendly platforms on river and lakes. Please enquire for more details.

STILLWATER COARSE

Todber Manor Fisheries (Big Hayes) &

Contact: John Candy, Manor Farm, Todber, Sturminster Newton. *Sat Nav:* DT10 1JB. *Tel:* 01258 820384. *Mobile:* 07974 420813. *Water:* 8.5 acre lake with 18 gravel swims. *Species:* Carp to 33lb 8oz. Perch 3lb 2oz. Bream 13lb, Pike 22lb 2oz. *Permits:* From on site tackle shop. *Charges:* £12 per day. £24 for 24 hours. *Season:* Open all year. *Methods:* No keepnets or sacks. Minimum 42" landing net. Unhooking mats must be used. Call for full details.

Todber Manor Fisheries (Little Hayes) &

Contact: John Candy, Manor Farm, Todber, Sturminster Newton. *Sat Nav:* DT10 1JB. *Tel:* 01258 820384. *Mobile:* 07974 420813. *Water:* 6 acre lake with 15 woodchipped swims. *Species:* Carp to 30lb. Bream 12lb. *Permits:* From on site tackle shop. *Charges:* £12 per day. £24 for 24 hours. *Season:* Open all year. *Methods:* No keepnets or sacks. Minimum 42" landing net. Unhooking mats must be used. Call for full details.

Todber Manor Fisheries (Paddock Lake) &

Contact: John Candy, Manor Farm, Todber, Sturminster Newton. *Sat Nav:* DT10 1JB. *Tel:* 01258 820384. *Mobile:* 07974 420813. *Water:* 1.5 acre lake with seven well spaced, woodchipped swims. *Species:* Carp 28lb 3oz, Catfish 84lb. Bream 10lb. *Permits:* From on site tackle shop. *Charges:* £12 per day. £24 per 24 hours. Whole lake £150 for 24 hours. *Season:* Open all year. *Methods:* Common sense rules apply. Call the tackle shop for full details.

Todber Manor Fisheries (Park Lake) &

Contact: John Candy, Manor Farm, Todber, Sturminster Newton. *Sat Nav:* DT10 1JB. *Tel:* 01258 820384. *Mobile:* 07974 420813. *Water:* 3 acre canal style lake with 38 wooden platforms. *Species:* Carp 12lb, Barbel 7lb 9oz, Tench 5lb, Roach 2lb, Bream 4lb 2oz, Hybrids 2lb plus. *Permits:* From on site tackle shop. *Charges:* £7 per day. Season ticket available. *Season:* Open all year. *Methods:* Common sense rules apply. Call the tackle shop for full details.

Todber Manor Fisheries (Wadmill Lake) &

Contact: John Candy, Manor Farm, Todber, Sturminster Newton. *Sat Nav:* DT10 1JB. *Tel:* 01258 820384. *Mobile:* 07974 420813. *Water:* 4.5 acre lake, 31 woodchipped swims. Gravel path all the way round. *Species:* Pike 22lb, Carp 28lb, Bream 9lb, Tench 6lb. *Permits:* From on site tackle shop. *Charges:* £10 per day. £20 - 24 hrs. Season tickets available. *Season:* Open all year. *Methods:* No keepnets. Large landing net and unhooking mats must be used.

Todber Manor Fisheries (Whitepost Lakes) &

Contact: John Candy, Manor Farm, Todber, Sturminster Newton. *Sat Nav:* DT10 1JB. *Tel:* 01258 820384. *Mobile:* 07974 420813. *Water:* Two 1 acre lakes, total 30 swims. *Species:* Carp to 12lb, Tench 3lb, Roach 1lb and Perch 3lb. *Permits:* From on site tackle shop. *Charges:* £7 per day. Season tickets available. *Season:* Open all year. *Methods:* Common sense rules apply. Call the tackle shop for full details.

A fish known as 'the bailiff' at a healthy 20lb 2oz from Coking Farm Fishery

WAREHAM

Silent Woman Lakes

Contact: David Sowry, Silent Woman Farm, Coldharbour, Wareham. *Sat Nav:* BH20 7PA. *Tel:* 01929 554153. *Water:* 3.5 acre lake with central island and 1.25 acre lake with central island. *Species:* Carp, Tench, Roach, Rudd, Pike. *Charges:* £1.50 hourly rate/Day ticket £15. Other prices on application. *Season:* Open all year. *Methods:* 2 rods per person. Barbless hooks. No boilies or Carp pellets. No keepnets. All fish to be returned. Fish antiseptic recommended.

Wareham and District Angling Society (Coarse Lakes)

Contact: Deano Watts, c/o Purbeck Angling Centre, 28 South Street, Wareham. *Tel:* 01929 550770. *Water:* See entry under River Fishing, Frome. 8 lakes including Breach Pond and Pitmans Pond. *Species:* Carp 25lb+, Bream 10lb+, Crucians 3lb+ and Tench 8lb+. *Permits:* Purbeck Angling. *Season:* Some 12 months, Others normal season applies. *Methods:* As specified in club book.

WEYMOUTH

Dorchester & District Angling Society (Coarse Lakes) &

Contact: Steve Sudworth, 3 Buddleia Close, Weymouth. *Tel:* 01305 835283. *Mobile:* 07816 175579. *Water:* Two 2 acre lakes - Witch Hazel and Lavender at Chickerel, Weymouth. See also River Fishing Stour entry plus coarse Lakes at Dorchester. *Species:* Witch Hazel: Carp to 30lb, Roach, Rudd and Perch. Lavender: Tench to 4lb plus, Bream, Skimmers, Roach, Rudd, Perch and a few Carp. *Permits:* Membership only available from above. *Season:* Lakes open all year. *Methods:* In members handbook.

Radipole Lake &

Contact: Weymouth Tackle Shops. *Sat Nav:* DT4 8TA. *Water:* 70 acres plus. Fishing only permitted in locations shown on licence. *Species:* Carp 30lb+, Roach and Rudd 2lb+, Pike,

Mullet, Tench, Eels and Perch. *Permits:* Reels and Deals, 61b St. Thomas Street, Weymouth: 01305 787848. Weymouth Angling Centre, 2 St. Edmonds Street, Weymouth: 01305 777771. Permits must be shown to RLAS bailiff on request. Bailiffs carry ID card. *Charges:* Per season charges: Adult £55, Junior (17 and under) £30, OAP/Disabled £40 (must show badge or disabled rod licence). No overnight fishing on day tickets. Per week charges: All tickets £25. Per day charges: Adult £6, Junior £6, OAP/Disabled £6. Tickets are half price from 1st December to 14th March except day tickets. *Season:* 16 June - 14 March. Parts of the lake are shut in winter for rare birds. See permit for more details. No angler may fish for more than 72 hours in one swim. They must move if they wish to continue fishing. *Methods:* 3 rod max, no lead weights, no live baiting, barbless hooks only, bivvies and keepnets permitted, no Carp over 3lb to be kept in keepnets. Lead weights can be used if over 28 grams. No fires or BBQ's.

Wally's Lakes
Contact: Rosewall Camping Reception, East Farm Dairy, Osmington Mills, Weymouth. *Sat Nav:* DT3 6HA. *Tel:* 01305 832248. *Water:* 1 acre Wally's Lake. 2.75 acre Meadow Lake. *Species:* Carp, Tench, Bream, Roach. *Permits:* Camping Park reception or riding stables reception. *Charges:* £10 per day Adults, £5 a day 15 years and under. Under 15's must be accompanied by responsible adult. Summer half day after 4 pm £5. *Season:* Open all year. Please phone first if travelling any distance. *Methods:* Barbless hooks, no keepnets, no particle bait. Maximum 2 rods. Night fishing by arrangement. No parking at lakeside. Full rules on site. Minimum 36" landing net. Catch mats must be used. No rubbish to be left.

Warmwell Holiday Park &
Contact: Steven Nicklinson, Warmwell, Weymouth. *Sat Nav:* DT2 8JE. *Tel:* 01305 854023. *Water:* 3 lakes. 2 acre Carp lake (fish to 34lb+) - 20 swims. 2 mixed fishing lakes. *Species:* Specimen Lake - Carp to 35lb, Pike to 30lb. Pleasure Lake - Bream 10lb, Carp 20lb, Tench 7lb, Perch 3lb. *Permits:* Day tickets available all year, but must be purchased in advance. Contact fishery manager on number above. *Charges:* Specimen Lake - £12 for 12 hours, £20 for 24 hours. Pleasure Lake - £8 Adult, £7 juniors. *Season:* Open all year. *Methods:* Specimen Lakes: Barbless hooks. No nuts, beans or pulses. 2 rods max. No keepnets. Unhooking mats must be used. Minimum 10lb line.

WIMBORNE

Clump Hill Farm Fishery &
Contact: Donna, Mannington, Wimborne. *Sat Nav:* BH21 7JT. *Mobile:* 07764 535211. *Water:* One acre lake. *Species:* Carp to 30lb+. Common, Crucian and Mirror. Chub 7lb. Perch 5lb 4oz. Roach, Rudd, Tench and Bream. *Permits:* On the bank. *Charges:* £7 per day for two rods. £5 OAP and under 14s. *Season:* Open all year 7am to 7.30pm or dusk if earlier. Night fishing only by prior arrangement. *Methods:* Barbless hooks only. No keepnets. No dogs. No radios.

Crooked Willows Farm
Contact: Mr & Mrs VJ Percy, Mannington, Wimborne. *Sat Nav:* BH21 7LB. *Tel:* 01202 825628. *Mobile:* 07543 283824. *Water:* 1.5 acres. *Species:* Carp to 26lb, Tench to 6lb, Chub 4lb, Perch 5lb, Roach 1lb, Rudd 1lb & Crucians 3lb. *Permits:* Available on bank. *Charges:* £5/day, Juniors £4. 24 hour £15 and must be booked in advance. Under 15s must be accompanied by an adult. *Season:* Dawn to dusk all year round. *Methods:* Barbless hooks only, no groundbait, no keepnets, no dogs, no rubbish and no hemp.

Whitemoor Lakes &
Contact: Paul, 400 Colehill Lane, Colehill, Wimborne. *Sat Nav:* BH21 7DA. *Tel:* 01202 884478. *Mobile:* 07932 466250. *Water:* 2 acre lake with 40 pegs and 1 acre canal with 20 pegs. Disabled toilet facilities. *Species:* Carp 35lb, Tench 9lb, Perch 4lb 9oz, Roach 2lb, Rudd, Bream 6lb 5oz. *Permits:* Tickets on the bank. Night fishing by arrangement. *Charges:* Adults £8, Juniors £6, OAP £6. Evenings £5. *Season:* No close season. *Methods:* No barbed hooks, no keepnets, no braid.

Wimborne and District Angling Club (Little Canford Ponds) &
Contact: Mr Rob Doyle, WDAC PO Box 6632, Poole. *Mobile:* 07740 675788. *Water:* Approx. 2 acres with facilities for the disabled including fully accessible fishing platforms. *Species:* Carp, Bream, Roach, Perch, Tench, Rudd, Pike. *Charges:* Fishing open to members only. Please contact Mr Doyle for further information.

Stillwater Trout

BRIDPORT

Mangerton Mill
Contact: Mrs Harris, Mangerton Mill, Mangerton, Bridport.
Sat Nav: DT6 3SG. *Tel:* 01308 485224. *Water:* 1 acre lake.
Species: Rainbow Trout. *Permits:* Post Office. *Charges:* £6
to fish. £9 up to 2 fish. £13 up to 3 fish. £17 up to 4 fish.
Season: 1 April - 31 December. *Methods:* Max hook size 10.

DORCHESTER

Flowers Farm Fly Fishers &
Contact: Alan J. Bastone, Flowers Farm, Hilfield, Dorchester.
Sat Nav: DT2 7BE. *Tel:* 01300 341351. *Water:* 5 lakes total
3.75 acres. *Species:* Rainbow & Brown Trout. Best fish in
2012 - 9lb 2oz Rainbow, 4lb Brown. *Permits:* Prices on
request (Tel/Fax: 01300 341351). *Charges:* 4 fish £31 per
day, 3 fish £25 half day, 2 fish £19 eve, 12 fish £126. *Season:*
Open all year 5.30am to dusk. *Methods:* Single fly, max size
10, Bank fishing only. We have a disabled friendly fishing
platform with nearby parking and toilet facilities.

Wessex Fly Fish Trout Lakes
Contact: Richard & Sally Slocock, Lawrences Farm,
Southover, Tolpuddle, Dorchester. *Sat Nav:* DT2 7HF. *Tel:*
01305 848460. *Water:* Five lakes and pools totalling four
acres. Also see entries under Frome and Piddle. *Species:*
Rainbow Trout average 3lbs. *Permits:* From the above
address. *Charges:* 2 fish ticket £18, 3 fish ticket £24, 4 fish
£28. 55's and over £16 for 2 fish, £7 for additional fish.
Season: Lakes: April 1st to October 31st. Half price tickets to
clear stock from 1 to 15 November only. *Methods:* Fly only.

LYME REGIS

Amherst Lodge
Contact: Mr B Stansfield, Amherst Lodge, St Mary's Lane,
Uplyme, Lyme Regis. *Sat Nav:* DT7 3XH. *Tel:* 01297 442773.
Water: 6 stream fed Trout lakes totalling 4 acres on the Dorset
Devon borders. *Species:* Rainbow to 5lb. Brown Trout(catch
and release only) to 4lb. *Permits:* Please go to rod room on
arrival. *Charges:* From £20 for two fish bag. Catch & release
£15 day or £10 up to 4 hours. *Season:* Open all year 9am
to dusk. Must book if arriving before 9am. Telephone in
advance. *Methods:* Small imitative patterns only. Barbless
for catch & release in water. In season upper lakes are dry
fly only. Mown walkways along banks allow some degree
of access for motorised wheelchairs.

Amherst Lodge
Near Lyme Regis
Tel: (01297) 442773
Six secluded, stream fed lakes
totalling 4 acres stocked with
Rainbows to 5lb and Browns to 4lb

Flowers Farm Trout Lakes
Open all year, 5.30am to dusk.
2013 prices
Full day £31 - 4 fish
Half day £25 - 3 fish
Evening £19 - 2 fish
12 fish ticket - £126
25 and 50 fish tickets - prices on application
Flowers Farm, Hilfield, Dorchester, Dorset.
Tel/Fax: (01300) 341351 Web: www.flowersfarmlakes.co.uk
E-mail: alan@flowersfarmlakes.co.uk

RINGWOOD

Hamer Trout Fishery
Contact: John White, Christchurch Angling Club, Unit 6,
Silver Business Park, Airfield Way, Christchurch. *Tel:* 01202
480009. *Water:* 5 acre stillwater Trout fishery. *Species:*
Rainbow and Brown Trout. *Permits:* Christchurch A.C.
membership. Guest tickets available if with CAC member.
Charges: Club member: 5 fish £20, 2 fish £12, sporting
ticket £14. *Season:* Open all year. *Methods:* Single fly only.

WIMBORNE

Whitesheet Trout Lakes
Contact: Christchurch Angling Club Office, Unit 6, Silver
Business Park, Airfield Way, Christchurch. *Tel:* 01202
480009. *Water:* Three lakes totalling seven acres. Also
Hamer Lake. Fishing for Christchurch Angling Club members
and their guests only. No day tickets for non members.
Species: Rainbow and Brown Trout. *Permits:* Local tackle
shops. *Charges:* Club member: 5 fish £20, 2 fish £12,
sporting ticket £14. Guest: 5 fish £35, 2 fish £20, sporting
ticket £24. *Season:* Open all year dawn to dusk. *Methods:*
Single fly only. See ticket for complete rules.

Remember a & means the fishery has disabled
facilities - contact them direct for further details

Where to Stay in Dorset

A pretty Mirror Carp from Highway Farm

WHERE TO STAY

Fisheries Enforcement Overview

Dilip Sarkar MBE
Angling Trust Fisheries Enforcement Manager

The Angling Trust – the sport's governing body – is driving forward fisheries enforcement and working closely with the police and Environment Agency. Here the Trust's Fisheries Enforcement Manager, retired police officer Dilip Sarkar MBE, explains this – and how we can all help...

Poaching and fish theft are of great concern to anglers – but it is little understood that these are criminal offences and not victim-less crimes. Fishing without permission is a Schedule 1 Theft Act offence ('Theft of Fishing Rights'), and the theft of fish is exactly that – theft, under Sections 1 – 7 of the Theft Act 1968. Historically the police have been confused regarding their role and powers when dealing with such reports – but at last this is changing. Via the England & Wales Poaching Priority Group (E&WPPG) we have forged strong links with the National Wildlife Crime Unit (NWCU), which has uploaded our 'Elementary Guide to Angling Law & Fisheries Enforcement' to the Police Online Knowledge Area (POLKA). This important advice can also be downloaded free of charge from our website: www.anglingtrust.net

Nationally, crime figures continue to fall - but not in the rural area. Consequently the police are focussing on Rural Crime - providing an unprecedented opportunity for us to educate the police and ensure that poaching and fish theft are included in the national and local force Rural Crime Strategies. Via the E&WPPG we have also recently contributed an expert 'Impact Statement' contextualising the negative financial and environmental effects of these offences - this will be appended to police operational orders and provided to the courts to ensure that offenders receive appropriate punishments.

The Environment Agency's (EA) role largely concerns rod licence checking and byelaws.

Angling Trust Fisheries Enforcement Manager Dilip Sarkar with a big river pike caught in January 2013. Magnificent fish like this must be protected – and many people are working hard to do just that.

The role of EA Fisheries Enforcement Officers is, however, a very difficult and wide-ranging one delivered with limited resources. It is crucially important to understand that today all law enforcement is 'intelligence led'. This means that all calls are logged, analysed, hotspots identified and resources deployed accordingly. The Agency is not resourced to respond immediately to all reported incidents but will target particular waters when sufficient intelligence confirms offences in a specific area. The importance of us all contributing to this process by reporting incidents and intelligence cannot be over emphasised: 0800 80 70 60.

Naturally we are anxious to support the EA's work as much as possible, and one significant initiative is the Voluntary Bailiff Service (VBS). At the time of writing (August 2013) this remains an operational pilot project in the EA South East Region, the national roll-out of which (in England) we are currently negotiating. All Volunteer Bailiffs (VBs) are subject to a Criminal Records Bureau check and are trained by the Angling Trust, EA and NWCU. In Phase One, VBs join an 'Angling Watch' and contribute to the essential intelligence gathering process. During the coarse close season of 2013, for example, the VBS ran Operation CLAMP DOWN, undertaking 165 patrols, reporting fourteen incidents of illegal fishing, and assisted the police with enquiries on two occasions. VBs work closely with EA Fisheries Enforcement Officers, and as the process evolves will ultimately be empowered and fully trained to check rod licences and deal with certain byelaw offences. Law enforcement volunteering is nothing new; the police are supported by both the Special Constabulary and Police Support Volunteers - and VBS has already proved enormously popular with anglers. We now have fifty-three VBs in EA SE, and well over 300 registered on our database pending us recruiting in their areas. Anyone interested in joining the VBS should in the first instance either email bailiffs@anglingtrust.net or call 07971 677638.

Enforcement works on the principle of 'Prevention; Intelligence; Enforcement (PIE). Naturally it is desirable to prevent offences happening at all, to which end education is vitally important. There continue to be problems, due to cultural differences, with certain Eastern European migrant anglers, in whose countries fish are killed for the pot. Consequently fish are pursued using the most efficient, and not necessarily sporting, methods, such as set lines, traps and gill nets - all of which are illegal here, where conservation, and catch and return underpin our angling law, rules and culture. The apprehending and prosecution of offenders is, of course, vitally necessary - but education is equally important. Our 'Building Bridges' initiative, managed by Rado Papiewski, pro-actively engages with migrant communities and angling clubs, working closely with the police and EA, in an effort to educate migrants regarding our laws and angling culture. 'Building Bridges', in fact, provides multi-lingual posters and leaflets which can be downloaded from our website and a free translation service to British angling clubs, through the Polish Anglers' Association.

The foregoing covers the main points of our Fisheries Enforcement Campaign to date, progress with which is made daily. What we must do is achieve 'joined up' thinking and working between all enforcement agencies involved – and ensure that anglers understand the law and how the system works: 0800 80 70 60. Calling that number, or your local police on 101 (or 999 in the event of a criminal offence in progress), and joining the Angling Trust to support our work in this critical area is the only way we anglers will make progress and get the system working for us. This is why the Trust, Agency, NWCU and Institute of Fisheries Management is creating a training course for angling club bailiffs – again, details can be found on our website; see you there!

Environment Agency fisheries enforcement officers have a very difficult job to do with limited resources; support them: 0800 80 70 60

South West Rivers Association

SWRA

Roger Furniss - Secretary

SWRA is the voice of riparian owners and game angling in the South West. It is the umbrella body of the individual river associations in the South West and a powerful lobbying body regularly consulted by the Environment Agency and Government. Its main aim is to see salmon and sea trout stocks and the sport of angling for them return to their former glory.

Since the abolition of statutory fisheries advisory committees to support the work of the Environment Agency SWRA is more important than ever.

As with many aspects of modern life, angling and our freedom to enjoy it have been threatened by an ever-growing bureaucracy. Our rivers are also subject to pressure from abstraction, pollution and public access. By enabling individual rivers to work together to speak with one voice SWRA continues to influence the political and environmental agenda in a number of key areas, including:

Abolition of Salmon and Sea Trout Netting

We lobby for recognition that rod fishing provides enormous social and economic benefits compared to net fishing.

Salmon Stocking Policy

We support effective stocking to compensate for the effects of environmental degradation. Our Hatchery Best Practice Group, supported by the Environment Agency and Westcountry Rivers Trust, is ensuring the best possible use of our volunteer hatchery teams.

Canoeing

We continue to support the policy of voluntary access agreements and have helped secure more acceptable ones on some rivers.

Abstraction

Over-abstraction remains a serious threat. In South Devon we are working with the Angling Trust to reduce the unacceptable levels of abstraction. The biggest and newest threat is the rapid growth in hydropower developments. Our Secretary is not only active at a local level but sits on the National Hydropower Stakeholder Group set up to ensure best practice.

Water Framework Directive

This European directive has given a great opportunity for anglers and riparian owners to become directly involved in the management of our rivers and their fisheries. SWRA is a lead player in ensuring we get the best outcomes from working in partnership with Defra, the Environment Agency and the Westcountry Rivers Trust.

If you would like to know more about the work of South West Rivers Association by joining the mailing list for its Newsletter, or wish to become an individual supporter, please contact the Secretary, Roger Furniss at:

swra@furniss2733.fsnet.co.uk

HAMPSHIRE

Find us on
Facebook

 @gethookedguide

HAMPSHIRE

RIVER FISHING

STILLWATER COARSE

STILLWATER TROUT

WHERE TO STAY

Map No	Advertiser	Sat Nav	Phone	Advert Page
	Game Fishing			
116	Christchurch Angling Club (Game and Coarse)		01202 480009	90
	Coarse Fishing			
117	Lake Farm Country Holidays	SP6 3EF	01425 654106	109
118	Ringwood & District Anglers Association (Coarse & Game)		01202 659393	97

Please note sat nav postcodes, where supplied, may not be totally accurate.

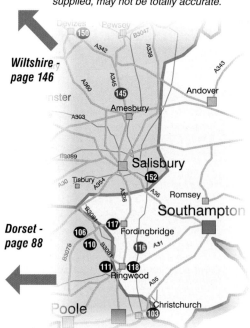

Wiltshire - page 146

Dorset - page 88

Only advertisers with fishing are located on this map. Their listings within this guide are highlighted in blue.

Hampshire River Fishing

THE 'HAMPSHIRE' AVON

The River Avon is one of England's most famous rivers, and is revered by all anglers for the quality of fish that live in it. This river creates a certain mystique that captivates the attentions of fishers from all walks of life.

The River Avon rises in the Vale of Pewsey and, with its tributaries the Bourne and Wylye, drains the chalk of Salisbury Plain. The River Nadder, which is joined by the Wylye near Salisbury, drains the escarpment of the South Wiltshire Downs and the Kimmeridge clays of the Wardour Vale. The River Ebble and Ashford Water also drain the South Wiltshire Downs and join the Avon downstream of Salisbury and Fordingbridge respectively.

Visit our dedicated sea fishing website
www.westcountryseaangling.co.uk

12yr old Annabella caught this magnificent 8lb Brown trout whilst on a fly fishing course on the river Test run by Graeme Lowndes

Below Fordingbridge, a number of streams drain the New Forest area. The Avon finally drains into Christchurch harbour, where it is joined by the Rivers Stour and Mude before discharging into the English Channel.

Britford (Coarse)

Contact: London Angler's Association, Izaak Walton House, 2A Hervey Park Road, London. *Tel:* 0208 5207477. *Water:* Several stretches of the Hampshire Avon. *Species:* Roach 3lb 12oz, Barbel 14lb, Chub 7lb, plus specimen Dace, Grayling, Perch & Pike. Bream 12lb. *Permits:* Day membership tickets available from Fishery Keeper on the bank - £10 Seniors per rod, maximum of 2 rods. £5 Juniors & OAP and registered disabled per rod, maximum of 2 rods. *Charges:* Senior: £43 - Junior: £24 - OAP/Reg. Disabled: £26 - Partners Ticket: £65 - Club affiliated membership available on request. Plus £15 (Seniors) or £7.50 (Juniors/OAP/Reg.Disabled) for Britford Coarse Fishing Ticket. *Season:* Current EA byelaws apply. *Methods:* See members handbook.

Britford (Game)

Contact: London Angler's Association, Izaak Walton House, 2A Hervey Park Road, London. *Tel:* 0208 5207477. *Water:* Several stretches of the Hampshire Avon. *Species:* Trout & Salmon. *Permits:* Day membership permit available from Fishery Keeper on bank. *Charges:* Salmon & Sea Trout £20 per day. Trout £10 per day. £30 Game Permits available to those purchasing Britford Coarse tickets and membership tickets. *Season:* EA byelaws apply. *Methods:* See members handbook.

Christchurch Angling Club (Salmon & Sea Trout)

Contact: Christchurch Angling Club Office, Unit 6, Silver Business Park, Airfield Way, Christchurch, Dorset. *Tel:* 01202 480009. *Water:* Many miles of double bank fishing on the Hampshire Avon, including the Somerley Estate, Winkton, Ringwood Fishery, Bisterne Fishery and River Frome. Also Sea Trout on the Dorset Stour. *Species:* Salmon 27lb+. Sea Trout 12lb+. *Permits:* Club Membership required. *Charges:* Membership: Adult £160 plus £15 joining fee, Conc. £110. Junior - (12 to under 18) £60. Somerley Estate Salmon membership is an additional £165. *Season:* Salmon: 1 Feb to 31 Aug. Sea Trout: 15 April to 31 Oct. *Methods:* Salmon: Fly only from 1 Feb to 15 May. Spinning permitted from 15 May to 31 Aug. Shrimp and Prawn permitted from 16 June to 31 Aug. Sea Trout fly, spinner and bait from 16 June.

Fordingbridge Park Day Ticket Fishing

Contact: Fordingbridge Town Council, Town Hall, 63 High Street, Fordingbridge. *Tel:* 01425 654134. *Water:* 500 yards on the Hampshire Avon. *Species:* Chub 6lb 2oz, Roach 3lb 6oz, Dace 1lb, Rainbow Trout 6lb, Eels 1lb, Pike 23lb, Perch 1lb, Carp 16lb. *Permits:* Day Tickets must be purchased in advance from Fordingbridge Information Office, Kings Yard, Salisbury St. Fordingbridge or Fordingbridge Post Office, Salisbury Street, Fordingbridge. *Charges:* £5 Adults per Day. £2.50 per day for Juniors (under 16's) and Senior Citizens (65 plus). *Season:* Coarse Fishing 16 June to 14 March, 7.30am to dark. Trout Fishing April to June by arrangement only. *Methods:* Max 2 rods per person. No fishing under power lines or in play area. Tickets must be purchased in advance.

Lifelands / Ringwood Fishery

Contact: Christchurch Angling Club Office, Unit 6, Silver Business Park, Airfield Way, Christchurch, Dorset. *Tel:* 01202 480009. *Water:* Christchurch Angling Club controlled double bank fishing on the Hampshire Avon at Ringwood. *Species:* Barbel 14lb, Chub 7lb, Dace 1lb, Pike 30lb, Carp 20lb, Roach 2lb, Grayling 2lb. *Permits:* Local tackle shops. *Charges:* Day ticket: Adult £10, Junior/conc. £5. *Season:* Coarse: 16 June to 14 March. *Methods:* See club rules for individual waters.

Ringwood and District A.A. (Hampshire Avon)

Contact: J Sudworth. *Tel:* 01202 659393. *Water:* Severals Fishery at Ringwood upstream of Ibsley bridge and a number of stretches around Fordingbridge. *Species:* Barbel to 16lb 11oz, Chub to 7lb 6oz, Roach 3lb plus, Pike 30lb plus, Bream 10lb plus, Perch, Carp, Dace, Salmon, Sea Trout, Brown Trout. *Permits:* Ringwood Tackle. Tel: 01425 475155. *Charges:* Adult £150, Junior £50, Concessions for OAP and Disabled (Joining fee £20 adult). *Season:* Slight variations to coarse season due to Salmon fishing. Current E.A. byelaws apply. *Methods:* Details in permit.

Royalty Fishery

Contact: Davis Tackle, 71 - 75 Bargates, Christchurch, Dorset. *Sat Nav:* BH23 1QE. *Tel:* 01202 485169. *Water:* 2 miles on Hampshire Avon (Royalty fishery). *Species:* Barbel - 16lb 8oz, Chub - 8lb, Roach - 3lb, Pike - 30lb, Bream - 10lb, Perch - 4lb 11oz, Carp - 34lb, Dace - 10oz, Brown Trout, Sea Trout and Salmon. *Charges:* £12.50 day ticket, Concessions - 65 or over/disabled or under 18 £8.50 from Davis Tackle. *Season:* Coarse fishing June 16 - March 14. *Methods:* Rolling meat, float fishing for Dace/ Roach. Legered pellets for Barbel.

Sandy Balls Fishing

Contact: Cycle Centre, Sandy Balls Holiday Centre, Godshill, Fordingbridge. *Sat Nav:* SP6 2JZ. *Tel:* 01425 657707. *Water:* 0.33 mile on River Avon. *Species:* Barbel, Perch, Trout, River Carp and Chub. *Charges:* £9 Adult. £5 Junior. *Methods:* No night fishing. Barbless hooks only.

DUN

The River Dun is the shortest of the Test tributaries, but one of the most substantial. It rises above Lockerley and flows down through Dunbridge. Soon after Dunbridge it becomes part of the Mottisfont Abbey Estate before joining the main river at Mottisfont.

Holbury Lane Lakes (River Dun)

Contact: Fishery Manager, Holbury Lane, Lockerley, Romsey. *Tel:* 01794 341619. *Mobile:* 07817 252441. *Water:* 700 yards of River Dun, a tributary of the River Test, plus four Trout Lakes (see Stillwater Trout, Romsey). *Species:* Brown Trout 1.5lb average. *Charges:* On application. *Season:* Pre booking essential. 1 May - 30 September. *Methods:* Single fly, max size 10. Priest and net must be carried by anglers.

ITCHEN

For some the River Itchen is the ultimate chalk stream. Much shorter than its counterpart the River Test (17 miles vs. 39 miles), the Itchen is formed by the Alre, Tichborne and Candover Brook, which come together just below Alresford. It is from here down to Winchester, no more than five miles through the Itchen valley, where the most sought after beats lie.

Lower Itchen Fishery

Contact: Lyndsey Farmiloe, Embley Ridge, Gardeners Lane, Romsey. *Tel:* 07885 175540. *Water:* 3.5 miles River Itchen. *Species:* Brown Trout, Sea Trout, Salmon, Grayling. *Charges:* Upon application. *Season:* Trout 18 April - 7 October. Salmon 1 March - 1 October.

> Remember a ♿ means the fishery has disabled facilities - contact them direct for further details

TEST

In every respect, the River Test is the pre-eminent chalk stream. Physically, it is the longest; 39 miles from source to estuary. Historically, it is generally regarded as the birthplace of modern fly fishing.

The Test rises in north Hampshire. It then travels on a south-west curve, growing in width and flow as first the Bourne, and then the Dever and the Anton join the main river.

Below Stockbridge the river becomes appreciably bigger, then the Wallop Brook and the Dun join the main river and it is only south of Romsey, a few miles from the sea that the River Test finally becomes one single channel.

Dever Springs Trout Fishery

Contact: Niall Staig, Barton Stacey, Winchester. *Sat Nav:* SO21 3NP. *Tel:* 01264 720592. *Water:* Half a mile of river Dever (tributary of the Test). Two spring fed lakes totalling 6 acres. *Species:* Brown Trout. *Permits:* River Day - 8am to dusk £55. River afternoon - From 12 - dusk £40. Additional lake ticket £25 if purchased at the same time. *Season:* Open all year. 8am to dusk. *Methods:* No catch and release on Lakes.

River Blackwater Fishing ♿

Contact: John Hardeley, Keepers Lodge, Whinwhistle Road, East Wellow, Romsey. *Tel:* 01794 324485. *Mobile:* 07816 187648. *Water:* Approx. one mile on River Blackwater (2 beats only). See also Woodington Trout Lakes, Romsey and Whinwhistle Coarse Fishery. *Species:* Wild and stocked Browns and Grayling. *Charges:* On application. £58- 2 fish ticket then catch and release. *Season:* Open all year. Closed Christmas day and Boxing day. Open 7am - 7pm. *Methods:* Full rules on site.

Timsbury Fishing (Test)

Timsbury, Romsey. *Tel:* 01264 365165. *Mobile:* 07759 331385. *Water:* 1.5 miles on the River Test. *Species:* Brown Trout, Grayling, Roach, Perch, Dace, Chub, Pike, Carp. *Permits:* By booking in advance. Please ask for directions. *Charges:* £90 per person game. £20 per person coarse. *Season:* Game: 2nd April to 30 Sept. Coarse: 1 October to 14 March. 8am - dusk. *Methods:* Upstream dry fly. Coarse season any method (no spinners).

Stillwater Coarse

ANDOVER

Andover Angling Association
Contact: Tracy or Mike, c/o Challis Tackle, 60 Mylon Road, Andover. *Tel:* 01264 361103. *Water:* Rooksbury Mill Lake - 2 acres. Foxcotte Lake - 2.75 acres. Anton Park Lake - 8 acres. *Species:* Rooksbury - mixed coarse. Foxcotte - mixed coarse. Anton Park - mixed coarse, predominately Pike in winter. *Permits:* Available from Challis Tackle. *Charges:* Rooksbury - £7.15, no concessions. Foxcotte - £5 one rod, £7 two rods, no concessions, club membership available. Anton Park - £5 one rod, £7 two rods. *Season:* All lakes open all year. *Methods:* Rooksbury - no live bait, no night fishing. Foxcotte - no live bait, night fishing by appointment only. Anton Park - no live bait, night fishing by appointment only.

CHRISTCHURCH

Orchard Lakes
Contact: Mr J Southcombe, New Lane, Bashley, New Milton. *Sat Nav:* BH25 5TD. *Tel:* 01425 612404. *Mobile:* 07790 915434. *Water:* 5 small lakes at Bashley, New Milton. Largest 2 acres. 50 peg match lake. *Species:* Carp 26lb, Roach 2lb, Barbel 4lb, Tench 6lb, Perch 4lb, Bream 3lb, Chub 3lb. *Permits:* From shop on site. *Charges:* All lakes - £10 per day. £7 concession. *Season:* Open all year 7am to dusk. *Methods:* Barbless hooks only. No keepnets.

RINGWOOD

Hurst Pond
Contact: Ringwood Tackle. *Tel:* 01425 475155. *Water:* 1.5 acre pond at Hedlands Business Park, Blashford, Ringwood, Hants. *Species:* Carp 22lb, Tench 6.5lb, Roach 2.5lb, Rudd 2lb, Perch 3lb 12oz, Crucians 2.5lb, Eels 5lb. *Charges:* £10 a day, £7.50 conc, £15 for 24 hours. Limited to 6 tickets a day - booking advised. *Season:* Open all year.

Ringwood and District A.A. (Coarse Lakes)
Contact: J Sudworth. *Tel:* 01202 659393. *Water:* 3 lakes at Northfield, plus 1 at Hightown on the outskirts of Ringwood. *Species:* Hightown - Mixed fishery with Carp to 49lb, Tench, Bream, Roach, Rudd, Pike, Eels. Northfield - Big Carp to 40lb, Tench to 12lb, Bream, Roach, Rudd, Pike. *Permits:* Ringwood Tackle, Tel: 01425 475155. *Charges:* Adult £150, Junior £50, concessions for OAP and disabled. Available at Ringwood Tackle, West St., Ringwood, 01425 475155. *Season:* All year fishing available. *Methods:* Details in Permit.

Ringwood and District A.A. (Rockford Lake)
Contact: Ringwood & District Anglers Association. *Sat Nav:* BH24 3NA. *Tel:* 01202 659393. *Water:* Approx 55 acres with depths up to 12 feet, this lake is our latest acquisition formally a Cemex Syndicate. *Species:* Numerous Carp 30lb - 40lb, specimen Bream 14lbs plus, Tench 12lbs plus,

Pike 28lbs plus and huge Perch. *Charges:* Joining Fee £20. Adult £150. Senior Citizen £95. Junior (under 18) £50. Junior (under 12) £10. Non fishing guest £12. Night fishing permit £96. *Season:* Dawn - 1 hour after sunset. *Methods:* No camping, boating, dogs, bathing, fires or bait boats. No Keepnets other than matches.

Somerley Lakes
Contact: Christchurch Angling Club Office, Unit 6, Silver Business Park, Airfield Way, Christchurch, Dorset. *Sat Nav:* BH24 3PF. *Tel:* 01202 480009. *Water:* Christchurch Angling Club controlled series of former gravel pits. Meadow Lake and King Vincent's Lake. Blashford/Spinnaker offers coarse fishing to members only during the coarse fishing season. *Species:* Carp 35lb plus, Pike 30lb, Bream 10lb, Perch 4lb, Roach, Tench and Rudd. *Permits:* From Avon Angling and Ringwood Tackle. *Charges:* Day ticket: Adult £12, junior/ conc. £7. Night fishing is available on Spinnaker to members at £5 per night. *Season:* 16 June to 14 March. Night fishing available to members only with prepaid permit from tackle shops. *Methods:* No nuts or pulses. Barbless hooks to be used. See club rules for individual waters.

Turf Croft Farm Fishery &
Contact: Keith, Stephen or Christine Duell, Forest Road, Burley, Nr Ringwood. *Sat Nav:* BH24 4DF. *Tel:* 01425 403743. *Mobile:* 07850 086021. *Water:* 8 acre lake - naturally spring fed. Over 100 years natural habitat with secluded swims. *Species:* Ghost Carp to 28lbs, Mirror Carp to 28lbs, Tench to 6lbs, Bream to 4lbs, Perch to 2lb, Rudd, Red Rudd, Golden

Tench to 5lb, Roach & Crucians to 2.5lbs. *Permits:* Day ticket only. No night fishing. Request by arrangements. *Charges:* £10 per two rods maximum. *Season:* Open all year. Dawn to dusk in winter. Summer 7.30am - 7.00pm. *Methods:* No boilies, no nut baits, no hemp, no keepnets, natural bait.

ROMSEY

Headlands Farm Coarse Fishery &

Contact: John Harris, Wellow, Romsey. *Sat Nav:* SO51 6BG. *Tel:* 01794 323801. *Mobile:* 07776 202000. *Water:* Two lakes now extended to 6 acres. *Species:* Mixed coarse in both lakes. One lake contains Pike. Wild fish - Carp 24.8oz, Pike 25.8oz, Perch 4.12oz, Roach 2.8oz, Bream, Gudgeon and Rudd. *Charges:* £10 day. £15 24 hours. £15 night fishing. £25 2 days and nights. Longer stays by quotation. *Season:* Open all year - 24 hours per day. *Methods:* Strict rules regarding litter and groundbait on site. No spinning. No flooding problems. No Trebles, Barbless Hooks. No Pole Fishing. No Dogs.

Longbridge Lakes (Lee)

Contact: Neil Freeman, Broadlands Estate. *Sat Nav:* SO51 9LF. *Mobile:* 07785 281349. *Water:* 3 acre lake. *Species:* Tench to 8lb, Carp 30lb, Bream, Perch, Crucians, Roach and Rudd. *Permits:* From local tackle shops or on the bank. *Charges:* Summer: 7am-7pm - £10 day, £16 for 24 hrs, £5 half day and concessions. Winter: 8am-6pm - £10 day, £16 for 24 hrs, £5 half day and concessions. *Season:* Open all year. *Methods:* Full rules at lake to be followed at all times. Strictly no boilies, nuts, beans or peas.

Whinwhistle Fisheries &

Contact: John Hardeley, Keepers Lodge, Whinwhistle Road, East Wellow, Romsey. *Sat Nav:* SO51 6BF. *Tel:* 01794 324485. *Mobile:* 07816 187648. *Water:* Four Coarse lakes: Keepers Lake and Whinwhistle Lake. See also Woodington Trout Lakes, Romsey and River Fishing on Test and Shear Water. *Species:* Mixed coarse. Perch to 4lb, Pike to 27lb and Carp to 23lb. *Permits:* Available on site. *Charges:* Under 12 years £5. 12 to 16 years £6. Adult one rod £8. Two rod £10. Concessions Monday to Friday £6. *Season:* Open all year. Closed Christmas day and Boxing day. *Methods:* Pellets only if bought at the fishery. Full rules on site. Disabled friendly pegs. Parking close to lake and wheelchair toilet facilities.

STOCKBRIDGE

Golden Pond Fishery &

Contact: Jeff Hounslow, Fullerton Road, Fullerton, Stockbridge. *Sat Nav:* SP11 7LA. *Mobile:* 07734 669738. *Water:* One acre lake with 16 pegs. *Species:* Mixed coarse. *Permits:* On the bank. *Charges:* Day ticket £8. Junior, OAP, Concessions £5. Night fishing £15. 24 hours £20. *Season:* Open all year. *Methods:* No whips. No nut baits. No boilies. Landing nets and unhooking mats to be used. Barbless hooks only.

> Remember a & means the fishery has disabled facilities - contact them direct for further details

Stillwater Trout

ANDOVER

Amport Trout Fishery

Contact: Will H-Byass, Wiremead Lane, Amport, Andover. *Sat Nav:* SP11 8AZ. *Mobile:* 07775 953273. *Water:* 1 acre spring fed lake. *Species:* Rainbow & Brown Trout 2lb plus. *Charges:* £40 for 4 fish, £25 for 2 fish, £180 exclusive use of fishery - 20 fish max. Please phone 07775 953273. *Season:* Open all year. *Methods:* Fly fishing only. No catch and release.

FORDINGBRIDGE

Damerham Fisheries

Contact: Mike Davies, The Lake House, Damerham, Fordingbridge. *Sat Nav:* SP6 3HW. *Tel:* 01725 518446. *Water:* 6 lakes. 1.5 mile Allan river. *Species:* Rainbow Trout (Sandy, Lavender, White & Electric Blue Rainbow Trout). *Permits:* Season Rods. *Charges:* Full Season Rod £2,040 (30 visits), 1/2 Season Rod £1,170 (15 visits), 1/4 Season Rod £850 (10 visits). Guest Day Rods £85. Fishing parties(small and large) £80 per head. Please phone to confirm prices. *Season:* March - October 2013. *Methods:* Fly only.

Rockbourne Trout Fishery

Contact: Rockbourne Trout Fishery, Rockbourne Road, Sandleheath, Fordingbridge. *Sat Nav:* SP6 1QG. *Tel:* 01725 518603. *Water:* 6 Spring fed lakes. *Species:* Rainbow Trout 19lb (summer 2010). Occasional specimen Brown Trout. Arctic Char have been introduced to our Lakes. *Permits:* From the fishery. *Charges:* Please telephone for prices. *Season:* Open all year except Christmas day. *Methods:* Fly only, max hook size 10 long shank, no droppers, tandem/double/treble hooks.

ROMSEY

Holbury Lane Trout Lakes

Contact: Fishery Manager, Holbury Lane, Lockerley, Romsey. *Sat Nav:* SO51 0JR. *Tel:* 01794 341619. *Mobile:* 07817 252441. *Water:* 4 lakes totalling 7.5 acres plus 700yds on the River Dun (see River Dun entry). *Species:* Rainbow and Blue Trout 2lb to 5lb. *Permits:* 10 or 25 fish ticket. *Charges:* 2 fish half day £31. 4 fish full day £49. *Season:* Winter hours 8.30 - 4.30, Summer 8.30 - 6.00. *Methods:* Single fly, max size 10, no catch and release, priest and net must be carried by anglers.

Moorhen Trout Fishery &

Contact: Wendy Rogers, Warnford, Southampton. *Sat Nav:* SO32 3LB. *Tel:* 01730 829460. *Water:* 3 acre spring fed lake adjacent to the River Meon. *Species:* Rainbows from 2lb to double figures. *Charges:* Catch and keep tickets from £19 - £44 (4 Fish). *Season:* Open all year from 8.30am until 7pm or dusk (whichever earliest). Please contact us for scheduled closure dates. Fishery closes every Monday and the whole of August.

A first ever rainbow trout caught by 11 year old Sion at a lake near Andover. Landed during a fly fishing course run by Graeme Lowndes.

Woodington Trout Fishery
Contact: John Hardeley, Keepers Lodge, Whinwhistle Road, East Wellow, Romsey. *Sat Nav:* SO51 6BE. *Tel:* 01794 324485. *Mobile:* 07816 187648. *Water:* Three Trout lakes: Springlake, Kingfisher Lake and The Leat are catch and release. See also Whinwhistle Coarse Fishing, Romsey and River Fishing on the Test. 1 mile of the river Blackwater. *Species:* Rainbow and Brown Trout. *Permits:* Available on site. *Charges:* 2 fish £20, 4 fish £36. 4 hour catch and release ticket £18. *Season:* Open all year 7am - 7pm. Closed on Christmas Day and Boxing day. *Methods:* Fly fishing. Must use entrance for Whinwhistle Coarse Fishery. No Boobies. 1 hook only.

STOCKBRIDGE

John O' Gaunts &

Contact: Mrs E Purse, 51 Mead Road, Chandlers Ford, Southampton. *Sat Nav:* SO20 6QG. *Tel:* 01794 388130. *Mobile:* 02380 252268. *Water:* 2 Lakes approx. 7 acres in Test Valley. *Species:* Rainbow Trout (various sizes). *Permits:* Available from Fishery. Tel: 02380 252268 or 01794 388130. *Charges:* £44 - 4 fish Full Day, £24 - 2 fish Half Day. *Season:* February 1st - November 30th inclusive, Wednesdays & Saturdays throughout December and January. *Methods:* Fly and Nymph only. No barbless hooks, no catch and release, no keepnets.

WINCHESTER

Dever Springs Trout Fishery &

Contact: Niall Staig, Barton Stacey, Winchester. *Sat Nav:* SO21 3NP. *Tel:* 01264 720592. *Water:* Two spring fed lakes totalling 6 acres. *Species:* Rainbow and Brown Trout. (Record Brown 28lb 2oz). Double figure specimens regularly caught. *Permits:* Day ticket: 4 fish ticket £70, 3 fish £55, 2 fish (from 12 noon - dusk) £45. *Season:* Open all year. 8am to dusk. *Methods:* Minimum 6lb leader. Max hook size 8. Dressed length not over 1 inch. No catch and release on lakes. Disabled friendly peg, ramp to lodge and parking near lake.

I love fishing in the South West of England!

Professor Mark Everard

I've fished all over the UK and much of Europe, the USA, Australia, various African countries as well as India. I value this diversity, with Indian fishing a particular thrill, but nothing touches coming home to the South West.

I first fished in the South West around 1965, that short holiday a more profound experience that any pilgrimage! The Hampshire Avon was a place of legend, fished by Mr Crabtree and Peter and routinely featuring as a piscatorial paradise in angling magazines. To be frank, it was an intimidating experience for a kid! The river ran at the pace of a train, great foaming weir pools interspersed with powerful runs of crystal water over golden gravel and wavering weeds which, periodically, parted to reveal dark shapes beneath. My 7 foot solid fibreglass rod and light floats were no match, but I contented myself with ever-voracious swarms of salmon parr or occasional boldly-striped perch and shimmering dace.

It was also a profound learning experience, a friendly local angler showing me how to rig up a leger properly and pointing out the kind of swims to look for. It was perhaps the first significant step towards me becoming a thinking angler, and for that I was rewarded with some larger chub and roach. I dreamed of being 'smashed up'; I loved the romance of connecting with something too powerful to hold! Certainly, there were barbel and other species there which could have made a mockery of my inadequate tackle, though none had the bad grace so to do!

That was long ago, but left an indelible mark. The latter half of my life has been spent in the West Country, and nowhere else is 'home'.

I lived by the Hampshire Avon for several years, learning its moods and nuances and adapting my approach accordingly. I was rewarded with fish of great beauty and, sometimes, not insignificant size. Roach of course, my personal obsession (or at least one of them), including a good number of fish over 2lb and an immense specimen of 3lb 6oz 4dr that made my eyes stand out on stalks!

For twenty-one years now, the smaller, more intimate Bristol Avon has been, and I'm sure will remain, home to me and my family. I knew little about the Bristol Avon before moving here, but an enquiring mind and adaptive approach introduced me to unsuspected marvels from its fewer fast runs and rather more slack depths. The Bristol Avon's roach have been an unsuspected joy! OK, I was always going to be catching roach given my near-obsession with them! But the river has rewarded me magnificently over the years. Nine of my eleven roach of three pounds or more have come from this river, including a river record of 3lb 2oz and three more equalling that weight! Today, roach stocks are in decline, but let's hope this is merely a lull in a longer-running natural cycle.

Dace too. I just love dace! Bars of platinum, vigorous and willing to oblige in the heat of summer or when air frosts paint the trees. The Bristol Avon has rewarded me with some exceptional fish over 1lb throughout the years, including two fish of 1lb 2oz 8dr: the river record and another to match it. Hampshire Avon dace have always been good to me, with many over 1lb. One fish I hooked at dusk in 1990 pulled the scales to 1lb 4oz 8dr, which my fishing buddy and I rounded down to 1lb 4oz realising only later that the British record was then 1lb 4oz 4dr! But an agreement is an agreement and, nearly a quarter century later, my dace remains the Ringwood and District Angling Association record as well as the Hampshire Avon river record.

I can't mention dace without talking about the fantastic shoals of dace in the lower River Exe. Oh, and big bream and pike too, and of course the shoals of roach and the odd monster barbel!

Then there are the canals in the vicinity, the Exeter Canal, the Tiverton Canal and their like, not to mention some of the rivers of the Somerset Levels, many of which hold surprises including respectable rudd and roach as well as pike, tench, eels and now even big carp. But if I am coarse fishing down that way, it is often to the secluded pools that I will head, because some of them (I will not give away too many secrets) hold some mind-boggling secrets!

Mark in a familiar pose, cradling another magnificent river roach from the South West!

And then there is the salmon fishing on the Tamar and other rivers, both small and large, across the peninsula! Oh, and those richly-spotted wild trout, perhaps four to the pound on a good day, eager to take a fly in the bleakly beautiful moorland where the trilling cries of curlews echo all around!

And all this talk of trout and dace calls to mind the brilliant sport to be enjoyed plug-fishing for bass from the rocks! That and the springtime black bream trips just a short way offshore, feeling for delicate tapping bites that may yield something tasty to take home for tea! I love my estuary mullet fishing too, guaranteeing you only frustration, but which rewards the roach angler rather better than those weaned on traditional sea tackle. The fight of a mullet on light tackle is awesome; bear in mind this is an Indian mahseer enthusiast talking! Suddenly I find myself salivating, wondering where I might cast a line next and wishing I had more time to spend by flowing, still and tidal waters!

Another thing I am passionate about in the South West is the way local people mobilise to take care of their rivers. The UK's rivers trusts are exemplary charitable organisations, dedicated to improving our waters. Much of the work of rivers trusts is in partnership with landowners and farming interests, seeking 'win-win' outcomes. Simple measures, such as the separation of clean roof water from dirty yard water, prudent fencing of watercourses, finding opportunities to reduce pesticide use or improve storage of farm chemicals can all represent benefits and savings to farmers in hard cash terms while simultaneously providing benefits to river systems. These benefits produce more opportunities for angling and the wider enjoyment of the river by many people, regardless of their interest in catching fish.

The focus of all the UK's rivers trusts also includes nature conservation, heritage, regional ecotourism and connections with local businesses, but fish themselves are often a conspicuous indicator of success, for which we anglers can be very pleased!

To find out more about rivers trusts in the UK visit - www.theriverstrust.org

I love the South West! As primarily a coarse angler who also loves to chase salmon, trout and all sort of sea fishes, I can think of nowhere else I'd rather call home, or that takes better care of its precious fishes.

Professor Mark Everard lives in the South West and is an avid angler for all species. An aquatic scientist, specimen angler and regular contributor to the angling press, TV and radio, Mark has also published fourteen books. Many of these concern fish and fishing, including 'Redfin Diaries' (Coch-y-Bonddu Books, 2013) and 'Britain's Freshwater Fishes' (Princeton Field Guides, 2013).

Going Fishing

Mark Lloyd - The Angling Trust
www.anglingtrust.net   Tel: 0844 7700616

It doesn't matter what type of fishing you're doing, getting ready is almost as much fun as actually fishing. My brother taught me to fish and he used to tell me to visualise everything I would be doing when I got to the water, and all the kit I would need to do it, in the hope that I might actually remember all my tackle for once. Of course when we got there I'd have forgotten my scissors, net, or worse, my reel. I still go through this exercise but packing up to go fishing has become more of a routine process and I rarely have those horrible moments when you realise that all your gear is completely useless because of one crucial missing item. Behind all these practical considerations however lies a steady throb of excitement, like a film soundtrack, as your mind pictures the water and the great fish that lurk beneath the surface. The feeling of that first contact when the fish takes and the thrilling relief of it played out and slipping into the net. All this unites us anglers and it is why we expend so much time, money and heartache on this fantastic pastime.

My favourite moments of all are those spent preparing for a weekend of sleeplessness in the west country chasing sea trout at night. It's a branch of our sport that few people try. Many are afraid of the dark and the strange noises from foxes, owls and even sheep that can sound like savage monsters when you hear them in the dark. Others worry about casting into the unknown, and tying knots without being able to see. Fishing at night creates a whole new layer of challenges and excitement, and this is part of what I love about it. It's always with an immense sense of adventure that I head off into the gloaming to wait for dark, for only then can fishing begin. I like to see several bats overhead, and the colour go out of the grass, before I cast a line. I start in the fast shallow run at the neck of a pool, with small flies before changing to larger flies and sometimes going a bit deeper to fish the pool itself.

The first fish to jump sends an electric shock of excitement through you. On still nights, you can actually hear the fish leave the water with a little slurp, and sometimes the flapping of the tail as it leaps into the night air, shortly followed by a resounding crash as if someone has thrown a breeze block into the river. In these little west country streams, the fish are improbably big, with some getting into double figures. When these jump, a little bit of doubt enters your mind about whether or not you really want something so big connected to your 7 weight fly rod in the middle of the night.

The take from a sea trout is unmistakable. There is something violently angry about it and when you can't use your eyes, all your other senses are heightened. It is usually some time before you really feel in control of these powerful fish, as they shoot around the pool like torpedoes, leaping and crashing on the surface, turning it to a silver foam that gleams in the gloom. Often, you catch nothing. Humidity, temperature, wind, water levels, fly choice, depth and plain luck all have to be right to make these fish take your fly. But the memory of what it felt like last time, and the dream of how it might be the next time, keep you casting repeatedly until long past dawn.

However sea trout numbers are not what they used to be. Abstraction, pollution, weirs, hydro-power turbines and commercial netting have all impacted on stocks. There's a lot of great work being done to put this right by the river trusts and the Environment Agency. The Angling Trust and Fish Legal are also fighting on all these fronts to try and restore all our rivers to better health. We do this because we all love all types of fishing, and the unique excitement that it offers. If you care about the future of fish stocks and the freedom to go fishing, please join us to support our work.

There's lots of sea trout fishing available in the South West and you can find more information about where to go in this guide and via the Rivers Trust web site. Once you've felt that take, you will never look back!

SOMERSET

Incorporating Bristol, Bath and North Somerset

Find us on
Facebook

@gethookedguide

RIVER FISHING

STILLWATER COARSE

STILLWATER TROUT

WHERE TO STAY

ADVERTISER LOCATION MAP

Map No	Advertiser	Sat Nav	Phone	Advert Page
	Game Fishing			
119	Clatworthy	TA4 2EJ	0845 600 4 600	139
120	Hawkridge	TA5 1AL	0845 600 4 600	139
121	Lance Nicholson River Fishing	TA22 9HB	01398 323409	118
122	Sutton Bingham	BA22 2QL	0845 600 4 600	139
123	Wimbleball	TA22 9NU	01398 371460	Back Cover
	Coarse Fishing			
124	Alcove Angling Club	BS16 3DS	01179 392827 or 07938 874330	157
125	Amalgamated Fisheries Ltd (Coarse & Game)		0117 9603378	149
126	Bridgwater Angling Association		01278 457022	118
127	Bullock Farm Fishing Lakes	BS21 6XA	01934 835020	135
128	Burnham-on-Sea Holiday Park	TA8 1LA	01278 783391	141
129	Durleigh Reservoir	TA5 2AW	0845 600 4 600	139
130	Edney's Fisheries	BA11 3RF	01373 812294 or 07941 280075	132
131	Emerald Pool Fisheries	TA9 3NL	01278 794707	133
132	Laburnum House Lodge Hotel	TA9 3RJ	01278 781830	121
133	Leverets Specimen Carp Lake		01749 890303	136
134	Northam Farm Holiday Park	TA8 2SE	01278 751244	131
135	Plantation Lakes Ltd	BS21 6XW	01934 832325	135
136	Summerhayes Fishery	TA6 6LW	01278 451043	127
137	Tan House Farm Lake	BS37 7QL	01454 228280	130
138	Taunton Angling Association		07712 867773	125
139	Thorney Lakes	TA10 0DW	01458 250811	135
140	Trinity Waters	TA5 2BQ	01278 450880 or 07720 542141	127
141	Viaduct Fishery & Lodges	TA11 6LJ	01458 274022	136
142	Warren Farm Holiday Centre	TA8 2RP	01278 751227	131
143	Warrens Holiday Village	BS21 6TQ	01275 871666	130
144	Withy Water	TA9 3NW	01278 783700	134

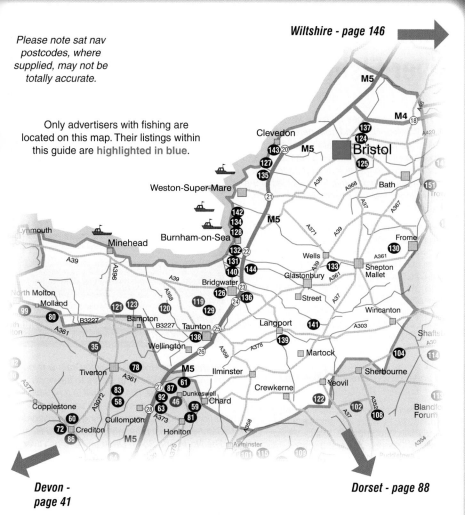

Please note sat nav postcodes, where supplied, may not be totally accurate.

Only advertisers with fishing are located on this map. Their listings within this guide are highlighted in blue.

Wiltshire - page 146

Devon - page 41

Dorset - page 88

Somerset River Fishing

AXE

The River Axe emerges from the Mendip Hills at Wookey Hole and from here to below Wookey the river is Trout water. The river deepens as it crosses low lying land at the foot of the Mendips to the sluices at Bleadon and Brean Cross, the tidal limit. Fish species in the lower reaches include Bream, Roach, Tench, Dace and Pike.

Weston-Super-Mare A.A &

Contact: Stuart Knill (Head Bailiff). *Tel:* 01934 414371. *Water:* River Axe, River Brue, South Drain, North Drain. Summer Lane Pond, Locking Pond. *Species:* Bream, Tench, Roach, Carp, Gudgeon, Perch, Rudd, Chub and some Dace. *Permits:* Weston Angling Centre or from Stuart Knill on number above. *Charges:* Season £30, Week £12, Day £5. Senior £30, Junior £15, OAP / Concession £15. *Season:* Old River Axe, Summer Lane and Locking Ponds - year round. *Methods:* No boilies, no nuts, no cat foods.

BARLE

See under Devon, Exe and tributaries.

Paddons

Contact: Mrs M. McMichael, Northmoor Road, Dulverton. *Tel:* 01398 323514. *Water:* 400 yards single bank on River Barle. *Species:* Brown Trout & Salmon. *Permits:* Lance Nicholson's, Dulverton. *Charges:* Day ticket - Adults £7, Juniors £4. *Season:* March 15 to September 30. *Methods:* Fly fishing. Must have valid rod licence obtainable from Lance Nicholson, Gloster House, High Street, Dulverton, Somerset. Tel: 01398 323409 or Dulverton Post Office.

BRIDGWATER AND TAUNTON CANAL

Cut in 1827 the canal provided a good commercial waterway between the two towns. The canal has been recently restored for navigation but there is only infrequent boat traffic. The canal offers excellent coarse fishing from the towpath for Roach, Bream, Tench, Rudd, Perch & Pike.

HUNTSPILL RIVER / SOUTH DRAIN / CRIPPS RIVER / NORTH DRAIN

The Huntspill River is a man made drainage channel, excavated in the 1940s and connected to the River Brue and South Drain

via the Cripps River. The North Drain was dug c1770 to drain low lying moors to the north of the River Brue. The Huntspill is a notable coarse fishery and is often the venue for national and local match fishing competitions. Catches consist primarily of Bream and Roach. The North and South Drain and Cripps River contain similar species and also offer good sport for the coarse angler.

Bridgwater Angling Association &

Contact: Mr A Danahy, 127 The Old Basin, Somerset Bridge, Bridgwater. *Tel:* 01278 457022. *Water:* 6 miles on the Bridgwater & Taunton Canal, Fishing on the rivers Brue, North & South Drain, King's Sedgemoor Drain, Langacre Rhine & The Huntspill. Stillwater fishing at Combwich, Walrow, Dunwear & Screech Owl. *Species:* All types of coarse fish. *Permits:* Available from Tackle outlets throughout Somerset area including Somerset Angling, 74 Bath Road, Bridgwater, Tel; 01278 431777. Taunton Angling Centre, 63 Station Road, Taunton, Tel; 01823 282518. Watts News, Edward Street, Bridgwater, Tel; 01278 422137. Scoops, 77 St Johns Street, Bridgwater. Veals Tackle 1a Church Street, Highbridge, Tel; 01278 786934. *Charges:* Adult Season 1 rod £35, 2 rods £50, 3 rods £70 4 rods £90. Senior citizens/Disabled 1 rod £25, 2 rods £37.50, 3 rods £55, 4 rods £70. Junior (7-11 years) 1 rod £6. Junior (12-17 years) 1 rod only £8 + £10 for 2 rods. Day ticket £7. Night fishing (24) hour

Josh with 3lb 12oz Chub caught on the River Tone

£12. Prices correct at time of publication subject to change. *Season:* E.A. byelaws apply. Bridgwater and Taunton Canal open all year. *Methods:* Full rules and map with permits.

BRISTOL AVON AND TRIBUTARIES

The River Avon flows from its sources near Sherston and Tetbury to its confluence with the Severn at Avonmouth some 117 kilometers and is fed by many tributaries on its way. The headwaters of the River Avon, the Tetbury and Sherston branches join at Malmesbury. Both are important Trout streams where fishing is strictly preserved and there is little opportunity for the visiting angler to fish these waters.

Malmesbury to Chippenham

Coarse fisheries predominate in this section, although Trout are stocked by fishing associations in some areas. Arguably one of the best fisheries in the country, this section contains a wide range of specimen fish. Local records include: Roach 3lb 2oz, Perch 3lb 3oz, Tench 8lb 5 1/2oz, Bream 8lb 8oz, Dace 1lb 2oz, Chub 7lb 10oz, Carp 20lb 8 1/4oz and Pike 33lb 3oz. Also many Barbel to 12lb have been reported.

Chippenham to Bath

Upstream from Staverton to Chippenham the Avon continues to be an important coarse fishery, both for the pleasure angler and match fisherman. The river flows through a broad flood plain and provides a pastoral setting. In the faster flowing sections chub, Roach, Dace and Barbel can be caught in good numbers.

Bath to Hanham

Between Hanham and Bath much of this length retains a rural character and is an important coarse fishery used by pleasure and match anglers. The National Angling Championships have been held here. Roach, Bream and Chub are the main catches and, in some favoured swims, Dace. Very good catches of Bream are to be had with specimen fish. 'Free' fishing is available through Bath from the towpath side between Newbridge and Pulteney Weir. Carp of 20lb have been reported caught downstream of Pulteney and Keynsham Weirs.

Hanham to Avonmouth

Between Netham Dam and Hanham Weir the river is affected by spring tides. The water has a very low saline content and this length of river provides reasonable coarse fishing. Below Netham Dam the river contains mostly estuarine species but some Sea Trout and Salmon have been seen.

Amalgamated Fisheries Ltd
Contact: Mrs P Leonard, 48 Abbots Road, Hanham, Bristol. *Tel:* 01179 603378. *Water:* Approx. 30 miles coarse fishing on Bristol Avon & Somerset Rivers & Streams including the Brue. Stillwaters at Lyneham, Calne, Bath and Pawlett near Bridgwater. Trout only water on Cam Brook near Radstock. Please contact the secretary for full details. *Species:* All coarse species. *Charges:* Full membership available from tackle outlets. Full members only may fish at Tockenham Reservoir. Day permits for all waters are available at Tackle Shops. Adults £45. Adult and child £60. Conc. Senior Citizens, Disabled and Juniors £25. Day permits. Adults £6. Senior Citizens and Juniors £3. *Methods:* Barbless hooks. No livebaiting.

Avon Valley Country Park (River Avon)
Contact: Jack Jenkins, Bath Rd, Keynsham, Bristol. *Tel:* 0117 9864929. *Water:* 1.5 miles on River Avon. *Species:* Tench & Coarse fish. *Charges:* Adults £8, Children £7.50, OAP £7.50. *Season:* Park open: Easter - 1 November 10am - 6pm every day. Current E.A. Byelaws apply on the river.

Bathampton Angling Association (Box Brook)
Contact: Dave Crookes, 25 Otago Terrace, Larkhall, Bath. *Tel:* 01225 427164. *Water:* 3 miles of Box brook (tributary of Avon). Split into 2 beats at Middle Hill and Shockerwick. *Species:* Brown Trout (occasional Rainbows) Grayling. *Permits:* Season permits only. *Charges:* Adults £70, Juniors £30, OAP £50. Season permits only. *Season:* Fishing from 1st April to 15 October inclusive. *Methods:* Traditional fly/ Nymph only.

Bathampton Angling Association (Bristol Avon Claverton)
Contact: Dave Crookes, 25 Otago Terrace, Larkhall, Bath. *Tel:* 01225 427164. *Water:* 2.5 miles Bristol Avon up and downstream from Claverton. *Species:* Bream to 6lbs, Chub to 5lbs, Roach to 2.5lbs, Pike to 25lbs, Barbel to 13lbs. *Permits:* Local fishing tackle shops. *Charges:* Adults £35, Juniors £15, OAP £13. Under 12's free. Members only. *Season:* Standard river close season, night fishing on application. *Methods:* Club byelaws apply.

Bathampton Angling Association (Bristol Avon Newbridge)
Contact: Dave Crookes, 25 Otago Terrace, Larkhall, Bath. *Tel:* 01225 427164. *Water:* 1.5 miles of Bristol Avon at Newbridge, downstream of Bath. *Species:* Bream to 10lbs, Chub to 4lbs, Roach to 2.5lbs, Pike to 20lbs plus. *Permits:* Local fishing tackle shops. *Charges:* Adults £35, Juniors £15, OAP £15. Under 12's free. £3 day tickets available to Non-members. Tickets must be purchased before fishing. *Season:* Standard river close season. *Methods:* Club byelaws apply.

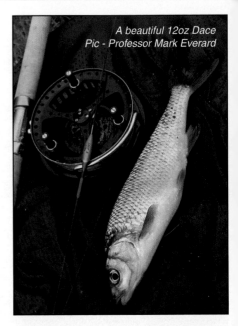

A beautiful 12oz Dace
Pic - Professor Mark Everard

Bathampton Angling Association (Bristol Avon Saltford)
Contact: Dave Crookes, 25 Otago Terrace, Larkhall, Bath. *Tel:* 01225 427164. *Water:* 1.5 miles of Bristol Avon at Saltford. *Species:* Bream to 8lbs, Roach to 2lbs, Chub to 3lbs. *Permits:* Local fishing tackle shops. *Charges:* Adults £35, Juniors £15, OAP £13. Under 12's free. £3 day tickets available to Non-members. Must be purchased before fishing. *Season:* Standard river close season. *Methods:* Club byelaws apply.

Bristol and West Federation of Anglers
Contact: Hon Sec. B Lloyd, 386 Speedwell Road, Kingswood, Bristol. *Tel:* 0117 9676030. *Mobile:* 07831 311582. *Water:* Bristol and West waters are; Swineford to Keynsham, Jack Whites Cottage (Londonderry Farm) all right hand bank downstream. *Species:* Roach, Chub, Carp, Barbel, Pike. *Permits:* Open to affiliated clubs including Amalgamated Fisheries Ltd.

Bristol City Docks Angling Club
Contact: Bob Taylor, 118 Northcote Road, Downend, Bristol. *Tel:* 01179 104738. *Mobile:* 07990 573831. *Water:* 3 miles on Bristol Avon from Chequers Weir to Netham. Feeder canal (Netham - docks), Bristol Docks system. *Species:* Skimmers, Bream, Roach, Dace, Chub, Pike, Eels, Carp, Tench and Perch. *Permits:* All Bristol tackle shops and Harbour Masters office, or from secretary above on 07790 573831. Free Fishing on Bristol Avon Chequers to Netham. *Charges:* Season: Senior & 2 Juniors under 12 £15, Seniors £12.50, Concessions, Disabled, Juniors, OAP £6.50, Day tickets in advance: Seniors £2.50 + Concessions £1, Day tickets on the bank issued by Bailiff: Seniors £5, Juniors/

Conc £2. *Season:* River - normal close season applies; Docks and Feeder Canal open all year. *Methods:* Docks: Pole and Feeder. Pole & Waggler on Feeder Canal. All normal river tactics on the Avon. Daily update information from Tony on 0117 9517250.

Frome Vale Angling Club
Contact: Nigel Vigus (Secretary), 32 Rock Lane, Stoke Gifford, Bristol. *Tel:* 01179 759710. *Water:* 1 mile River Frome. Bristol Avon - Keynsham - Swinford approx. 3 miles. *Species:* Roach, Bream, Tench, Pike, Perch, Chub and Carp. *Permits:* As above. *Charges:* Per season: Seniors £25 - Junior No charge - OAP/Disabled £10. Day tickets not available. *Season:* Closed season 15th March - 15th June inclusive. *Methods:* Barbless hooks on all waters.

Frys Match Group
Contact: Mr Merv Sivell. *Mobile:* 07811 746484. *Water:* 63 Pegs - 2 mile stretch single bank fishing. *Species:* Carp, Barbel, Bream, Roach. *Permits:* Membership available to all, please contact Merv Sivell. *Charges:* Please ring for prices. *Season:* E.A. Byelaws apply. No night fishing.

Keynsham Angling Association (Bristol Avon)
Contact: Keynsham Angling Association. *Mobile:* 07973 736519. *Water:* Four miles on Bristol Avon (Swineford to Chequers). *Species:* Most species. *Charges:* Members only fishing. Membership details from club website. Adult membership £18. Juniors under 16/OAP/Disabled £9. *Season:* Current E.A. Byelaws apply. *Methods:* Details in members handbook. On rivers Chew and Avon there are no restrictions other than current E.A. Byelaws.

Mardon Angling Club
Contact: Mr Austin, 65 Grange Avenue, Hanham, Bristol. *Tel:* 0117 9839776. *Mobile:* 07941 360212. *Water:* Open to all. Regular monthly meetings, full match calendar. We fish waters throughout Somerset and Swindon area. Members can also fish Bristol Avon from Jack White's to Swineford as Club is member of Bristol and West Federation of Anglers. *Species:* Most coarse species. *Charges:* Please contact above. Charges £12 per annum, children under 16 free. *Season:* All year. *Methods:* All members must observe specific rules of each fishery.

BRISTOL FROME
The Bristol Frome rises at Dodington and offers a fair standard of coarse fishing on the lower sections. The upper section contains limited stocks of Brown Trout, Roach and Perch. This tributary of the River Avon is culverted beneath Bristol and discharges into the Floating Harbour.

BRUE
The River Brue is a Trout fishery from its source above Bruton to Lovington. From here to Glastonbury a number of weirs

provide areas of deep water and coarse fish predominate, notably Chub and Roach, together with Bream, Dace and Pike. Similar species may be found between Glastonbury and Highbridge where the river is channelled across the Somerset Levels and connected with a number of drainage channels such as the Huntspill River and North Drain.

Glaston Manor Angling Association
Contact: Adam Mitchell, NFU Office, Cathedral View, Wookey Hole Rd., Wells. *Tel:* 01749 673786. *Water:* Brue - approx. 15 miles both banks; Lydford on Fosse to Westhay. 3 miles on River Sheppey plus South Drain from Catcott Bridge back to source. Also see entry in Stillwater Coarse, Glastonbury. 1.75 miles approx. on North Drain. *Species:* Roach, Chub, Bream, Dace, Perch, Gudgeon, Pike, Tench and Carp. *Permits:* Thatchers Tackle, Wells. Tel: 01749 673513. Somerset Angling, 74 Bath Rd, Bridgwater. Tel: 01278 431777 or Thyers Tackle, 1a Church Street, Highbridge. Tel: 01278 786934. *Charges:* Prices upon application. *Season:* Current E.A. byelaws apply. *Methods:* No live bait permitted, full rules on day ticket and annual permit.

Highbridge Angling Association (River)
Contact: Mr C Brewer. *Tel:* 01278 786230. *Water:* Basin Bridge, East Huntspill. *Species:* Carp to 33lb, Pike to mid 20's, all other coarse species. *Permits:* Thyers Tackle, Highbridge - 01278 786934. Also available from other local

tackle shops. *Charges:* Prices upon application. *Season:* March 15th - June 16th closed season. *Methods:* No live baiting, full list with ticket.

Merry Farm Fishing

Contact: Mr Peter Dearing, Merry Farm, Merry Lane, Basonbridge. *Sat Nav:* TA9 3PS. *Tel:* 01278 783655. *Water:* 600 yards on the River Brue. *Species:* Pike 20lb plus, Bream 7lb, Tench 6lb, Chub 2lb, Carp 18lb, Roach 1.5lb, Gudgeon, Ruffe, Perch 4lb. *Charges:* £1 per day. *Season:* 16 June to 14 March. *Methods:* No tackle restrictions. No night fishing.

Walleden Farm Fishery (Brue) &

Contact: Andrew Wall, East Huntspill, Highbridge. *Tel:* 01278 786488. *Mobile:* 07703 857732. *Water:* Section of River Brue. *Species:* Roach, Bream, Chub, Carp, Perch, Pike. *Permits:* From the above. *Season:* Open all year. River fishing closed season 15th March - 15th June. *Methods:* Any legal method.

CAM AND WELLOW BROOKS

The Cam and Wellow Brooks, rising on the north side of the Mendip Hills, flow through what was a mining area and now provide good quality Trout fishing controlled by local fishing associations.

Cameley Lakes (River Cam)

Contact: J. Harris, Hillcrest Farm, Cameley, Temple Cloud, Nr Bristol. *Tel:* 01761 452423. *Water:* Fishing on River Cam. See also entry under Stillwater Trout, Bristol. *Species:* Rainbow and Brown Trout, Wild Trout. *Permits:* Full details on request.

CHEW

The River Chew rises near Chewton Mendip and flows through the Bristol Waterworks Reservoirs at Litton and Chew Valley Lake. The river continues through Chew Magna, Stanton Drew, Publow, Woolard and Compton Dando to its confluence with the River Avon at Keynsham. A mixed fishery for most its length and is particularly good for Roach, Dace and Grayling below Pensford.

Bathampton Angling Association (River Chew)

Contact: Dave Crookes, 25 Otago Terrace, Larkhall, Bath. *Tel:* 01225 427164. *Water:* One mile of River Chew at Compton Dando, near Keynsham. *Species:* Roach, Chub, Grayling, Brown Trout, Rainbow Trout, Dace, Perch. *Permits:* Local fishing tackle shops. *Charges:* Adults £35, Juniors £15, OAP £13. Under 12s free. Members only. *Season:* Open all year. Fly and worm for Trout from 15 March to 15 June inclusive. *Methods:* Club bye-laws apply.

Keynsham Angling Association (River Chew)

Contact: Keynsham Angling Association. *Mobile:* 07973 736519. *Water:* 2.5 miles on the River Chew (Compton Dando to Keynsham). *Species:* Most species. *Charges:* Members only fishing. Membership details from club website. Adult membership £18. Juniors under 16/OAP/Disabled £9. *Season:* Current E.A. Byelaws apply. *Methods:* Details in members handbook. On rivers Chew and Avon there are no restrictions other than current E.A. Byelaws.

Knowle Angling Association (River Chew)

Contact: Keith Caddick, 41 Eastwood Crescent, Brislington, Bristol. *Tel:* 01179 857974. *Mobile:* 0794 634 7581. *Water:* 5 miles of upper and lower River Chew, 2.5 miles River Yeo. Wellow Brook Wild trout fishing - 0.75 mile single bank fishing at Wellow, 1.5 mile single bank at Stoney Littleton and 2 miles single banks at Writhlington. 5 Trout lakes - Publow, Taylors Farm, Clutton, Broadoak Farm and Acker Pool. Plus fishing at Chew Magna reservoir (see Stillwater Trout, Bristol). *Species:* Brown Trout 1.5 to 4lb and Rainbow Trout 1.5 to 6lb. *Permits:* From Keith Caddick. Guests of members only. *Charges:* Annual membership £125. Over 65 £100. Junior £27. All new members pay extra £5 entrance fee. *Season:* All rivers 1 April - 15 October. Lower Chew open all year. Trout 1st April to 15 October. Coarse Fish and Grayling 16 June to 14 March. *Methods:* Fly only on upper Chew. Any method on Lower Chew. Any method on River Yeo. Wellow Brook Fly only.

EXE AND TRIBUTARIES

See description under Devon, river fishing.

Beasley Mill

Contact: P. Veale, Lance Nicholson, 9 High Street, Dulverton. *Tel:* 01398 323409. *Water:* Approx. 1 mile double bank on Barle at Dulverton. *Species:* Trout and occasional Salmon. *Permits:* As above. *Charges:* £15 Trout, £25 Salmon. *Season:* 15 March - 30 September. *Methods:* Any legal method.

Broford Fishing

Contact: P. Veale, Lance Nicholson Fishing, Tackle & Guns, 9 High Street, Dulverton. *Tel:* 01398 323409. *Water:* Approx. 5 miles bank fishing on Little Exe. *Species:* Wild Brown Trout with occasional Salmon. *Permits:* As above. *Charges:* £15 per day - Trout. £25 per day - Salmon. *Season:* 15 March - 30 September. *Methods:* Fly only for Trout. Any legal method for Salmon.

Dulverton Angling Association

Contact: P. Veale, Lance Nicholson Fishing, Tackle & Guns, 9 High Street, Dulverton. *Tel:* 01398 323409. *Water:* Approx. 5 miles bank on Exe & Hadeo and River Barle. Membership open to all. *Species:* Brown Trout & Salmon. *Permits:* No charge - Members only. *Charges:* Adults £30. Junior £1. (All juniors under 16 must be accompanied by an adult). *Season:* 15 March - 30 September. *Methods:* Any legal method.

Remember a & means the fishery has disabled facilities - contact them direct for further details

Exe Valley Fishery (River Exe)

Contact: Nick Hart, Exebridge, Dulverton. *Sat Nav:* TA22 9AY. *Tel:* 01398 323008. *Water:* Half a mile of single bank on the Exe. Three fly only lakes at Dulverton. *Species:* Salmon Trout and Grayling. *Permits:* Day Tickets from Hart Fly Shop. *Charges:* Contact for details. *Season:* EA Byelaws apply. *Methods:* Trout and Grayling fly only. Salmon fly or spinner.

ISLE

The River Isle rises near Wadeford and soon after its source is joined by a tributary from Chard Lake. Trout are found as far as Ilminster but below the town coarse fish predominate. The profile of the river is fairly natural though a number of shallow weirs provide increased depth in places. Species caught in the lower stretches include Chub, Dace and Roach.

Chard and District Angling Club

Contact: John Barron. *Tel:* 01460 63593. *Water:* Approx. 1.5 miles on the River Isle. Also Perry Street Pond, see entry under Stillwater Coarse. *Species:* Dace, Roach, Chub, Perch, Bream, Gudgeon. *Permits:* Barron, 2 Holyrood St., Chard. Tel: 01460 63593. *Season:* Closed season 14 March to 16 June on river.

Ilminster and District A.A. (River Isle)

Contact: P. Lonton, Mashala, Ilton, Ilminster. *Tel:* 01460 52519. *Water:* Approx. 6 miles on the River Isle. *Species:* Roach, Chub, Perch, Bream, Dace, Pike. *Permits:* Day tickets from Ilminster Warehouse. Membership details from the secretary. Annual membership tickets from Ilminster Warehouse, Tackle UK Ltd, Tackle Box, Chard. *Charges:* £22 annual membership. Junior £6. OAP £15. Day Adult - £6, Day Junior - £3, OAP/Disabled - £6. *Season:* Current E.A. Byelaws apply. *Methods:* Club rules apply.

KENN AND BLIND YEO

The New Blind Yeo is an artificial drainage channel which also carries some of the diverted water of the River Kenn. Both waters contain good Roach with Bream, Rudd, Carp, Perch, Tench and Pike.

Clevedon and District F.A.C.

Contact: Mr Newton, 64 Clevedon Rd, Tickenham, Clevedon. *Tel:* 01275 856107. *Water:* 6 miles - Blind Yeo / River Kenn. *Species:* Roach, Bream 7lb, Rudd, Eels, Perch 1.5lb, Pike 25lb & Tench 5lb. *Permits:* NSAA Permit at all local tackle shops available until March 2014 after which date Clevedon and District F.A.C. will issue their own permits to fish the water. Please Tel: 01275 856107. *Charges:* Season - Seniors: £28, Juniors/OAP: £15; Weekly - £15; Daily - £5. *Season:* June 16th - March 14th inc. *Methods:* Waggler/Stick, Pole, Ledger, no live baits, no coarse fish to be used as dead bait.

KENNET AND AVON CANAL

There are some 58 kilometres of canal within the Bristol Avon catchment area which averages one metre in depth and thirteen metres in width. The Kennet & Avon Canal joins the River Avon at Bath with the River Kennet between Reading and Newbury. The canal was opened in 1810 to link the Severn Estuary with the Thames. The canal, now much restored, provides excellent fishing with Carp to 25lb, Tench to 5lb also Roach, Bream, Perch, Rudd, Pike and Gudgeon.

Bathampton Angling Association (Kennet & Avon Canal)

Contact: Dave Crookes, 25 Otago Terrace, Larkhall, Bath. *Tel:* 01225 427164. *Water:* 7.5 miles of Kennet and Avon canal. From Bath to Avoncliffe. *Species:* Bream to 4lbs, Chub to 3.5lbs, Roach to 2lbs, Pike to 20lbs, Carp to 24lbs, Tench to 3lbs, Perch to 4lbs, Eels to 3lbs. Roach/Bream Hybrids to 5lbs. *Permits:* Local fishing tackle shops. *Charges:* Adults £35, Juniors £15, OAP £13. Under 12's free. £3 day tickets available to non members must be purchased before fishing. *Season:* Open all year. *Methods:* Club bylaws apply.

THE KINGS SEDGEMOOR DRAIN

The Kings Sedgemoor Drain is an artificial drainage channel dug c1790. As well as draining a large area of moor it also carries the diverted water of the River Cary and excess flood flows from the River Parrett. The KSD is a very well known coarse fishery and is used for both local and national match fishing competitions. Fish species present include Roach, Bream, Tench, Perch and Pike.

PARRETT

The River Parrett rises in West Dorset and there is some Trout fishing as far as Creedy Bridge upstream of the A303. Below this point a number of weirs and hatches result in deeper water and slower flows. The resulting coarse fishery contains a wide variety of species including Roach, Bream, Rudd, Chub, Dace, Carp, Crucian Carp and Pike. Similar species are found in the lowest freshwater section at Langport where the Rivers Isle and Yeo join the Parrett to form a wide deep river which becomes tidal below Oath Sluice.

Langport and District Angling Association &

Contact: Dave Jolly, 30 King Street, Yeovil. *Tel:* 01935 420836. *Water:* 5 miles on the River Parrett. Normal closed season applies to river. *Species:* All common coarse species except Barbel. *Permits:* Fosters Newsagency, Bow Street,

Langport. *Charges:* Annual £17, junior £5, Disabled/OAP £8. Senior day £4, Junior day £1 (day tickets for river only). *Season:* Closed season on river only. Membership from 16 June to 15 June inc. No night fishing. *Methods:* No live baiting. No dead baiting with coarse fish.

Somerset Levels Association of Clubs
Contact: Newton Abbot Fishing Association, Ian Donaldson (Hon. Secretary), PO Box 229, Totnes, Devon. *Water:* See entry under Newton Abbot Fishing Association Devon, Stillwater Coarse. Rights to numerous parts of the Parrett, Brue, and other stretches of drain in the Langport area. *Species:* All coarse species.

Stoke Sub Hamdon and District A.A. (River)
Contact: Mr Derek Goad (Secretary), (H.Q. at Stoke Working Mens Club), 2 Windsor Lane, Stoke-Sub-Hamdon. *Tel:* 01935 824337. *Water:* Upper Stretches River Parrett approx. 10km. *Species:* Carp, Tench, Roach, Rudd, Bream, Perch, Dace, Chub, Pike, Eel, Gudgeon, Ruffe. Trout fishing also available. *Permits:* Season permits only. Available from Post Office, Montacute Post Office and Tackle UK, Yeovil. Also available from secretary and treasurer. *Charges:* Season tickets: Senior £15, Junior/OAP £8. Juniors under 12 must be accompanied by an adult. *Season:* Trout 1 April - 31 October. Coarse river 16 June - 14 March. *Methods:* Trout: No maggot. River Coarse: No restrictions.

Tiverton and District Angling Club (River Parrett)
Contact: Exe Valley Angling, 19 Westexe South, Tiverton, Devon. *Tel:* 01884 242275. *Water:* Various stretches on several rivers in Somerset including Isle, Brue and North Drain. See also entry under Stillwater Coarse, Devon, Tiverton. *Permits:* Please ring Exe Valley for details. Also available from: Exeter Angling Centre, Enterprise Angling, Taunton, Topp Tackle, Taunton. Minnows Caravan Park - beside Grand Western Canal. *Charges:* Senior: Day £5, Annual £30. Junior £3. OAP Day £5, Annual £15. Junior Annual £10. *Season:* Coarse: closed 15 March to 16 June. Trout: open from 15 March to 30 September. Salmon: open 14 February to 30 September.

SOMERSET FROME
The Somerset Frome is the main tributary of the Bristol Avon. It drains a large catchment area which is fed from the chalk around Warminster and limestone from the eastern end of the Mendips. There are numerous weirs and mills mostly disused. The tributaries above Frome provide ideal conditions for Brown Trout with fishing on the River Mells. The middle and lower reaches provide excellent coarse fishing.

Airsprung Angling Association (Frome)
Contact: Bill Turner, 124 Langford Rd, Trowbridge, Wiltshire. *Tel:* 01225 766219. *Water:* River Frome at Stowford Farm (near Farleigh, Hungerford). See also entry under Wiltshire, River Fishing, Kennet & Avon Canal. *Species:* Carp, Bream, Chub, Roach, Rudd, Dace, Tench, Perch, etc. *Permits:* Wiltshire Angling, 01225 763835; West Tackle, Trowbridge, 01225 755472. Trowbridge Road Post Office, Bradford-upon Avon. *Charges:* Full Licence £25/season. *Season:* Subject to normal close season. *Methods:* Details from Association.

Avon and Tributaries Angling Association
Contact: Rob Whish. *Tel:* 01392 430422. *Water:* Somerset Frome, Cam, Wellow, Midford Brooks. *Species:* All Coarse species and Trout. *Permits:* No day tickets, guest ticket from individual members. Membership details from telephone number above.

Frome Angling Association (River)
Contact: Gary Collinson, 2 Bath Street, Frome. *Tel:* 01373 471437. *Water:* 12 miles River Frome. *Species:* River: Roach, Chub, Bream. *Permits:* Please ring Gary Collinson. *Charges:* £20 Senior, £10 Junior Under 16 and OAP. Day tickets £3. *Season:* 16 June to 14 March, unless changes in legislation occur. *Methods:* No restrictions.

TONE
The River Tone rises on the edge of Exmoor National Park and not far from its source it feeds into and out of Clatworthy reservoir. From here to Taunton there are some twenty miles of fast flowing Trout river, though Grayling, Dace and Roach appear near Taunton where weirs provide increased depth. Through the town and just below, Chub, Dace and Roach predominate but at Bathpool the river becomes wider, deeper and slower. Roach, Bream, Carp, Tench and Pike are the typical species in this stretch which continues to the tidal limit at New Bridge.

Taunton Angling Association (Tone)
Contact: Kieran Granville. *Mobile:* 07712 867773. *Water:* 6 miles on River Tone (See also entries under Taunton and Bridgwater Canal & Stillwater Coarse). *Species:* Roach 2lb, Pike 29lb, Dace 1lb, Bream 10lb, Tench 7lb, Perch 5lb, Carp 30lb, Grayling 2.5lb, Chub 6.5lb. *Charges:* Senior season £45, Junior £10. Senior weekly £20, Senior day £7, Junior daily £4, OAP/Disabled £28, Under 12 season £5. Night fishing £65 in addition to Senior season ticket only. *Season:* Closed from 15 March to 16 June. *Methods:* All fish (including Pike and Eels) to be returned alive.

Taunton Fly Fishing Club (Tone)
Contact: John Connolly, 35 Manor Road, Taunton. *Tel:* 01823 274272. *Water:* Six beats on the River Tone upstream of Taunton. *Species:* Brown Trout, Grayling. *Permits:* No day tickets - members only. *Charges:* Full member £90 (plus £90 joining fee). Junior £15. Joint members £120 (plus £120 joining fee). Prices may change for 2014. *Season:* Brown Trout 1 April to 15 October. Grayling 16 June to 14 March. *Methods:* Fly only.

Wellington Angling Association

Contact: Grahame Woodward, 1 Waterloo Rd, Wellington. *Tel:* 01823 663236. *Water:* Membership strictly only available to persons living within postcode TA21. Approx. 3 miles on River Tone. Both banks from Runnington - Ash Farm, East Nynehead. *Species:* Brown Trout. Grayling, small head of coarse fish. *Charges:* Currently waiting list with joining fee. Joining fee £15, annual membership £12, day tickets £5 for visiting anglers from Carstock, Mantle Street, Wellington. *Season:* As EA season - 1 April to end October. *Methods:* No spinning.

WEST SEDGEMOOR DRAIN

This artificial channel was excavated in the 1940s on the lines of existing watercourses. Coarse fish species present include Bream, Roach, Tench and Carp.

Taunton Angling Association (W. Sedgemoor Drain) ♿
Contact: Kieran Granville. *Mobile:* 07712 867773. *Water:* 2 miles of West Sedgemoor Drain, easy access for disabled anglers (also see entries under Stillwater Coarse). *Species:* Bream 7lb, Roach 2.5lb, Eels 2lb, Tench 8lb, Pike 29lb, Perch 4lb, Rudd 2lb, Carp 30lb. *Charges:* Senior season £45, Junior £10. Senior weekly £20, Senior day £7, Junior daily £4, OAP/Disabled £28, Under 12 season £5. Night fishing £65 in addition to Senior season ticket only. *Season:* Closed from 15 March to 16 June. *Methods:* All fish (including Pike and Eels) to be returned alive.

YEO

The River Yeo rises near Sherborne and between here and Yeovil the river is a coarse fishery, though tributaries such as the River Wriggle have Brown Trout. Below Yeovil a number of weirs produce areas of deep water and the resulting fishery contains good Dace together with Roach, Chub, Bream and Pike.

Ilchester and District A.A.

Contact: Mr B Bushell (Chairman), 1 Friars Close, Ilchester, Yeovil. *Tel:* 01935 840767. *Water:* River Yeo above and below Ilchester. *Species:* Chub, Roach, Dace, Bream, Gudgeon, Tench, Perch and Carp. *Permits:* Tackle shops in Yeovil. Tackle UK Ltd. Ilchester Post Office. *Charges:* Season ticket £14. OAP/junior £7. Weekly ticket £6. Day ticket £3. *Season:* Open 16 June to 15 March. *Methods:* Current E.A. Byelaws apply. Club rules on ticket and fishery map.

Mudford Angling Club

Tel: 01935 476777. *Water:* 3.5 miles double bank on River Yeo. *Species:* Chub, Bream, Dace, Roach. *Charges:* Club membership available from Tackle UK: 01935 476777.

N. Somerset Association of Anglers ♿

Contact: Mr Newton, 64 Clevedon Rd, Tickenham, Clevedon. *Tel:* 01275 856107. *Water:* Blind Yeo, Kenn, Brue, Apex Lake, Newtown Ponds & Walrow Ponds, Tickenham Boundry

---

Rhyne, North Drain (also see entry Stillwater Coarse, Highbridge). *Species:* Roach, Bream, Eels, Perch, Rudd, Carp, Pike, Tench. *Permits:* NSAA Permits available at all local Tackle Shops until March 2014 after which date permits will be issued from same outlets for Clevedon and District F.A.C. Please Tel: 01275 856107 or Highbridge Angling Association on Tel: 01278 786230. *Charges:* Season: Seniors £28. Juniors/OAP/ Disabled £15. Weekly: £15. Day £5. *Season:* June 16th - March 14th inclusive. Apex Lake & Newtown Ponds: closed March 1st - 31st inclusive. *Methods:* Apex Lake and Newtown Ponds: Barbless hooks, no live or dead baits, no floating baits, min. breaking strain line 2.5lb. Some disabled friendly platforms on River Yeo, please contact Mr Newton for more information.

Northover Manor Water

Contact: Mark Haddigan, Ilchester. *Tel:* 01935 840447. *Water:* 50 yards single bank fishing on the Yeo. *Species:* Roach, Bream and Carp. *Charges:* Please enquire at Reception. *Season:* E.A. Byelaws.

Yeovil & Sherborne Angling Association (River Club Card)

Contact: Richard Cattle, 14 Millford Road, Yeovil. *Tel:* 01935 473515. *Water:* 4 miles rivers. Long Load Drain. Long load river above road bridge, approx 1 mile fishing on both banks. *Species:* Roach, Bream, Carp, Dace Chub, Perch, Rudd, Tench. *Permits:* Membership details from above & local tackle shops. *Charges:* No day tickets. River Club card £15. Junior £10. Contact the above or local tackle shops. Sherborne lake separate licence needed, but will cover for all club waters. *Season:* 16 June to 14 March on non enclosed stillwaters.

Stillwater Coarse

BATH

Amalgamated Fisheries Ltd (Shackells Lake)
Contact: Mrs P Leonard, 48 Abbots Road, Hanham, Bristol.
Tel: 01179 603378. *Water:* 3 acre Shackells Lake near Bath
plus various stillwaters at Lyneham, Calne, and Pawlett near
Bridgwater. *Species:* All coarse species including Carp to
21lb. *Charges:* Adults/Ladies £45. Adult and child £60.
Senior Citizen/Disabled and Juniors £25. All Tackle Outlets.
Day Permits. Adult £6. Senior Citizen/Disabled/Juniors.
Full members only may fish Tockenham Lake. *Season:*
Lakes open all year. Shackells Lake closed from May 1st
to June 16th. *Methods:* Maximum 2 rods, no metal cans
or glass allowed on banks, no freshwater fish to be used
as livebait. Full rules and maps available at Tackle Outlets
or above address.

Bathampton Angling Association
Contact: Dave Crookes, 25 Otago Terrace, Larkhall, Bath. *Tel:*
01225 427164. *Water:* Small pond at Weston village in Bath.
Species: Carp to 10lb, Roach to 1.5lb, Bream to 2lb, Hybrids
to 1lb, Tench to 4lb. *Permits:* Bacons Tackle Box, 83 Lower
Bristol Road, Bath. Scott Tackle, 42 Soundwell Rd., Bristol.
Charges: Adults £35, Juniors £15, OAP £13. Under 12's
free. Members only special day permits must be purchased
in advance at £3 per day. *Season:* Open all year. *Methods:*
Special rules apply. Available from secretary or from shop.

Bathampton Angling Association (Hunstrete Ponds) &
Contact: Dave Crookes, 25 Otago Terrace, Larkhall, Bath.
Tel: 01225 427164. *Water:* 3 lake complex at Hunstrete, near
Pensford. Total 11 acres 120 pegs. *Species:* Bream to 8.5lbs,
Chub to 2.5lbs, Roach to 2.5lbs, Pike to 22lbs, Carp to 36lbs
plus, Tench to 10.5lbs, Perch to 2.5lbs, Crucians to 2lbs, Eels
to 7lbs. *Permits:* Local fishing tackle shops (members only).
Charges: Adults £35, Juniors £15, OAP £13. Under 12's free.
Additional special day permit at £3 must be obtained before
fishing. *Season:* Open all year fishing times vary according
to time of year. No night fishing. *Methods:* Copies of rules
available from secretary and tackle shops. Also displayed
on notice boards at lakeside.

Bathampton Angling Association (Newton Park Pond)
Contact: Dave Crookes, 25 Otago Terrace, Larkhall, Bath.
Tel: 01225 427164. *Water:* 2.5 acre lake at Newton Park,
near Bath. *Species:* Bream to 2.5lbs, Chub to 7lbs, Roach
to 3lbs+, Pike to 24lbs, Carp to 27lbs. *Permits:* Local
fishing tackle shops (members only). *Charges:* Adults £35,
Juniors £15, OAP £13. Under 12's free. Additional special
day permit at £3 must be obtained before fishing. Members
only. *Season:* Open all year fishing times vary according
to time of year. No night fishing. *Methods:* Copies of rules
available from secretary and tackle shops. Also displayed
on notice boards at lakeside.

Stunning Koi from Emerald Pool

Farleigh Wood Fishery (Coarse)
Wood Cottage, Tellisford, Bath. *Sat Nav:* BA2 7RN. *Tel:* 01373
831495. *Water:* 1 acre coarse fishing lake. *Species:* Carp to
double figures. *Charges:* £5 a day. *Season:* Open all year.
Car Park. *Methods:* List of rules at fishery.

BRIDGWATER

Amalgamated Fisheries Ltd (Pawlett Ponds)
Contact: Mrs P Leonard, 48 Abbots Road, Hanham, Bristol.
Tel: 01179 603378. *Water:* Pawlett Ponds : 4 ponds totalling
5 acre, Tockenham Reservoir at Lyneham, Sabre Lake at
Calne plus various stillwaters at Lyneham, and Bath. *Species:*
All coarse species including Carp to 27lb. *Charges:* Full
Members only at Tockenham. Adults/Ladies £45. Adult
and child £60. Senior Citizen/Disabled and Juniors £25.
Day Permits available from Pawlett Post Office and Veals
in Highbridge. Adult £6. Senior Citizens/Disabled/Junior
£3. *Season:* Lakes open all year. Shackells Lake closed
from May 1st to June 16th. *Methods:* Maximum 2 rods, no
metal cans or glass allowed on banks, no freshwater fish to
be used as livebait.

Beeches Fishery
Contact: Andrew Bradbury. *Tel:* 01278 423545. *Water:*
9 ponds set in 5 acres of designated county wildlife site.
Species: Carp (Crucians, Common, Mirror), Roach, Rudd,
Tench, Perch and Eels. *Permits:* Limited day tickets, only
available in advance from Andrew Bradbury on the above
telephone number. *Charges:* Valid EA rod licence required.
Season: Close season - March to June. No night fishing.

Bridgwater Angling Association (Coarse Lakes) &
Contact: Mr A Danahy, 127 The Old Basin, Somerset Bridge,
Bridgwater. *Tel:* 01278 457022. *Water:* See entry under
Taunton and Bridgwater Canal. Various stillwaters. Stillwater
fishing at Combwich, Walrow, Dunwear & Screech Owl.
Species: All types of coarse fish. *Permits:* Available from

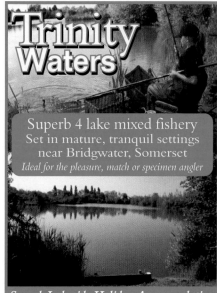

STILLWATER COARSE

Tackle outlets throughout Somerset area including Somerset Angling, 74 Bath Road, Bridgwater, Tel; 01278 431777. Taunton Angling Centre, 63 Station Road, Taunton, Tel; 01823 282518. Watts News, Edward Street, Bridgwater, Tel; 01278 422137. Scoops, 77 St Johns Street, Bridgwater. Veals Tackle 1a Church Street, Highbridge, Tel; 01278 786934. *Charges:* Adult Season 1 rod £35, 2 rods £50, 3 rods £70 4 rods £90. Senior citizens /disabled 1 rod £25, 2 rods £37.50, 3 rods £55, 4 rods £70. Junior (7-11 years) 1 rod £6. Junior (12-17 years) 1 rod only £8 + £10 for 2 rods. Day ticket £7. Night fishing (24 hour) £12. Prices correct at time of publication subject to change. *Season:* Open all year except Screech Owl (traditional Coarse close season). *Methods:* Disabled access at all lakes except Screech Owl. No reserving swims.

Browns Pond
Contact: Sedgemoor District Council, Off Taunton Rd (A38), Bridgwater. *Sat Nav:* TA6 4QE. *Tel:* 0845 408 2540. *Water:* 2.5 acres. *Species:* Carp to 22lb, Tench to 5lb, Bream to 6lb, Perch to 2lb & Roach. *Charges:* Please phone for details. *Season:* No closed season. *Methods:* No night fishing, barbless hooks only, no live bait, no Carp sacks.

Burton Springs Fishery (Specimen Lake)
Contact: Adam Hilling, Lawson Farm, Burton, Nr Stogursey, Bridgwater. *Sat Nav:* TA5 1QB. *Tel:* 01278 732135. *Mobile:* 07838 152968. *Water:* Approx. 2 acre lake. *Species:* Tench to 7lbs, Perch to 4lbs, Bream to 5.5lbs, mixed Carp to 30lbs (Mirror, Common, Leather, Grass, Ghost). *Permits:* Self Service at fishing lodge/on bank. *Charges:* £10 per day, 2 rods, £20 for 24hrs. Night fishing strictly by arrangement, bookings and payment taken over phone. *Season:* Dawn to dusk, please ring for times. *Methods:* Barbless hooks only, no nuts or peas. Fishery rules to be followed at all times.

Cokerhurst Farm
Contact: Derrick Chappell, 87 Wembdon Hill, Wembdon, Bridgwater. *Sat Nav:* TA6 7QA. *Tel:* 01278 422330. *Mobile:* 07850 692065. *Water:* 0.75 acre lake. *Species:* Carp to 25lb. *Charges:* Day £5. Night fishing £15. *Season:* Open all year. *Methods:* Barbless hooks only. No keepnets for larger fish. Night fishing by prior arrangement.

Durleigh Reservoir
Contact: Wessex Water. *Sat Nav:* TA5 2AW. *Tel:* 0845 600 4600. *Water:* 80 acre reservoir. *Species:* Carp, Roach, Bream, Perch, Tench and Pike. *Permits:* Contact Ranger Paul Martin on 01278 424786. *Charges:* Day Ticket £7(1 rod). Day ticket £9 (2-3 rods). Day concession £5 (1 rod). Day concession £7 (2-3 rods). Block of 6 tickets £35 (1 rod). Block of 6 tickets £45 (2-3 rods). *Season:* Open all year except Christmas day, Boxing day, New Years Eve and day.

Plum Lane Fishery
Contact: Mrs J. Goodland, Plum Lane, Dunwear, Bridgwater. *Sat Nav:* TA6 5HL. *Tel:* 01278 421625. *Water:* 1 acre pond. *Species:* Predominately Carp to 10lb plus Tench. Roach and Skimmers. *Permits:* On site. *Charges:* £5 per adult (1 rod). *Season:* Open all year. *Methods:* Barbless hooks only. No keepnets. No Braid. Advice available on site.

Summerhayes Fishery &
Contact: Peter Wakeling, Somerset Bridge, Huntworth. *Sat Nav:* TA6 6LW. *Tel:* 01278 451043. *Mobile:* 07866 557896. *Water:* 5 lakes. 100 pegs to 10 acres on 24 acre fishery. *Species:* Carp to 26lb, Bream, Tench, Roach, Rudd, Perch, Ghost Carp to 16lb. *Permits:* On site only. *Charges:* £7 day, £5.50 Concessions. Season ticket Adult £75, Junior/ Concession £75 for 1 rod. £10 for 2 rods. Disabled access. *Season:* Open all year dawn to dusk. Night fishing by prior arrangement, max 6 people. *Methods:* Barbless hooks, no nuts. Maximum 2 rods. Fishery keepnets must be used, £1 hire.

STILLWATER COARSE

Taunton Road Ponds
Contact: Sedgemoor District Council, Off Taunton Rd (A38), Bridgwater. *Sat Nav:* TA6 4QE. *Tel:* 0845 408 2540. *Water:* 3.5 acres. *Species:* Large Carp to 32lb, Tench to 6lb, Bream to 13lb 6oz, Perch to 3lb, Rudd to 2lb, Skimmer Bream to 12oz & Roach to 8oz. *Charges:* Please phone for details. *Season:* No closed season. *Methods:* No night fishing, barbless hooks only, no live bait, no Carp in keepnets, no Carp sacks.

The Sedges ♿
Contact: Jamie & Denise Cook, River Lane, Dunwear, Bridgwater. *Sat Nav:* TA7 0AA. *Tel:* 01278 445221. *Mobile:* 07980 128404. *Water:* 3 lakes totalling 6.5 acres. *Species:* Perch 3lb, Tench 9lb, Rudd & Roach 1lb, Bream 5lb, Carp 22lb. *Charges:* On bank: £7 adult day, children accompanied by adult £7. OAP/disabled £7. Eve after 4pm £5. *Season:* Open all year dawn to dusk. No entry before 6am. *Methods:* No Carp sacks, barbless hooks only, unhooking mats to be used. Strictly no nuts, boilies, fixed leads or feeders. Landing nets supplied and must be used.

Trinity Waters ♿
Contact: John and Sue Herring, Trinity Waters, Straight Drove, Chilton Trinity, Bridgwater. *Sat Nav:* TA5 2BQ. *Tel:* 01278 450880. *Mobile:* 07720 542141. *Water:* Currently 5 lakes: 6.5 acres, 3 acres, 2 acre and 1 acre. *Species:* Rudd 2lb. Roach 2lb. Perch 3lb. Tench 8lb. Golden Tench 5lb. Bream 11lb. Mirror, Common 20lb and Grass Carp 25lb. Plus Chub and Barbel to 5lb. Mirror and Common to 30lb plus in specimen lake. *Permits:* On site only. *Charges:* £6.50 per day, £8.50 two rods. £4 juniors and conc. Match rates on request. Specimen Lake £15 day, £20 for 24 hour, £30 for 48 hour. Wildmarsh lake 6.5 acres - £20 for 24hrs, £30 for 48hrs. *Season:* Open all year dawn to dusk. *Methods:* Barbless hooks. No fixed rigs. Keepnets can be used, must be dry before going in water. Separate keepnets for carp and silvers. Close parking and toilets. Disabled friendly on all waters.

Willow Fisheries ♿
Contact: Peter Lane, Marsh Lane, Huntworth, Bridgwater. *Sat Nav:* TA7 0AQ. *Mobile:* 07799 877724. *Water:* 1 acre lake and 0.75 acre pond in Huntworth. *Species:* Carp, Specimen

Perch, Bream, Rudd, Roach and Tench. *Permits:* From above. *Charges:* Please phone. *Season:* Open all year. Night fishing permitted. *Methods:* Full rules at fishery.

BRISTOL

Alcove Angling Club ♿
Contact: Bryan Cleevely, 31 Roseberry Park, Redfield, Bristol. *Tel:* 01179 392827. *Mobile:* 07938 874330. *Water:* One lake Bristol area at Alcove Lido. Also 3 lakes in South Gloucs. Secure gated access to all car parks. Phone for further information and about disabled fishing. *Species:* Carp 28lb, Bream 7lb, Roach, Tench 8lb, Rudd, Pike, Perch and Crucian Carp. *Charges:* Annual memberships only - No Day tickets. Annual memberships Adult £50. Partners of members £10, Children under 12 free, Junior 12 to 17 £16, OAP £28. Disabled £28 (helper £1). Children must be accompanied by an adult at all times. *Season:* No close season. *Methods:* As specified in membership card. Night fishing at Alcove Lido only. Barbless hooks or Micro Barb only. 1 kilo of bait per day.

Bagwood Lake
Contact: Woodland Golf Club - David Knipe, Trench Lane, Almondsbury, Bristol. *Sat Nav:* BS32 4JZ. *Tel:* 01454 619319. *Mobile:* 07973 797555. *Water:* One coarse lake. 4 acre. *Species:* Carp. *Permits:* On site, pay in shop. *Charges:* 12 hour ticket £12. 24 hours £18. Junior 12hr £9. 24hr £12. Tickets valid from 7am to 7pm. 2 rods per person or 3 rods per swim. *Season:* Please phone prior to travelling.

Boyd Valley Lake
Contact: Avon Aquatics, 72-76 High Street, Staple Hill, Bristol. *Sat Nav:* BS15 6EE. *Tel:* 01179 327659. *Water:* 1.5 acre lake. *Species:* Carp to 20lb, Tench, Roach and Bream, Barbel. *Permits:* Day tickets from Avon Aquatics. *Charges:* £7 per day. *Season:* Open all year. *Methods:* Barbless hooks to be used.

Bristol PSV Club ♿
Contact: Mike Wilson. *Mobile:* 07850 731137. *Water:* Well established club, fishing waters such as Viaduct and Lands End in Gloucester, Bristol, Bath & Somerset. 45 matches a year. Meeting 1st Tuesday of every month in the Midland

STILLWATER COARSE

Spinner on London Road, Warmley. *Charges:* Membership £20 per year. Juniors welcome. Call in to the Midland Spinner. *Methods:* Disabled anglers welcome please telephone in advance for further information.

Cross Hands Angling Club
Contact: Roy Golding - Secretary. *Mobile:* 07770 264910. *Water:* The Crest lake - 30 pegs. Hunters lake 1 at Clutton - 20 pegs, lake 2 at Clutton 6 pegs. Ashleigh Farm, Horton, Chipping Sodbury - 35 pegs. Section of River Frome. *Species:* Carp to 16lb. Tench, Bream, Roach. *Permits:* Members only - Limited membership available from above, junior section, OAP Section. Total adult member - 150 max. OAP and Junior - unlimited. *Charges:* Junior £10 p/year, OAP £30 p/year, Seniors £50 p/year. *Season:* Open all year. Hunters Lakes are closed 14 March to 16 June. *Methods:* No boilies, no groundbait, barbless hooks.

Duchess Pond
Contact: Wayne Tooker (Leaseholder), 2A Aintree Drive, Downend, Bristol. *Mobile:* 07980 091286. *Water:* 2 acre pond. *Species:* Mixed fishery plus Carp to 30lb. *Permits:* Direct from Wayne on bank. *Charges:* £5 Adults, £100 season ticket. £15 for 24hrs. *Season:* Open all year Dawn to dusk. Night fishing available. *Methods:* Full rules displayed at Fishery.

Eastville Park Lake
Contact: Bristol City Council, Brunel House, St. Georges Street, Bristol. *Sat Nav:* BS16 1BQ. *Tel:* 01179 223719. *Species:* Various coarse species. *Permits:* Free fishing for responsible anglers. *Season:* Please ring for opening times. *Methods:* Fishing permitted on south side of lake only. Please respect nature reserve on opposite bank.

Ham Green Fisheries
Contact: Mr Hunt, Chapelpill Lane, Hamgreen. *Sat Nav:* BS20 6DB. *Tel:* 01275 849885. *Mobile:* 07818 640227. *Water:* Two lakes. 1 acre 25 peg. 2 acre open bank. *Species:* 1 acre lake stocked with Carp, Roach, Rudd, Perch, Pike, Bream, Skimmers and Golden Tench. 2 acre lake all the above with Carp to 30lb and Bream 16lb. *Permits:* Mr Hunt, 21 Station Rd, Portishead, Bristol; also on lake side from Bailiff. *Charges:* £5 on bank for small lake. All night fishing £15. £10 on bank for big lake. Prices may change for 2014

due to restocking of Carp. *Season:* No closed season. 7am to 8pm from 16 June to 13 October. 8am to 5pm from 1 November to 30 April. Night fishing strictly by arrangement, booking essential by telephone to Mr Hunt. *Methods:* No live bait, barbless hooks preferred, no keepnets for fish over 1lb. Children must be accompanied by an adult. Hooking mats to be used.

King William IV Angling Association ♿
Contact: Jerry Pocock, 86 Tower Road South, Warmley, Bristol. *Tel:* 01179 492974. *Mobile:* 07852 294212. *Water:* Open to all in the area. Regular meetings and matches. Further details from Jerry.

Kingswood Disabled Angling Club + Over 55's
Contact: Rodney Buff, 54 Leicester Square, Soundwell, Bristol. *Mobile:* 07900 051113. *Water:* Bristol based Coarse fishing club meeting monthly. New members welcome. Must be registered disabled at local Social Services Office. Regular fishing trips and matches organised. Please phone for further information or to join waiting list. *Charges:* £10 adult annual membership.

Paulton Lakes
Contact: John Wiles, Ruthin Villa, High Street, High Littleton, Bristol. *Sat Nav:* BS39 7NX. *Tel:* 01761 472338. *Mobile:* 07709 471414. *Water:* Two lakes located off Bristol Road, Paulton. Approx. 2.5 acres with a total of 25 swims. *Species:* Island Lake: Carp 25lb, Roach 3lb, Chub 10lb, Tench 6lb, Eels 6lb. King Lake: Carp 15lb, Grass Carp, Tench 6lb, Chub, Roach, Rudd. *Permits:* Day tickets from A.M. Hobbs, The Island, Midsomer Norton. Tel: (01761) 413961 and from Central Garage, High Street, Paulton. Tickets must be purchased in advance - not available on the bank. *Charges:* £7 per day ticket. Concessions for Junior/OAP. Season tickets available. *Season:* Open all year, season tickets 1st May. Fishing from dawn to one hour after dusk. Night fishing by syndicate only. *Methods:* Full details on ticket. Barbless hooks, no Carp in keepnets, unhooking mats must be used, no pre-baiting or ground baiting.

Royal British Legion Kingswood
Contact: Mr Lloyd, 386 Speedwell Road, Kingswood, Bristol. *Tel:* 0117 9676030. *Mobile:* 07831 311582. *Water:* Fishing on rivers and stillwaters. Open to all anglers especially Royal British Legion members, regular matches.

Saint Georges Park Lake
Contact: Bristol City Council, Brunel House, St. Georges Street, Bristol. *Tel:* 01179 223719. *Water:* Small lake. *Species:* Stocked with coarse fish. *Permits:* Free fishing for responsible anglers. *Season:* Please ring for opening times. *Methods:* Fishing permitted on south side of lake only. Please respect nature reserve on opposite bank.

Tan House Farm Lake
Contact: Mr & Mrs James, Tan House Farm, Yate, Bristol. *Sat Nav:* BS37 7QL. *Tel:* 01454 228280. *Water:* Quarter mile lake. *Species:* Roach, Perch, Carp, Bream, Tench, Rudd. *Permits:* Day tickets from Farm House. *Charges:*

Adult £5 per rod plus £1 for extra rods, Children & OAP £4. *Methods:* No Ground bait, dog & cat food, boilies, barbless hooks only. No Trout pellets.

BURNHAM-ON-SEA

Burnham-on-sea Holiday Village
Contact: Elaine Organ, Burnham-on-Sea Holiday Village, Marine Drive, Burnham-on-Sea. *Sat Nav:* TA8 1LA. *Tel:* 01278 783391. *Water:* Two lakes. First lake about 2.5 acres. Second around 4 acres. *Species:* Both lakes hold Carp up to 30lb, Bream 10lb 2oz, Tench 7lb 6oz, Eels 6lb 9oz, Roach 1lb, Rudd 1lb, Pike 20lb 3oz, Perch to 1lb. *Permits:* Spar shop on site (Tel 01278 783156). *Charges:* On application. *Season:* Open March - November. *Methods:* Barbless hooks only. No Carp over 10lb in keepnets. Night fishing by bookings only. Noise kept to a minimum.

Highbridge Angling Association (Apex Lake)
Contact: Mr C Brewer. *Tel:* 01278 786230. *Water:* Apex lake, Marine Drive, Burnham-on-sea. *Species:* Mixed coarse fish. Carp to 20lb, Bream to 8lb, Roach to 3lb and Chub to 5lb. *Permits:* From local tackle dealers. *Charges:* Prices upon application. *Methods:* No night fishing.

Holiday Resort Unity
Coast Road, Brean Sands, Burnham-on-Sea. *Sat Nav:* TA8 2RB. *Tel:* 01278 751235. *Water:* 0.5 acre pond. *Species:* Carp 26lb, Pike 23lb, Tench 3lb, Roach 1/2lb, Bream 3lb. *Charges:* Not in peak season. *Season:* All year. *Methods:* Pond - No keepnets or ground bait.

CHARD

Chard and District Angling Club (Coarse Lakes)
Contact: John Barron. *Tel:* 01460 63593. *Water:* Perry Street Pond - 1.5 acres. Chard Reservoir - 48 acres. Sadborow Pond near Thorncombe. Also 1.5 miles on Isle see entry under River Fishing. *Species:* Roach, Bream, Carp, Tench, Perch, Eels, Rudd. *Permits:* Perry Street Ponds - members only, Membership details from Barrons, 2 Holyrood St., Chard. Tel: 01460 63593. *Charges:* Chard reservoir £10 per day on the bank (£8 club members). Perry Street ponds free to members only. *Season:* Open all year. *Methods:* Full list of rules from fishery notice board and membership book.

Chard Reservoir

Contact: John Barron. *Tel:* 01460 63593. *Water:* 48 acre reservoir. *Species:* Coarse fish. *Permits:* On the bank. *Charges:* 24 hour ticket - £10 non members. £8 members of Chard and District A.C.

CHEDDAR

Cheddar Angling Club

Contact: Mr Richard Heard, P.O. Box 1183, Cheddar. *Mobile:* 07796 990205. *Water:* 200 acre Cheddar Reservoir. *Species:* Pike 30lb, Perch 1lb, Tench 7lb, Roach 1lb and Eels 6lb. *Permits:* Permits are NOT available at the reservoir. Only from: Crossroads Filling Station A371, between Axbridge and Cheddar. Thatchers Pet and Tackle, 18 Queen St, Wells. Veals Fishing Tackle, Bristol. Somerset Angling, Bridgwater. Colins Tackle, Weston-Super-Mare. Thyers Fishing Tackle, Church St., Highbridge. *Charges:* Seniors season £45, Juniors season £20, Seniors day £6, Juniors day £3. *Season:* No closed season. *Methods:* No live baiting, Moderate ground baiting, No dead baiting from 16 June to 30 September. No night fishing. Dawn to dusk only. Unhooking mats recommended. Rod limits: seniors maximum 3 rods, juniors one rod only. (Please check re-rods).

COLEFORD

Breach Valley Fishing

Contact: Lower Vobster, Coleford, Radstock. *Sat Nav:* BA3 5LY. *Tel:* 01373 812352. *Mobile:* 07950 771219. *Water:* 2 ponds totalling 1.5 acres approx. *Species:* Carp to 28lb, Roach, Tench, Perch and Bream. *Charges:* Day tickets on bank £7. *Season:* Open Saturday June 11th to end of March, dawn to dusk. *Methods:* No keepnets, no boilies, barbless hooks.

CONGRESBURY

Silver Springs Fish Farm &

Contact: Liz Patch, Silver Street Lane, Congresbury. *Sat Nav:* BS49 5EY. *Mobile:* 07837 809005. *Water:* General coarse lake: 4.5 acres. Specimen Carp lake: 4.5 acres. *Species:* General: Carp to mid twenties, Rudd, Roach to 3lb, Tench, Chub, Bream, Perch and Gudgeon. Specimen: Mirrors and

commons to high 20's/low 30's. *Permits:* On site. *Charges:* General: £7, After 2pm £5, Conc. £5. Specimen: £10, After 2pm £7, Conc. £7. *Season:* General: All year dawn till half hour before dusk. Specimen: All year. *Methods:* General: Barbless hooks. Specimen: No poles, no keepnets, no nuts, barbless hooks only.

CORFE

Taunton Angling Association (Wych Lodge Lake) &

Contact: Kieran Granville. *Mobile:* 07712 867773. *Water:* Wych Lodge Lake, 3 acre large Carp lake (also see entries under River & Canal Fishing). *Species:* Large Carp up to 27lb, Roach 2lb, Rudd 2lb, Perch 4lb and Skimmer Bream

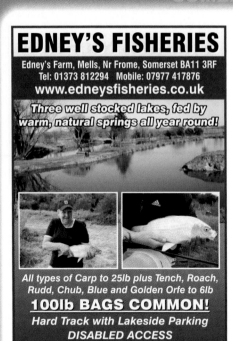
1lb. *Permits:* Only from Taunton Angling Centre (restricted to 15 pegs) Tel: 01823 282518. Please bring season ticket as proof of membership when purchasing day permit. Separate day ticket available for non season ticket holders. *Charges:* Senior season £45, Junior £10. Senior weekly £20, Senior day £7, Junior daily £4, OAP/Disabled £28, Junior Season up to and including 15 years £10. Night fishing £65 in addition to Senior season ticket only. *Season:* Open all year. *Methods:* No Carp in keepnets, no lighting of fires, no litter. Disabled access. Micro barbs can be used.

CREWKERNE

Highlands Dairy Lake &
Contact: J. Wyatt, Highlands Dairy Farm, Hewish, Crewkerne. *Sat Nav:* TA1 8QY. *Tel:* 01460 74180. *Water:* Two 1 acre lakes and one 0.5 acre lake. *Species:* Carp, Tench, Rudd, Roach, Perch. *Permits:* At house. *Charges:* £5 per day. £6.50 to include night fishing. *Season:* Open all year. *Methods:* No keepnets for Carp. Barbless hooks only.

FROME

Barrow Farm Pond
Contact: John Nicholls, Barrow Farm, Witham Friary, Frome. *Sat Nav:* BA11 5HD. *Tel:* 01749 850313. *Mobile:* 07734 978988. *Water:* Half acre lake. *Species:* Carp, Perch and Tench. *Charges:* £5 adult. £3.50 children and OAP. *Season:* February to September. Phone for details. *Methods:* No restrictions.

Edneys Fisheries &
Contact: Richard or John Candy, Edneys Farm, Mells, Frome. *Sat Nav:* BA11 3RF. *Tel:* 01373 812294. *Mobile:* 07941 280075. *Water:* 3 lakes totalling approx.3 acres. Hard standing and parking at all lakes. Recently cleaned out lake 1 and refurbished pegs. *Species:* Carp 25lb, Tench 9lb, Roach, Rudd, Golden Rudd, Perch, Common, Mirror, Linear, Leather and Ghost Carp. Golden and Blue Orfe to 6lb and Perch 4lb 14oz in lake 2. Chub in lakes 2 and 3. *Permits:* Yearly tickets £85 Adults, £65 Under 14. *Charges:* Adults £6, Under 14 yrs £4. Night tickets £6 for all. *Season:* 24hrs all year. *Methods:* Barbless hooks, no nuts, no feeding of boilies, no fish over 2lb in keepnets.

Witham Friary Lakes
Contact: Mr Miles, Witham Hall Farm, Witham Friary, Nr Frome. *Sat Nav:* BA11 5HB. *Tel:* 01373 836239. *Water:* Two lakes totalling approx. 2 acres. *Species:* Carp, Roach, Tench, Perch, Gudgeon. *Permits:* On site. *Charges:* £5 day - £10 night (dusk - 8 am). *Season:* All year. *Methods:* Barbless hooks only.

GLASTONBURY

Glaston Manor Angling Association (Moorland Fishery)
Contact: Adam Mitchell, NFU Office, Cathedral View, Wookey Hole Rd., Wells. *Tel:* 01749 673786. *Water:* Moorland Fishery (stillwater), Meare and Burtle Ponds, Burtle (3 ponds in about 12 acres). See also entry under River Fishing, Brue. *Species:* Tench, Carp, Bream, Roach, Rudd, Perch, Crucian. *Permits:* Thatchers Tackle, Wells. Tel: 01749 673513. Somerset Angling, 74 Bath Rd, Bridgwater. Tel: 01278 431777 or Thyers Tackle, 1a Church Street, Highbridge. Tel: 01278 786934. *Charges:* Prices upon application. *Season:* Current E.A. byelaws apply. *Methods:* Full rules on permit.

HIGHBRIDGE

Emerald Pool Fishery &
Contact: Mr Alan Wilkinson, Emerald Pool Fishery, Puriton Road, West Huntspill, Highbridge. *Sat Nav:* TA9 3NL. *Tel:* 01278 794707 *Mobile:* 07974 862503. *Water:* 4 lakes in total. 1.5 acre lake, plus 'Sapphire Lake' - 20 peg disabled angler friendly pool for adults and juniors. Jade 30 pegs, Ruby 21 pegs, 108 pegs now on site. *Species:* Bream, Golden Orfe, Roach, Rudd, Tench, Perch, Barbel 5lb. Emerald Lake - Small Carp to 11lb. Jade 30 pegs, Carp, Barbel, Bream and Tench. Sapphire Lake Carp 10lb, Tench 5lb. Ruby Lake 1 to 5lb Carp. *Permits:* Environment Agency rod licence required on this water. *Charges:* £7 one rod. £2 for additional rods per person. 24 hour session £24 per person. *Season:* All year. *Methods:* Barbless hooks only. No Carp sacks, fixed rigs, tiger nuts. Do not leave rods unattended. Groundbait allowed in moderation. No keepnets.

Highbridge Angling Association (Coarse Lakes)
Contact: Mr C Brewer. *Tel:* 01278 786230. *Water:* 3 Lakes at Walrow. *Species:* Carp to mid 30's, Pike to mid 20's, Bream to 12lb, Tench to double figures and all other coarse species.

STILLWATER COARSE

Wheelyboat Trust trustee Danny Peet with a 31½lb pike caught on a fly in a Wheelyboat from Chew Valley Lake

Permits: Thyers Tackle, Highbridge - 01278 786934. Also available from other local tackle shops. *Charges:* Prices upon application. *Season:* Open all year.

N. Somerset Association of Anglers (Coarse Lakes) &

Contact: Mr Newton, 64 Clevedon Rd, Tickenham, Clevedon. *Tel:* 01275 856107. *Water:* See also entry under Yeo. Apex lake: 6 acre lake, Newtown: 3 acre lake, Walrow ponds: 2 acre lake, 3 acre lake and 6 acre lake. *Species:* Apex: Carp to 18lbs, Bream to 7lb, Pike to 15lb, Roach, Rudd. Newtown: Carp to 24lb, Pike to 27lb, Bream 7lb, Roach, Rudd, Perch. Walrow: Carp to 26lb, Bream 11lb, Tench 10lb, Pike 24lb, Roach, Rudd, Perch. *Permits:* Local tackle shops, purchased in advance of fishing available until March 2014 after which date permits will be issued from same outlets for Clevedon and District F.A.C. Please Tel: 01275 856107 or Highbridge Angling Association on Tel: 01278 786230. *Charges:* £5 day, £15 week, £28 season, junior/OAP/disabled £15. *Season:* Apex & Newtown Lakes - closed March 1st - 31st inclusive. Walrow Pond - open all year. *Methods:* Apex & Newtown Lakes: Barbless hooks, min. 2.5lb BS line, no live or dead bait, no floating bait. Disabled friendly platforms on Apex Lake with easy access.

Withy Water &

Contact: Jim Baker, Cedar Shade Farm, Withy Rd, East Huntspill, Highbridge. *Sat Nav:* TA9 3NW. *Tel:* 01278 783700. *Mobile:* 07891 557246. *Water:* 2 acre lake set in 4 acres with 20 well spaced swims. *Species:* Carp 8lb, Bream 4lb, Roach 3lb, Perch 2lb, Rudd 2lb and Tench 2lb. *Charges:* £6 day ticket (2 rods). Children £3.50. *Season:* Open all year. No night fishing. *Methods:* Barbless hooks, maximum 2 rods, no nuts, fishery landing nets must be used. No keepnets. Disabled friendly toilets on site. Nearby carpark.

ILMINSTER

Ilminster and District A.A. (Coarse Lake)

Contact: P. Lonton, Mashala, Ilton, Ilminster. *Tel:* 01460 52519. *Water:* Dillington Estate Pond (contact club secretary). 200 yards on canal at Ilminster Recreation Grounds. *Species:* Carp, Roach, Chub, Perch, Bream, Tench, Crucians. *Permits:* Ilminster Warehouse, Yeovil Angling Centre. Membership details from the Secretary. *Charges:*

Day tickets £5. £22 annual membership. £15 OAP/Disabled. Junior £6. *Season:* Open all year. *Methods:* Club rules apply.

KEYNSHAM

Avon Valley Country Park (Coarse Pond)

Bath Rd, Keynsham, Bristol. *Sat Nav:* BS31 1TP. *Tel:* 0117 9864929. *Water:* Small Coarse pond. *Species:* Carp to 12lb. *Charges:* Adults £8, Children £7.50, Senior £7.50. *Season:* Park open: 2nd April - 31st October every day 10am-6pm. *Methods:* Barbless hooks only, no keepnets.

Keynsham Angling Association (Coarse Lake)

Contact: Keynsham Angling Association. *Mobile:* 07973 736519. *Water:* Century Ponds two lakes 0.6 acres each, see also entry under River Chew. *Species:* Mixed fishery with Carp to over 20lb, Tench, Crucians, Bream, Roach, Gudgeon etc. *Charges:* Day ticket for club members £3.75. White Gate Garden Centre, Stockwood, Bristol. *Season:* Open all year 7.00am to 6.00pm winter, 7.00am to 10.00pm summer. Closed alternate Sunday mornings until 1pm and Christmas Day all day. *Methods:* Barbless hooks. No Carp in keepnets. Two rods maximum per angler.

KINGSTON SEYMOUR

Acorn Carp Fishery &

Contact: Bev Bartlett, Lampley Road, Kingston Seymour. *Sat Nav:* BS21 6XS. *Tel:* 01934 834050. *Water:* 3.5 acre main lake. Top Match Lake - 15 pegs. The Paddock - 40 peg match lake. *Species:* Main lake: Carp 10lb to 30lb plus. Top Match lake: Carp 0.5lb to 12lb, Perch Roach, Tench, Bream. *Charges:* Lots of ticket options. Main lake from £10. Top

STILLWATER COARSE

Match Lake £7. The Paddock £7. *Season:* April to end Sept 7am - 7pm. Oct to end March 7.30am - 6pm. *Methods:* Barbless hooks. Unhooking mats. Large nets. No braided mainline, tiger nuts, or peas.

Bullock Farm Fishing Lakes
Contact: Philip & Jude Simmons, Bullock Farm, Back Lane, Kingston Seymour. *Sat Nav:* BS21 6XA. *Tel:* 01934 835020. *Water:* 5 Lakes totalling 6.25 acres, including specialist Carp lake. *Species:* Carp - Common, Mirror, Ghost, Crucian, Grass, Purple and Koi. Tench, Roach, Rudd, Chub, Bream, Skimmer Bream, Golden Orfe, Golden Tench. *Permits:* Only at lakeside. *Charges:* £7 day ticket, £5 OAP/Under 14s/Disabled. Season tickets & Match rates available. *Season:* Open all year round Dawn - Dusk. No night fishing. *Methods:* No boilies, bloodworm or dried nuts. Barbless hooks, no braided line. Fish friendly keepnets only, No dogs, under 14's to be accompanied by an adult. Common sense.

Plantations Lakes
Contact: Angela and William Travis, Middle Lane Farm, Middle Lane, Kingston Seymour, Clevedon. *Sat Nav:* BS21 6XW. *Tel:* 01934 832325. *Mobile:* 07990 543600. *Water:* 0.75 acre carp lake, 2.5 acre coarse lake, 1.75 acre match lake. *Species:* 9 Species of coarse fish incl. Barbel, Crucian Carp. 3 Species of Carp in Carp lake. *Charges:* £8 Adult (£2 extra rod), £6 Juniors/OAP/Disabled (£2 extra rod). Please enquire for membership details. *Season:* All year. *Methods:* Barbless hooks.

LANGPORT

Langport and District Angling Assn. (Coarse Lake)
Contact: Dave Jolly, 30 King Street, Yeovil. *Tel:* 01935 420836. *Water:* Coombe Lake near Langport - 1.6 acres. *Species:* A few, very difficult to catch Carp. Tench 6.5lb, Roach 0.5lb, Perch 2lb plus, Bream 7lb, Chub 4lb. *Permits:* Season ticket holders only - no day tickets. *Charges:* Annual £17, Junior £5, Disabled/OAP £8. No day tickets for lake. *Season:* No closed season. No night fishing. *Methods:* Barbless hooks, no boilies, no Carp in keepnets.

Thorney Lakes
Contact: Richard or Sally England, Thorney Lakes, Muchelney, Langport. *Sat Nav:* TA10 0DW. *Tel:* 01458 250811. *Mobile:* 07803 005042. *Water:* 4 acres of water. *Species:* A selection of coarse fish including large Carp. *Permits:* On the bank. *Charges:* £7 per day, £5 per half day after 4 pm, £5 for OAP & Children under 16. *Season:* 16 March - 31 January. *Methods:* Barbless hooks, no boilies, nuts or pulses, all nets to be dipped on site, no night fishing.

MARTOCK

Ash Ponds
Contact: Pat Rodford, Ash Ponds, Burrough Street, Ash, Martock. *Sat Nav:* TA12 6NZ. *Tel:* 01935 823459. *Water:* Three 1 acre ponds. *Species:* Carp to 30lb, Tench to 7lb and Bream 3lb. *Permits:* On the bank. *Charges:* £5 Day. £5 Night. *Season:* No closed season. *Methods:* Barbless hooks.

STILLWATER COARSE

SHEPTON MALLET

Jon Thorners Fishing Lake &
Contact: Jon Thorner, Pylle, Shepton Mallet. *Sat Nav:* BA4 6TA. *Tel:* 01749 830138. *Water:* 2 acre 300m fishing lake. *Species:* Mirror Carp, Tench and Roach. *Charges:* £6 per person per day. *Season:* All year round. *Methods:* Barbless hooks only. 2k ground bait max. Fish over 4lb must not be placed in keepnet of sack. Unhooking mats required for large fish. Max 12lb line. All fish to be returned to lake. Fishing from platform pegs only.

SHEPTON MONTAGUE

Higher Farm Fishery &
Contact: Robert and Christina Dimond, Higher Farm, Shepton Montague, Wincanton. *Sat Nav:* BA9 8JJ. *Tel:* 01749 812373. *Water:* Three lakes, 3 acres in total. *Species:* Common, Mirror and Ghost Carp to 20lb. Green and Golden Tench, Bream, Rudd and Roach. *Permits:* All day tickets are sold on the bank. *Charges:* £7 adults full day, £5 adults half day. £4 under 14. £8 night fishing. *Season:* Open all year. *Methods:* No nuts, barbless hooks only. Full rules at the fishery.

SOMERTON

Viaduct Fishery &
Contact: Mr Steve Long, Viaduct Fishery, Cary Valley, Somerton. *Sat Nav:* TA11 6LJ. *Tel:* 01458 274022. *Water:*

Six coarse lakes. *Species:* Mirror Carp 27lb, Crucian Carp, Common Carp 25lb, Perch 4lb, Roach 2lb, Bream 6lb, Tench 8lb and Golden Tench, Rudd. *Permits:* From on site tackle shop. *Charges:* Day ticket £7, Under 16 £5, Summer eve ticket £5. Winter Half day ticket £5. £2 charge for second rod. Match bookings taken. *Season:* Open all year. *Methods:* No nuts or boilies, barbless hooks size 8 max, no fixed rigs, no braid, fishing from pegs only.

STREET

Peggy's Lake
Contact: Shane Alway. *Mobile:* 07789 760213. *Water:* Approx. 4 acre Specimen Carp lake. 2 acre Match lake. *Species:* Coarse fish including Carp 30lb 12oz, Common Carp 30lb 10oz, Grass Carp 16lb 4oz, Tench 8lb plus Pike 15lb plus. *Permits:* Please contact Shane on number above. *Charges:* Please telephone. *Season:* Closed season May - June. *Methods:* No nuts, 3 rods max. Barbed hooks only. Fisherman only allowed on one lake at a time.

Taunton Angling Association (Walton Ponds)
Contact: Kieran Granville. *Mobile:* 07712 867773. *Water:* Walton Ponds, 1 pond (also see entries under River & Canal Fishing). *Species:* Carp 25lb, Tench 5lb, Roach 2lb, Rudd 2lb, Skimmer Bream 1lb, Bream 7lb. *Permits:* Night fishing £65, available from club chairman. Application forms in local tackle shops. *Charges:* Senior season £45, Junior £10. Senior weekly £20, Senior day £7, Junior daily £4, OAP/Disabled £28, Under 12 season £5. Night fishing £65 in addition to Senior season ticket only. *Season:* Open all year. *Methods:* No Carp in keepnets. Antiseptic dip tanks to be used at this venue. Micro barbs are permitted.

TAUNTON

Follyfoot Farm
Contact: Rupert Preston, Follyfoot Farm, North Pertherton. *Sat Nav:* TA6 6NW. *Mobile:* 07748 400904. *Water:* Three acre Carp lake. *Species:* Mirror, Koi and Common to 30lb. *Permits:* Tickets to be acquired at shop or if closed ring Rupert on 07748 400904. *Charges:* £10 per day. £20 for 24 hours. *Season:* Open all year dawn to dusk. Night fishing by prior arrangement only. *Methods:* No keepnets, barbless

hooks only, no dogs or radios. Full rules at the fishery. Only unhooking mats and landing nets supplied by the fishery to be used.

HBS Fisheries &

Contact: Richard Bult, Rydon, West Newton, Bridgwater. *Tel:* 01823 412389. *Mobile:* 07966 239436. *Water:* Specimen Lake - 2.5 acres with varying depths and lots of features. Stocked with 50 fish between 12lbs and 30lbs. Match Lake - Half an acre with depths to 10ft stocked with Rudd, Roach, Tench, Bream and Carp to 10lbs. *Species:* Carp, Tench, Roach, Rudd, Bream, Perch. *Charges:* Specimen lake annual ticket is £275 (Day & Night fishing). Match Lake annual tickets are £50 per year. (Day and Night Fishing). *Season:* No Closed Season. *Methods:* Full list of rules and regulations available on request. Both lakes have level access to swims and parking. Please telephone for further information regarding access for disabled persons.

Ridge Farm Fisheries

Contact: Janet and Ivan Sharland, Ridge Farm, Bathealton, Taunton. *Sat Nav:* TA4 2AQ. *Tel:* 01984 623319. *Water* One 0.5 acre lake. One 0.75 acre lake. *Species:* Carp 17lb and over, Ghost Common and Mirror, Bream 4lb, Golden Tench. *Charges:* £6 per day. *Season:* All year except Xmas Day. *Methods:* No keepnets and barbless hooks only. Bales only on hook but not as groundbait.

Taunton Angling Association (Bridgwater & Taunton Canal)

Contact: Kieran Granville. *Mobile:* 07712 867773. *Water:* Approx. 6 miles. (See also entries under Taunton and Bridgwater Canal & Stillwater Coarse). *Species:* Carp 20lb, Roach and Rudd 2lb, Perch 5lb, Tench 7lb, Pike 25lb. *Permits:* Available in all local tackle shops. *Charges:* Senior season £45, Junior £10. Senior weekly £20, Senior day £7, Junior daily £4, OAP/Disabled £28, Under 12 season £5. Night fishing £65 in addition to Senior season ticket only. *Season:* No closed season. *Methods:* All gates must be closed, no dogs, all juniors (under 12's) must be accompanied by an adult. Micro barbs are permitted.

Taunton Angling Association (Maunsel Ponds)

Contact: Kieran Granville. *Mobile:* 07712 867773. *Water:* Maunsel Ponds (three ponds). See also entries under River & Canal Fishing. *Species:* Carp 27.5lb, Tench 9lb, Roach 2lb, Bream 12lb, Crucians 1.5lb and Perch 5lb. *Permits:* Night fishing £65 available from club chairman. Application forms in tackle shops. *Charges:* Senior season £45, Junior £10. Senior weekly £20, Senior day £7, Junior daily £4, OAP/Disabled £28, Under 12 season £5. Night fishing £65 in addition to Senior season ticket only. *Season:* Open all year. *Methods:* No Carp in keepnets. Please use car park. Micro barbs are permitted.

Taunton Angling Association (Thurlbear Pond)

Contact: Kieran Granville. *Mobile:* 07712 867773. *Water:* Near Netherclay at Taunton. 1 acre. *Species:* Carp 16lb, Roach 1 - 1.5lb, Orfe 3lb. Bream 7lb, Perch 2-3lb. *Permits:* Available in local tackle shops. *Charges:* Senior season £45,

Junior £10. Senior weekly £20, Senior day £7, Junior daily £4, OAP/Disabled £28, Under 12 season £5. Night fishing £65 in addition to Senior season ticket only. *Season:* All year. *Methods:* All Taunton Angling Association rules apply. All gates must be kept closed. Anglers park in area provided only.

WEDMORE

Lands End Farm Fishery &

Contact: Michael Duckett, Heath House, Wedmore. *Sat Nav:* BS28 4UQ. *Tel:* 07977 545882. *Water:* Tealham - 2.25 acre 24 peg match lake. Johns Walter - 2 acre, 30 peg match lake. Tadham - specimen lake 1.75 acres 16 peg. Sidney's - match lake, 2 acres 24 peg open to general public. *Species:* Carp to 27lb (Common, Mirror, Ghost) Grass Carp to 18.5lb, Bream to 8lb, Tench to 7lb 4oz and Roach 2lb, Rudd, Chub, Ide, Perch, Barbel, Golden Orfe to 4lb and F1's. *Permits:* From office on site. *Charges:* £7/day. After 4pm summer nights £5. £5 Concessions /OAP/Junior/Disabled. *Season:* Open all year. 7am to dusk in the summer. *Methods:* Barbless hooks only, no keepnets, no dog biscuits, no bread, boilies or nuts. Boilies allowed only on specimen lake.

Velocity Angling Complex &

Contact: Phil Chambers, Blakeway Road, Wedmore. *Sat Nav:* BS28 4HB. *Mobile:* 07767 794096. *Water:* Over 30 acres, Silverwood Lake 22 acres, Oakdene Lake 5 acre, Pearl Pool 0.6 acres. *Species:* Silverwood Lake - Carp to 30lb, Pike to 20lb. Oakdene Lake - Carp to 20lb, Bream and Tench - 10lb, Pike to 20lb, Rudd and Roach. Pearl Pool - Carp, Tench, Rudd and Roach. *Permits:* Silverwood Lake Gold Syndicate only. Oakdene Lake Bronze Syndicate only. Pearl Pool - Syndicate only. *Charges:* Contact Phil for full rules and booking information. *Season:* Please contact Phil. *Methods:* No live bait. No barbless hooks. Full fishery rules on site.

WESTHAY

Avalon Fisheries

Contact: Vic Bush or Leigh Nutland. *Sat Nav:* BA6 9TT. *Mobile:* 07855 825059. *Water:* Moors Match Lake: 6 acres, 48 pegs. Heath Lake: 22 pegs of which 10 are available for night fishing. *Species:* Carp to mid 20's, Tench 8.5lb, Bream 9lb 2oz, Perch 3lb, Roach, Rudd. *Permits:* Site office and

First ever fish - a Rainbow Trout for Stuart Gooding. Beginners Fly Fishing Course at Wimbleball May 2013 Pic - John Dawson

on the bank. Mobile phone 07855 825059. *Charges:* Moors Match Lake: Adult 1 rod £7. 2 rods £9. Evening ticket (after 4.30) 1 rod £4. 2 rods £6. Junior, OAP, Concessions: 1 rod £4. 2 rods £6. Evening: 1 rod £3. 2 rods £5. Heath Specimen Lake: Adult day 2 rods £10. 24 hour ticket £20. *Season:* No closed season - Open dawn to dusk. *Methods:* Moors Lake: No cat or dog meat. No boilies, bloodworm or joker. Coarse feed pellets only allowed. Heath Lake: Boilies are allowed. Trout and Halibut pellets as hookbait only. Please check rules before fishing.

WINTERBOURNE

Winterbourne Duck Pond
Contact: Winterbourne Parish Council. *Tel:* 01454 776922. *Water:* Half acre lake at Winterbourne. *Species:* Carp. *Charges:* No charge for fishing. *Season:* All year. *Methods:* No cereal groundbaits. No keepnets. Please return any fish caught unharmed back to lake.

YEOVIL

The Old Mill Fishery
Contact: Paul Newman, Tucking Mill Farm, Stoford, Yeovil. *Sat Nav:* BA22 9TX. *Mobile:* 07791 037091. *Water:* Four 1.5 acre lakes plus fishing on a tributary of the River Yeo and a canal. *Species:* 21 different species of coarse fish. River contains Roach, Dace, Chub and Barbel. Well stocked lakes with Carp to 25lb, Perch 3lb, Barbel 8lb, Bream 4lb. *Permits:* On the bank. *Charges:* Permit for lakes and river £6/day (£4 under 16yrs and OAP). £3 evening ticket 4pm onwards in summer. Club bookings taken. *Season:* Open all year 6.30am to dusk. Night fishing by arrangement. *Methods:* Barbless hooks only. Keepnets allowed, but no Carp to be retained in keepnets.

Stillwater Trout

BRIDGWATER

Burton Springs Fishery (Trout Lake)
Contact: Adam Hilling, Lawson Farm, Burton, Nr Stogursey, Bridgwater. *Sat Nav:* TA5 1QB. *Tel:* 01278 732135. *Mobile:* 07838 152968. *Water:* Approx. 2 acre lake. *Species:* Brown, Rainbow, Tiger & Blue Trout. *Permits:* Self service at fishing lodge/on bank. *Charges:* 4-fish ticket £26, 2-fish/6hr £20, sporting ticket £15. Please read rules in Lodge. *Season:* Open all year, dawn to dusk, please ring for times. *Methods:* Fly only. Barbless hooks only, only Rainbow Trout may be taken.

Hawkridge Reservoir
Contact: Wessex Water. *Sat Nav:* TA5 1AL. *Tel:* 0845 600 4 600. *Water:* 32 acre reservoir. *Species:* Brown and Rainbow Trout. *Permits:* Gary Howe (Ranger) Tel: 01278 671840. *Charges:* Day Ticket £20 (5 fish limit); Concession Day £17(5 fish limit); Evening ticket £12 (2 fish limit, no concessions); Days, book of 6 tickets £100; Concessions book of six tickets £85; Season Ticket £320 (4 fish limit) 100 fish limit, only 4 visit per week allowed; Boats £15 day, £10 evening. *Season:* Open 1st March - 6 October, 2013.

BRISTOL

Avon Fly Fishers Club
Contact: Bill Pugh, Bill Pugh Pets & Fishing, 410 Wells Road, Red Lion Hill, Knowle. *Tel:* 0117 9770280. *Water:* Fishing competitions and social evenings. *Permits:* New members welcome.

Blagdon Lake &
Contact: Bristol Water Fisheries, Woodford Lodge, Chew Stoke, Nr Bristol. *Sat Nav:* BS40 7UD. *Tel:* 01275 332339. *Water:* 440 acre lake at Blagdon near Bristol. 20 rowing boats for hire. *Species:* Rainbow Trout, best 16lb 4oz. Brown Trout, best 10lb 4oz. *Permits:* Woodford Lodge, Chew Valley Lake and Blagdon Lodge. *Charges:* Day, evening, season and boat tickets available. Concessions for OAP, junior etc. Contact for current prices. *Season:* Mid March to 30 November. *Methods:* Fly fishing only. Fishing for Pike by any method is not allowed.

Bristol Reservoir Flyfishers Association &
Contact: Martin Cottis (Sec.), 67 Four Acre Road, Downend, Bristol. *Tel:* 0117 9140157. *Mobile:* 07747 843548. *Water:* Fishing on Bristol Waterworks reservoirs. Blagdon, Chew Valley and Barrows. Competitions organised from bank and boat. Tuition offered. Full winter programme of activities including: tackle auctions, fly tying sessions, beginners and improvers casting sessions, guest speakers and quiz nights. *Species:* Rainbow and Brown Trout, fly fishing for Pike. *Permits:* Day tickets direct from Bristol Water. Club does not sell day tickets. *Charges:* £5 joining fee. Annual membership £10 full members, £5 pensioners and registered disabled,

Fishing in beautiful surroundings

STILLWATER TROUT

joining fee £1 juniors - annual membership fee juniors free. *Season:* End March to end of November (extension of season on banks and at Barrow Tanks). *Methods:* Fly fishing only.

Cameley Lakes

Contact: J. Harris, Hillcrest Farm, Cameley, Temple Cloud. *Sat Nav:* BS39 5AQ. *Tel:* 01761 452423. *Water:* One 2.5 acre lake and three 1 acre lakes. *Species:* Rainbow Trout, Brown Trout 1lb - 5lb. *Permits:* From car park. *Charges:* £30 Day ticket 4 fish. £25 half day 2 fish. *Season:* Open all year - 8am till sundown. *Methods:* Fly fishing only. Hooks no larger than 1 inch.

Chew Valley Lake &

Contact: Bristol Water Fisheries, Woodford Lodge, Chew Stoke, Nr. Bristol. *Sat Nav:* BS40 8XH. *Tel:* 01275 332339. *Water:* 1200 Acre lake. 32 motor boats for hire. Special boat available for disabled anglers. *Species:* Rainbow Trout, best 14lb 9oz, Brown Trout best 17lb. Pike to over 40lbs. *Permits:* Woodford Lodge, Chew Lake. *Charges:* Day, evening, boat, afternoon, evening and season permits available. Contact for current prices. *Season:* Mid March - 30 November. *Methods:* Fly fishing only. Pike fishing in spring and autumn only.

Jacklands Fishing Lakes

Contact: Caroline Eastwood, Jacklands Bridge, Tickenham, Nailsea. *Sat Nav:* BS21 6SG. *Tel:* 01275 810697. *Mobile:* 07767 255025. *Water:* 1.5 and 1 acre lakes. *Species:* Rainbow Trout 2-3lb and coarse fish. *Permits:* Available

from Farm shop. *Charges:* Day permit £6 plus £6 per kilo or £16 for 2 fish ticket rising to £26 for 5 fish ticket. *Season:* Open all year Tuesday - Sunday plus Bank Holidays 8am to dusk. *Methods:* Trout - fly only. Coarse - barbless hooks.

Knowle Angling Association (Trout Lakes)

Contact: Keith Caddick, 41 Eastwood Crescent, Brislington, Bristol. *Tel:* 01179 857974. *Mobile:* 0794 634 7581. *Water:* 5 lakes - Publow, Taylors Farm, Clutton, Broadoak Farm and Acker Pool. Plus fishing at Chew Magna reservoir, (also see listing in River Fishing, Chew). *Species:* Rainbow and Brown Trout up to 8lb. Carp up to 18lbs. *Permits:* For guests of members only from Keith Caddick. *Charges:* Annual membership £125. Over 65 £100. Juniors £27. All new members pay extra £5 entrance fee. *Season:* Chew Magna Reservoir open all year for Rainbows. Brown Trout from 1 April to 15 October. Lakes open all year. *Methods:* Fly only on lakes and upper Chew.

Litton Lakes

Contact: Bristol Water Fisheries, Woodford Lodge, Chew Stoke, Nr. Bristol. *Sat Nav:* BA3 4PW. *Tel:* 01275 332339. *Water:* 7 acre and 11 acre lakes at Coley, Nr Chewton Mendip. One rowing boat on each lake. *Species:* Brown & Rainbow Trout. *Permits:* Woodford Lodge, Chew Valley Lake. *Charges:* Booking gives exclusive use of both lakes. Corporate packages and tuition available. Contact for current pricing. *Season:* Open all year. *Methods:* Fly fishing only.

STILLWATER TROUT

The Barrows

Contact: Bristol Water Fisheries, Woodford Lodge, Chew Stoke, Nr Bristol. *Tel:* 01275 332339. *Water:* Three lakes of 25 acres (No. 1) 40 acres (No. 2) 60 acres (No.3) at Barrow Gurney, Nr. Bristol. Arguably the best bank fishing of all the Bristol Water Fisheries. *Species:* Rainbow Trout, best 10lb. Brown Trout, best 9lb 1oz. *Permits:* Self service kiosk at the fishery car park. *Charges:* Day, evening and season permits available. Contact for current pricing. *Season:* March 1st - November 30th. *Methods:* Fly fishing only.

DULVERTON

Exe Valley Fishery

Contact: Nick Hart, Exebridge, Dulverton. *Sat Nav:* TA22 9AY. *Tel:* 01398 323008. *Water:* 3 Lakes fly totalling 7 acres plus half mile River Exe. *Species:* Lake - Rainbow Trout (record 19lb 9oz). River - Brown Trout, Grayling and Salmon. *Charges:* Rod hire £10. 2 fish £20. 3 fish £23. 4 fish £25. 5 fish £27. River - £15 Trout and Grayling, £30 Salmon. *Season:* Lake open all year. River 15 March to 30 Sept. *Methods:* Lake fly only. Any method lake on site. River fly only, barbless hooks, catch and release.

Luckyard Farm

Contact: Carlton Stephens, Luckyard Farm, Wheddon Cross, Exmoor. *Sat Nav:* TA24 7HF. *Tel:* 01643 851220. *Mobile:* 07969 171415. *Water:* One 0.5 acre spring fed lake. *Species:* Rainbow Trout. *Charges:* Limited day tickets, please phone before travelling. *Season:* All year.

Wimbleball &

Contact: South West Lakes Trust, Angling & Watersports Centre, Brompton Regis, Dulverton. *Sat Nav:* TA22 9NU. *Tel:* 01398 371460. *Water:* Reservoir 374 acres. *Species:* Rainbow Trout fishery. Boats available including a Wheelyboat. To guarantee boats please book at least 24hrs in advance via the centre. Rod average 2012: 3.7 fish per rod per day. Fishery record 12lb 11oz. *Permits:* Self service at Hill Barn Farm, Wimbleball or online from our website. Fishing is also available via the Westcountry Rivers Trust Passport Scheme, Tel: 01579 372140. *Charges:* Full day £20, Concession £17, Evening £16. Catch and release Tickets £13. Child £6. Boats £15 per day. Season permits also available from Summerlands Tackle (01237 471291). *Season:* 15 March - 31 October 2013. *Methods:* Catch and release available (barbless hooks must be used), fly fishing only.

Wimbleball Fly Fishing Club

Contact: Dave Ridgway, 12 Gaunts Road, Pawlett, Bridgwater. *Tel:* 01278 685631. *Water:* Regular fishing days, bank and boat. Fishing Wimbleball and other stillwaters. Tuition can be arranged for juniors. *Permits:* All details available from Wimbleball Fishing Lodge. Available on site. *Charges:* Club membership prices: Adult £9.50, husband & wife £14, senior (over 60) £7.50, disabled £7.50, family £16, junior (up to 16) £5.

FROME

St. Algars Farm Lake

Contact: Angus Mackintosh, St. Algar's Farm, West Woodlands, Frome. *Sat Nav:* BA11 5ER. *Tel:* 01985 844233. *Water:* Two acre lake. *Species:* Rainbow Trout. *Charges:* 4 fish limit £20 (April and Oct), £16 (April - Oct). 2 fish limit £15 (April and Oct), £12 (April - Oct). *Season:* 1st April - 31 October. *Methods:* Normal rules for fly fishing.

TAUNTON

Hawkridge Fly Fishing Club

Contact: Bob Palmer, 13 Meadow Gardens, Stogursey, Bridgwater. *Tel:* 01278 734665. *Mobile:* 07855 580105. *Water:* Primarily fishing on Hawkridge Reservoir. Monthly competitions in season. Club meetings after matches normally 1st Sunday of the month. *Species:* Rainbow and Brown Trout. Blues, Tigers and Golden Trout. *Permits:* From the fishing lodge at Hawkridge Reservoir. *Charges:* £9.50 Adult. Concession £6.50. Juniors £6.50. *Season:* New fly fishermen welcome, young and old. *Methods:* Fly fishing only. Boats available.

Otterhead Lakes

Contact: John Connolly, 35 Manor Road, Taunton. *Tel:* 01823 274272. *Water:* Two small lakes on the Blackdown Hills. *Species:* Brown Trout (wild). *Permits:* No day tickets - members only. *Charges:* Full member £90 (plus £90 joining fee). Junior £15. Joint members £120 (plus £120 joining fee). Prices may change for 2014. *Season:* 15 March to 30 Sept. *Methods:* Fly only.

WIVELISCOMBE

Clatworthy Reservoir &

Contact: Wessex Water. *Sat Nav:* TA4 2EJ. *Tel:* 0845 600 4 600. *Water:* 130 acre reservoir. *Species:* Rainbow and Brown Trout. *Permits:* Contact ranger Dave Pursey on 01984 624658. *Charges:* Day Ticket £20. (5 fish limit); Concession Day £17 (5 fish limit); Evening ticket £12 (2 fish limit, no concessions); Days, book of 6 tickets £100. Concessions book of six tickets £85; Season Ticket £320 (4 fish limit) 100 fish limit only 4 visit per week allowed; Boats £15 day, £10 evening. Wheelyboat £10. *Season:* Open 13 March - 6 October, 2013. *Methods:* A Wheelyboat is available for use.

YEOVIL

Sutton Bingham Fly Fishers Association &

Contact: Mr Anthony Griffin (sec), 4 Drakes Meadow, East Coker, Yeovil. *Tel:* 01935 862683. *Water:* Hold regular competitions throughout the season. For members only. Tuition available. Fly tying classes held during the close season. *Species:* Brown Trout to 6lb, Rainbows to 9lb. *Permits:* Day tickets on site. *Charges:* New members always welcome. Adult and junior £5 per year. *Season:* Mid March to end September. *Methods:* Disabled facilities.

Where to Stay in Somerset

Sally Pizii giving fly casting instruction

Sutton Bingham Reservoir &

Contact: Wessex Water. *Sat Nav:* BA22 9QH. *Tel:* 0845 600 4 600. *Water:* 142 acre reservoir. *Species:* Rainbow and Brown Trout. *Permits:* Contact ranger Ivan Tinsley on 01935 872389. Advisable to book boats in advance. *Charges:* Day Ticket £20(5 fish limit); Concession Day £17 (5 fish limit); Evening ticket £12 (2 fish limit, no concessions); Days, book of 6 tickets £100; Concessions book of six tickets £85; Season Ticket £320 (4 fish limit) 100 fish limit, only 4 visit per week allowed; Boats £15 day, £10 evening. Wheelyboat £10. *Season:* Open 13 March - 6 October, 2013. *Methods:* A Wheely boat is available for use.

The Wheelyboat Trust

The Wheelyboat Trust is a small national charity dedicated to providing disabled people with hassle-free and independent access to waterborne activities such as angling, pleasure boating and nature watching. Formed in 1985 as The Handicapped Anglers Trust, it has so far supplied more than 150 specially designed wheelchair accessible Wheelyboats to fisheries, water parks and other venues open to the public all over the UK.

There are currently 16 Wheelyboats available for disabled anglers to use in the South West providing access to game and coarse fishing, nature watching and pleasure boating. Wheelyboats are self-operated and can be helmed by the disabled angler. They all have bow doors that lower to provide roll on, roll off wheelchair access either from the bank or slipway. They drift well, especially with a drogue, or can be fished at anchor. Booking is essential and it is recommended 24 hours notice is given. Lifejackets must be worn and are provided free of charge by the fishery.

New Wheelyboats are being launched all the time. For the latest list of all UK venues and for more information on the work of the Trust, visit the website or contact the Director. The Wheelyboat Trust is a registered charity and relies upon the generosity of charitable organisations, companies and individuals to enable it to continue providing this important service on behalf of disabled people. Donations can be made via the Trust's website: **www.wheelyboats.org**

The Wheelyboat Trust. Reg charity 292216
Andy Beadsley, Director. Tel: 01798 342222,
e-mail wheelyboattrust@btconnect.com
Rex Harpham, SW Regional Coordinator
Tel: 01822 615953
e-mail rex.harpham@gmail.com

Westcountry Wheelyboat Venues

Avon			
Bristol Sailability - Bristol Docks	Pleasure boating	0117 968 8244	www.bristolsailability.org.uk
Chew Valley Lake - Chew Stoke	Trout & pike fishing	01275 332339	www.bristolwater.co.uk
Cornwall			
Siblyback Lake - Liskeard	Trout fishing, pleasure boating	01579 346522	www.swlakestrust.org.uk
Stithians Reservoir - Redruth	Trout fishing, pleasure boating	01209 860301	www.swlakestrust.org.uk
Tamar Lakes - Bude	Coarse fishing, pleasure boating	01288 321712	www.swlakestrust.org.uk
Devon			
Burrator Reservoir - Dartmoor	Trout fishing	01822 855700	www.swlakestrust.org.uk
Haven Banks OEC - Exeter	Pleasure boating	01392 434668	www.haven-banks.co.uk
Kennick Reservoir - Bovey Tracey	Trout fishing	01647 277587	www.swlakestrust.org.uk
Roadford Lake - Okehampton	Trout fishing, pleasure boating	01409 211507	www.swlakestrust.org.uk
Wistlandpound Reservoir - Kentisbury	Trout fishing, pleasure boating	01598 763221	www.calvert-trust.org.uk
Dorset			
River Frome - Wareham	Pleasure boating	01929 550688	www.warehamboathire.co.uk
River Stour - Christchurch Quay	Pleasure boating	07813 278698	
Somerset			
Clatworthy Reservoir - Taunton	Trout fishing	01984 624658	www.wessexwater.co.uk
Maunsel Lock Canal Centre - Bridgwater	Pleasure boating	01278 663160	www.maunsellock.co.uk
Sutton Bingham Reservoir - Yeovil	Trout fishing, pleasure boating	01935 872389	www.wessexwater.co.uk
Wimbleball Lake - Brompton Regis	Trout fishing, pleasure boating	01398 371460	www.swlakestrust.org.uk

In November 2009 Lt. Will Davies wrote "A Letter From Helmand" to Trout & Salmon magazine, wonderfully articulating that thoughts of days on the river bank were a great mental restorer in the somewhat fraught circumstances he was dealing with.

Christopher Robinson replied to the Editor that Will's letter struck many a chord. He had a wonderful 11 years soldiering, always taking his fishing rod to far flung places. His son was Afghanistan-bound soon and is also a passionate fisherman. Time spent on a riverbank is indeed a huge healer. He ended by saying that he had asked Will to fish with him next summer and maybe other readers might ask returning personnel to join them for a days fishing?

As a result of these letters it became clear that there was a great deal of support for the concept of offering restorative time on the riverbank to Service personnel returning from Operational Duty. Bill Howell wrote to Christopher Robinson and Andrew Flitcroft, Editor of Trout and Salmon, suggesting the concept of Fishing for Forces.

Our aim is to provide a day's fishing for those returning from Operational Duty, whether it's part of a group day out at a local fishery or a day out with a local fisherman, helping ease their path back into a normal life, with lifetime support should they take up the sport.

All service men and women from the Navy, Army or Air Force who have been affected by any conflict, wherever and whenever are eligible.

We are always grateful for any offers to provide fishing for service men and women, if you think you can donate in any way please get in touch.

Bill Howell. Tel: 0207 385 2135 / 07850 373 760 Email: Bill@fishingforforces.org

www.fishingforforces.org

Fishing is not on the top of the list of things to do when you have been through the trauma of breast cancer, and trying to get your life back together again. But as the members of an organisation called Fishing For Life have discovered it is exactly what this group has helped them to do.

SWFFL provides a network of friends and support to help breast cancer patients with 'moving on' and coping with difficult times, as well as the ability to share information and experiences with people who can empathise. Thanks to the generosity of various waters and all the volunteers these days are free for the members to attend and also provide them with a social and supportive network.

Fishing For Life is not all about fishing but ME time and a soul finding time in beautiful locations, back with nature by still waters. If fishing is not really your idea of fun there is always a cup of coffee and plenty of chat and time for a walk. We always encourage friends and family to support, do their own thing while the members are having fishing instruction and then join in the refreshments afterwards.

Since founding in 2008 on Wimbleball we have grown to 6 groups, Kennick in Devon, Siblyback in Cornwall, Blagdon in Bristol and the Pennines, in Bolton. Group number 6 was launched in June 2013 in Dorset. As we have grown and moved from the south west we call the other groups Fishing For Life. In time we hope to have groups all over England so anyone who has suffered or is living with breast cancer can enjoy what our unique groups have to offer support, friendship, Me time, caring volunteers who listen and lots of fun and laughter!

In June 2013 we were thrilled to be awarded The Queens Award for Voluntary Service.

For more information ring Gillian on 01398 371244 or email: holworthyfarm@aol.com

www.southwestfishingforlife.org.uk

Yes, a woman can fly fish!

Sally Pizii

"Excuse me for saying so, my dear, but you do cast extremely well". This comment was made to me a few years ago whilst I was out fishing, what a lovely compliment I thought, but the more I thought about it, the more I wondered, was I not expected, as a woman, to cast so well?

Then there was the time when a fishery manager asked me what line I was using, I explained and asked why he wanted to know. "Ah well", he said "I thought you were using a shooting head, as you were getting the line out a good distance." No, I replied, it's just my skill! Am I not supposed to be able to put out a good length of line? Later I moved down the bank next to two young men. As I cast my fly to a rising trout, one of them turned and said, "I see you have had some practice." By this time I was feeling furious, yes I have had some practice, I regularly practice casting in my back garden. Golfers practice, tennis players practice, I practice. I want to be good and get better, is that so strange?

I know that not many women fly fish, but those that do, usually turn out to be pretty good. You see very few women 'false casting' more than two or three times when they cast a fly. Now watch the men, 4,5,6 false casts, some of you really like to keep your arm well exercised! Casting is all about making the rod work, no wonder you get tired so easily! Give it a break, accept that woman can fish and cast successfully, it is all about technique not brawn - we women take our fishing seriously. When we are at the water's edge by all means offer a helping hand or advice, we all need to learn, but don't patronise us.

Recently, whilst fishing a boat qualifier competition at a reservoir, I caught a very large trout. As the boats were landing the ranger asked if any large fish had been caught so he could take a photograph. No! was the reply in unison, so he left. Did anyone ask me? was I not expected to catch anything other than the usual stockie? So when I weighed in my four fish at 9lb 9ozs and then said "hang on, here is my fifth fish" and produced a 10lb 12oz rainbow everyone stared

Sally with 'that' rainbow!

in disbelief. I just laughed, their faces! Needless to say, I won the qualifier.

My life has taken many strange twists and turns. After I had given up my work as an infant teacher, I went on to train as a fly fishing coach. I took my GAIA award (formally called STANIC) and then went on to train as a Level 2 coach. From there I trained to become a Coach Educator so that I could deliver the coaching courses and train new coaches. They are often surprised to find that they are being trained by a woman, but once they get over it, they are fine.

In my free time, I volunteer with South West Fishing for Life as a coach and help ladies who have had breast cancer learn to fly fish. It is such good exercise for them and the wonderful surroundings soothe away their concerns and worries, if only for a couple of hours. This led to my husband and I being asked to represent the organisation we work with, at a garden party at Buckingham Palace. What an honour and what fun. It was also a wonderful excuse to buy a new dress - with fish on, well, what did you expect?

My husband and I run fly fishing courses for the over 50's, through Age UK Somerset. What fun and what a laugh, the participants are lovely and come from all walks of life. They appreciate the gentle approach that a woman can give to a coaching session and the secret knowledge that she imparts, as to how one can outwit a fish! As one of the participants said, "there was cheerful instruction that made us as keen as mustard, great fun."

The last decade has been a wonderful experience, I have met some fantastic people, fished at some delightful fisheries and learnt so much from all those who are involved in angling. Yes, women can fly fish and really enjoy themselves at the same time!

WILTSHIRE
and Gloucestershire

 Find us on
Facebook

 @gethookedguide

RIVER FISHING

STILLWATER COARSE

STILLWATER TROUT

WHERE TO STAY

WILTSHIRE

Map No	Advertiser	Sat Nav	Phone	Advert Page
	Game Fishing			
145	Avon Springs Fishing Lakes	SP4 8HH	019806 53557 or 07774 801401	155
146	Lechlade & Bushyleaze Trout Fisheries (Gloucs)	6L7 3QQ	01367 253266	161
	Coarse Fishing			
147	Amalgamated Fisheries Ltd (Coarse & Game)		0117 9603378	149
148	Blackland Lakes Holiday Centre	SN11 0NQ	01249 810943	150
149	Cuckoo's Rest Fishery	BA13 4EL	01373 826792 or 07850 431472	154
150	Lakeside Rendezvous	SN10 2LX	01380 725447	152
151	Tucking Mill	BA2 7DB	0845 600 4 600	139
152	Waldens Farm Fishery	SP5 3RW	01722 710480 or 07766 451173	153

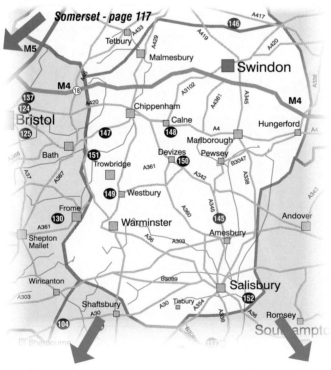

Please note sat nav postcodes, where supplied, may not be totally accurate.

Only advertisers with fishing are located on this map. Their listings within this guide are highlighted in blue.

Somerset - page 117

Dorset - page 88

Hampshire - page 106

ADVERTISER LOCATION MAP

Wiltshire River Fishing

AVON HAMPSHIRE
For detailed description of the Avon, see under Hampshire river fishing.

Calne Angling Association
Contact: Miss J M Knowler, 123a London Road, Calne. *Tel:* 01249 812003. *Water:* River Avon, River Marden. *Species:* Barbel to 8lb, Pike to 8lb, Carp to 10lb, Bream to 6lb, Rudd to 8oz, Roach to 2.5lb. *Permits:* T.K.Tackle. *Charges:* Please enquire at T.K.Tackle. *Season:* River: June - March. *Methods:* No restrictions.

Salisbury and District Angling Club
Contact: Andrea Topintzis, The Cartshed, New Bottom Road, Stratford-Sub-Castle, Salisbury. *Tel:* 01722 321164. *Water:* Several Stretches on River Avon at Little Durnford (premium Trout fishery & Grayling), Amesbury, Ratfyn Farm & Countess Water. Also fishing on Dorset Stour (mixed fishery), River Wylye (premium Trout & Grayling), Nadder (Trout & Coarse), Bourne & Ratfyn Lake at Amesbury. Premier stocked chalkstream fishing. *Species:* All species Coarse and Game. Roach to 3lbs, Chub to 6lbs plus, Barbel to 10lbs plus, Pike to 20lbs plus. Wild Trout, Grayling plus migratory Trout and Salmon. *Permits:* Enquire via Secretary at office@salisburydistrictac.co.uk or club address. Day tickets for certain fisheries on Avon and Nadder around Salisbury and Amesbury from Eadies Sports and Fishing Tackle, Catherine Street, Salisbury. Tel: 01722 328535. Hills Cycles, 2 Smithfield St., Amesbury, Tel: 01980 622705. *Charges:* Premium game membership has waiting list which is now open. Price around £195 for 2013. Coarse, mixed non premium membership open. Price around £94 for 2013. *Season:* Lakes: 1 June - 31 March. Rivers: Coarse 16 June - 14 March. Trout: 1 April - 15 October. Salmon: 1 February - 31 August. *Methods:* As per rules for each fishery.

Services Dry Fly Fishing Association
Contact: Major (Retd) CD Taylor - Hon Secretary, c/o G2 Sy, HQ 43 (Wessex) Brigade, Jellalabad Barracks, Tidworth. *Tel:* 01980 656648. *Mobile:* 07850 790066. *Water:* 7 miles on River Avon from Bulford upstream to Fifield. *Species:* Brown Trout & Grayling. *Permits:* Fishing Restricted to Serving & Retired members of the Armed Forces and MOD civilians. Membership details from Secretary. *Charges:* On application. *Season:* 24 April - 14 October. Grayling until 31st December. *Methods:* Only upstream fishing permitted, dry fly exclusively during May & dry fly/nymph thereafter.

Wroughton Angling Club
Contact: Phil Sloan, 35 Maunsell Way, Wroughton, Swindon. *Tel:* 01793 813980. *Mobile:* 07747 641632. *Water:* 1.25 miles Rivers Avon and Marden at Chippenham, Reservoir at Wroughton, plus 1 mile at Christian Malford. *Species:* (weights are from lake 2008 season) Roach, Perch 3lb, Bream, Pike, Barbel 12lb 4oz, Chub, Carp 30lb, Tench 12lb Crucian 2.7lb. *Permits:* Contact Phil Sloan on details above. *Charges:* £32 per year. Juniors free until age of 12. £15 OAP and Conc. Day tickets through Andrew Sloan. *Season:* Closed mid March. Re-opens 1 May. *Methods:* No night fishing. No peanuts, particle baits, dog biscuits or nuts of any description.

AVON WILTSHIRE
See under Bristol Avon.

Avon Springs Fishing Lake (River)
Contact: BJ Bawden, Recreation Road, Durrington, Salisbury. *Tel:* 01980 653557. *Mobile:* 07774 801401. *Water:* 1 mile Wiltshire Avon at Durrington. Two Trout lakes, see entry under Stillwater Trout, Salisbury. *Species:* Brown Trout and Grayling. *Charges:* £60 day ticket. River and Lake ticket £70. *Methods:* Fly only.

Upavon Farm
Contact: Peter C Prince, No 3, The Old Tractor Yard, Rushall, Near Pewsey. *Sat Nav:* SN9 6EN. *Tel:* 01980 630008. *Mobile:* 07770 922544. *Water:* 0.75 miles on Hampshire Avon in Wiltshire. *Species:* Brown Trout, both stocked and Wild, up to 3lb average 1.5lb. Wild Grayling to 2lb average 1lb. *Permits:* Day, Season Permits. *Charges:* Trout day ticket 15 April - 15 May £50, 15 May - 30 June £75, 30 June - 30 September £50. Grayling day rate £30. £500 for a season. *Season:* Brown Trout commences 15 April, ends 30 September. Grayling fishing thereafter. *Methods:* Catch and release, barbless hooks excepting annual season ticket holders.

Wiltshire Fishery Association
Contact: Bryan Gordon-Smith. *Water:* An association of riparian owners and fishing club representatives. The association covers the River Avon catchment above Salisbury and its tributaries.

BRISTOL AVON
Malmesbury to Chippenham

Coarse fisheries predominate in this section, although Trout are stocked by fishing associations in some areas. Arguably one of the best fisheries in the country, this section contains a wide range of specimen fish. Local records include: Roach 3lb 2oz, Perch 3lb 3oz, Tench 8lb 5 1/2oz, Bream 8lb 8oz, Dace 1lb 2oz, Chub 7lb 10oz, Carp 20lb 8 1/4oz and Pike 33lb 3oz. Also many Barbel to 12lb have been reported.

Airsprung Angling Association (Bristol Avon)
Contact: Bill Turner, 124 Langford Rd, Trowbridge. *Tel:* 01225 766219. *Water:* See also entry under Kennet & Avon Canal. Bristol Avon at Bradford on Avon, Pondfields. *Species:* Carp, Pike, Bream, Chub, Roach, Rudd, Dace, Tench, Perch, etc.

RIVER FISHING

Permits: Wiltshire Angling, 01225 763835; West Tackle, Trowbridge, 01225 755472. Trowbridge Road Post Office, Bradford-upon Avon. *Charges:* On application. Full Licence £25/season. *Season:* Subject to normal close season. *Methods:* Details from Association.

Amalgamated Fisheries Ltd
Contact: Mrs P Leonard, 48 Abbots Road, Hanham, Bristol. *Tel:* 01179 603378. *Water:* Approx. 30 miles coarse fishing on Bristol Avon near Malmesbury from Daniels Well to Keynsham. Somerset Rivers & Streams including the Brue. Stillwaters at Lyneham, Calne, Bath and Pawlett near Bridgwater. Trout only water on Cam Brook near Radstock. Please contact the secretary for full details. *Species:* All coarse species. *Charges:* Full membership available from tackle outlets. Full members only may fish at Tockenham Reservoir. Day Permits for all waters are available at Tackle Shops. Adults £45. Adult and child £60. Conc. Senior Citizens and Disabled and Juniors £25. Day Permits. Adults £6. Senior Citizens and Juniors £3. *Methods:* Barbless hooks. No livebaiting.

Avon Angling Club (Bristol Avon)
Contact: R.P. Edwards, 56 Addison Road, Melksham. *Tel:* 01225 705036. *Water:* 4 miles of Bristol Avon. See also entry under Kennet and Avon Canal. *Species:* Roach, Bream, Tench, Chub, Barbel, Perch, Pike, Eels. *Permits:* Wiltshire Angling, Trowbridge. Premier Angling, Chippenham or call 01225 705036. *Charges:* Day ticket £4. Full Licence £15. Junior/OAP Licence £5. *Season:* Current EA Byelaws apply. *Methods:* No blood worm or joker to be used.

Chippenham Angling Club ♿
Contact: Kevin Williams. *Mobile:* 07740 723603. *Water:* 5 miles on River Avon. Carp lakes at Corsham and stillwater coarse at Bromham. *Species:* Barbel 14lb, Chub 5lb, Roach 2.5lb, Bream 10lb, Perch 4lb, Pike 33lb, Tench 9lb, Carp 20lb (all weights approximate). *Permits:* Premier Angling, Chippenham: 01249 659210. *Charges:* Please telephone for prices. *Season:* 16 June - 15 June.

Swindon Isis Angling Club (Bristol Avon)
Contact: Peter Gilbert, Button Mill, Baunton, Cirencester, Gloucestershire. *Mobile:* 07785 542795. *Water:* Two miles of the Bristol Avon at Sutton Benger above Chippenham. See also lake under Stillwater Coarse Swindon. *Species:* Bream 9lb 9oz, Perch 4lb, Tench 9lb, Barbel 15lb, Pike 28lb, Roach 2lb 7oz, Eels to 5lbs and usual species. *Permits:* Tackle shops in Swindon, Cirencester, Chippenham, Cheltenham and Calne. *Charges:* As per lake entry and day tickets available £5. *Season:* From 16 June to 14 March. *Methods:* No bans.

KENNET AND AVON CANAL
There are some 58 kilometres of canal within the Bristol Avon catchment area which averages one metre in depth and thirteen metres in width. The Kennet & Avon Canal joins the River Avon at Bath with the River

Kennet between Reading and Newbury. The canal was opened in 1810 to link the Severn Estuary with the Thames. The canal, now much restored, provides excellent fishing with Carp to 25lb, Tench to 5lb also Roach, Bream, Perch, Rudd, Pike and Gudgeon.

Airsprung Angling Association (Kennet & Avon)
Contact: Bill Turner, 124 Langford Rd, Trowbridge. *Tel:* 01225 766219. *Water:* Two kilometres on Kennet and Avon Canal from Beehive Pub to Avoncliffe Aqueduct at Bradford-on-Avon. Kings Arms Hilperton Road Bridge to Crossguns, Avoncliff. *Species:* Carp, Bream, Chub, Roach, Rudd, Dace, Tench, Perch, etc. *Permits:* Wiltshire Angling, 01225 763835; West Tackle, Trowbridge, 01225 755472. Trowbridge Road Post Office, Bradford-upon Avon. *Charges:* Day ticket £4. Full licence £25. *Season:* Open all year. *Methods:* No night fishing, No fishing on match days in pegged areas. No radios etc. No fishing within 25 metres of locks etc. No bloodworm or joker; be aware of overhead cables.

Avon Angling Club (Kennet and Avon)
Contact: R.P. Edwards, 56 Addison Road, Melksham. *Tel:* 01225 705036. *Water:* 2.5 miles of Kennet and Avon Canal. See also entry under Bristol Avon. *Species:* Bream, Tench, Roach, Carp. *Permits:* Wiltshire Angling, Trowbridge. Premier Angling, Chippenham or call 01225 705036. *Charges:* Day ticket £4. Full licence £15. Junior/OAP licence £5. *Season:* All year.

Devizes A.A. (Kennet & Avon Canal) ♿
Contact: T.W. Fell, 21 Cornwall Crescent, Devizes. *Tel:* 01380 725189. *Water:* 15 miles from Semington to Pewsey, also 6.5 acre lake. *Species:* Carp 15 - 29lb, Roach, Tench, Pike to 26lb, Bream. *Permits:* Local tackle shops in: Devizes - Bernies Bait, Snuff St., Devizes, Wiltshire. Tel: 01380 730712. Wiltshire Angling: 5, Timbrell St., Trowbridge, Wiltshire, Tel: 01225 763835. Melksham - Carp Shack, Enterprise Centre, Trowbridge. Chippenham, Calne, Swindon. Anglers must be in possession of current Environment Agency rod licence. *Charges:* Adult £30 per season. Senior citizen £13. Junior (8-12) £9 or (12-16) £13. Day tickets £4.50 (not sold on the bank). 14 day ticket £9. *Season:* E.A. byelaws apply. *Methods:* Six free of charge pegs suitable for disabled anglers by prison bridge. Must display disabled blue badge and be in possession of E.A. rod licence. Please remember to take litter home.

Marlborough and District A.A
Contact: Chris Potter. *Tel:* 01672 516587. *Mobile:* 07717 803663. *Water:* Kennet & Avon Canal (12 miles approx). Also Heron Lake. *Species:* Roach, Perch, Pike, Tench, Bream, Carp. *Charges:* Full membership £40 plus £5 joining fee, Junior up to 16 £15, OAP £20. *Season:* Open all year. Membership from 1 Jan - 31 Dec. *Methods:* No live baiting. Barbless hooks only on lake.

Pewsey and District Angling Association
Contact: Jim Broomham, 85 Broad Fields, Pewsey. *Tel:* 01672 563690. *Mobile:* 07967 719604. *Water:* 4 Miles

RIVER FISHING

Kennet & Avon canal. Milkhouse Bridge (East) to Lady's Bridge (West). *Species:* Roach, Tench, Carp, Bream, Perch, Pike, Rudd and Chub. *Permits:* The Wharf, Pewsey (Day tickets only). Season tickets from Woottons, 5 North St, Pewsey. *Charges:* Day tickets Senior £5 / Junior/OAP £3. £6 on bank. *Season:* No closed season. *Methods:* Rod and line.

NADDER

The River Nadder rises near Tisbury draining the escarpment of the South Wiltshire Downs and Kimmeridge Clay of the Wardour Vale. The River Wylye joins the Nadder near Wilton before entering the main River Avon at Salisbury.

The Nadder is well known as a mixed fishery of exceptional quality; there is a diverse array of resident species including Chub, Roach, Dace, Bream, Pike, Perch, Brown Trout and Salmon. Much of the fishing is controlled by estates and syndicates although two angling clubs offer some access to the river.

Compton Chamberlayne

Contact: Simon Cooper, Fishing Breaks, The Mill, Heathman Street, Nether Wallop, Stockbridge, Hampshire. *Tel:* 01264 781988. *Water:* Seven beats on part of the Compton Chamberlayne Estate. *Species:* Brown Trout. *Permits:* By

phone or e-mail from Fishing Breaks. *Charges:* April 26th - May 14th £153. May 15th - June 13th £208. June 14th - July 31st £153. August 1st - October 15th £129. *Season:* April - October. *Methods:* Dry fly & Nymph only.

Tisbury Angling Club

Contact: Mr B Broom (membership sec.). *Tel:* 01722 743255. *Water:* 3 miles on River Nadder. 3.5 acre lake and 2.5 acre lake. *Species:* Roach, Chub, Dace, Pike, Bream, Perch, Carp, Brown Trout. *Permits:* £5 per day Guest tickets or contact Mr Alan Bonner 079137 44935. *Charges:* Season: Senior £35, Junior £7.50, OAP £17.50. Day - only available to member and their guests, £8.75 for partners (dawn to dusk): Seniors £5, Juniors £3. New members welcome. *Season:* 16 June to 14 March on river and Wardour Lake. Dinton Lake open all year.

STOUR

See under Dorset, river fishing.

Stourhead (Western) Estate

Contact: Sally Monkhouse, Estate Office Gasper Mill, Stourton, Warminster. *Tel:* 01747 840643. *Water:* 6 ponds and lakes, largest being 1.5 acres, on the headwaters of the Stour. *Species:* Wild Brown Trout. *Permits:* Weekly permit £30. *Charges:* Season permit for fly fishing £100, no day tickets. *Season:* April to October - no time restrictions.

WYLYE

The River Wylye rises near Kingston Deverill and flows off chalk, draining the western reaches of Salisbury Plain. The river confluences with the River Nadder at Wilton near Salisbury, then joins the main River Avon which flows south to Christchurch. This river is best described as a 'classic' chalk stream supporting predominantly Brown Trout; hence most fisheries here are managed for fly fishermen. The fishing is predominantly controlled by local syndicates and estates.

Fisherton De La Mere
Contact: Simon Cooper, Fishing Breaks, The Mill, Heathman Street, Nether Wallop, Stockbridge, Hampshire. *Tel:* 01264 781988. *Water:* One beat on River Wylye. *Species:* Brown Trout. *Permits:* By phone or e-mail from Fishing Breaks. *Charges:* April 17th - May 17th £98. May 18th - June 16th £135. June 17th - October 15th £98. *Season:* April - October. *Methods:* Dry Fly and Nymph only.

Langford Lakes (River Wylye)
Contact: Wiltshire Wildlife Trust, Duck Street, Steeple Langford, Salisbury. *Tel:* 01722 792011. *Water:* Wylye - 0.75 mile. *Species:* Brown Trout, Grayling. *Charges:* £40 Trout, £30 Grayling per rod. *Season:* April 15th - Oct 14th Trout season. Oct 15th - March 14th Grayling season. *Methods:* Full details at Fishery.

Wilton Fly Fishing Club
Contact: Mr Mike Tebbs, Rivendell, Newtown, Heytesbury, Warminster. *Mobile:* 01985 841192. *Water:* Over 7 miles of chalkstream on the River Wylye (including carriers) and 3 miles on River Till. *Species:* Wild Brown Trout, fish of 2-3lb caught every season. New record 2008 7lb 5.5oz. Average 12oz to 1.5lb. Large head of Grayling to over 2lb 12oz. *Permits:* Season membership only via Secretary. *Charges:* Prices on application to secretary. *Season:* Trout 16 April to 15 October. Grayling 16 June to 14 March. *Methods:* Trout: Dry fly and upstream nymph only. Grayling: Dry fly and upstream nymph only in Trout season. Trotting also allowed from 15th October to 14th March. Barbless hooks.

Stillwater Coarse

BRADFORD ON AVON

Rushy Lane Fishery &
Contact: Mike or Val, South Wraxall, Bradford-on-Avon. *Sat Nav:* BA15 2RP. *Tel:* 01249 714558. *Mobile:* 07780 635333. *Water:* 3 lakes one with specimen Carp and two with mixed fish. *Species:* Tench 3.5lb and Roach 1lb. Specimen Lake 5 has Carp to 32lb. No 3 and 4 lakes stocked with Tench to 5lb and Roach to 2lb. *Permits:* By telephone only. *Charges:* On application. *Season:* Open all year. *Methods:* Dawn to

dusk, no night fishing, no nets on all ponds, no boilies, no beans, no nuts, barbless hooks only. Parking near lakes and level peg, so please contact us for further details for suitability for disabled persons.

CALNE

Amalgamated Fisheries Ltd (Sabre Lake)
Contact: Mrs P Leonard, 48 Abbots Road, Hanham, Bristol. *Tel:* 01179 603378. *Water:* 3 acre Sabre Lake at Calne plus various stillwaters at Lyneham, Bath and Pawlett near Bridgwater. *Species:* All coarse species including Carp to 23lb. *Charges:* Adults/Ladies £45. Adult and child £60. Senior Citizen/Disabled and Juniors £25. Day Permits. Adult £6. Senior Citizen/Disabled/Junior £3. Available at all Tackle Outlets. *Season:* Lakes open all year. Shackells Lake closed from May 1st to June 16th. *Methods:* Maximum 2 rods, no metal cans or glass allowed on banks, no freshwater fish to be used as livebait.

Blackland Lakes
Contact: Mr Sam Walden, Blackland Lakes Holiday and Leisure Centre, Stockley Lane, Calne. *Sat Nav:* SN11 0NQ. *Tel:* 01249 810943. *Mobile:* 07974 135825. *Water:* 1 acre and 0.75 acre. *Species:* Carp to 27lb, Tench to 4lb, Roach to 3.5lb, Bream to 11lb, Perch to 3.5lb. *Permits:* Day tickets. *Charges:* Standard Adult £7, Standard Junior (14-16) £6, Standard Junior under 14 £6. Peak adult £10, Peak Junior (14-16) £8, Peak Junior under 8 £6. Extra rod £1 - maximum

2 rods. Night tickets available at same rates. Peak season runs April 1 - Sept 30. *Season:* Open all year. *Methods:* Barbless hooks, no ground bait, no large fish or Bream and Carp in keepnets.

Bowood Lake
Contact: Estate Office, Bowood, Calne. *Sat Nav:* SN11 0LZ. *Tel:* 01249 812102. *Water:* 35 acre lake. *Species:* Coarse. *Permits:* Available from the estate office. Season permits only - waiting list. *Charges:* Prices on application. *Season:* June to March. Dawn to dusk.

CHIPPENHAM

Chippenham Angling Club (Coarse Lake) &
Contact: Kevin Williams. *Mobile:* 07740 723603. *Water:* See entry under Avon. Carp Lake at Corsham also Burbrooks Lake. *Species:* Carp 20lb, Roach 2lb, Perch 3lb, Tench, Rudd. *Permits:* Members only, no day tickets. *Methods:* Barbless hooks only. Only silver fish in keepnets - no Carp. No boilies, nuts or groundbait. No floating baits.

Dodford Lake
Contact: Mr & Mrs Ewart, Dodford Farm, Christian Malford, Chippenham. *Sat Nav:* SN15 4DE. *Tel:* 01249 891606. *Water:* Four acre lake. 44 pegs. *Species:* Carp to 15lb, Roach and Bream. *Permits:* Day tickets can be purchased from the bailiff on the bank, who checks on a regular basis throughout the day. Match booking enquiries and bookings telephone 01249 891606. Matches to last a maximum of 6 hours. Minimum No. of pegs for matches: 10. *Charges:* £6 per day. Concessions £5. Under 11 £4. *Season:* Open all year. *Methods:* Full list of rules at lake. No night fishing.

Ivy House Lakes & Fisheries
Contact: Jo, Ivyhouse Lakes, Grittenham, Chippenham. *Sat Nav:* SN15 4JU. *Tel:* 01666 510368. *Mobile:* 07748 144788. *Water:* 1 Acre and 6 Acre lakes. 2 Canal type sections. *Species:* Carp, Bream, Roach, Tench, Chub, Perch, Crucians, Grass Carp, Trout. *Permits:* On the bank day tickets, no night fishing. *Charges:* Day tickets £7 (1 rod), £8 (2 rods). £4 (1 rod) £5 (2 rods) Ladies, OAP etc. Match booking £5. *Season:* All year. Gates open 6am - closed 1 hour after dusk. *Methods:* Boilies, tiger nuts and all meats banned, ground bait in moderation. No fixed feeders.

Sevington Lakes &
Contact: Fiona and Andrew Butler, Sevington Farm, Sevington, Chippenham. *Sat Nav:* SN14 7LD. *Tel:* 01249 783723. *Mobile:* 07414 728765. *Water:* Natural spring fed lakes approx. 2 acres. Parking next to most swims. Secure parking for night fishing. *Species:* Mirror, Common and Crucian Carp to 42lbs plus Perch, Roach, Tench and Rudd. *Charges:* Day ticket £7 (2 rods) £3 extra rod (3 rods max.). Night fishing £14 (24hrs). All under 16's must be accompanied by responsible adult when night fishing. *Season:* Open all year, night fishing by arrangement only to avoid disappointment. *Methods:* Barbless hooks. No keepnets. No bait boats at busy times.

Not sure who caught this Carp at Blackland Lakes but they both look pretty pleased!

Silverlands Lake
Contact: Mr S & Mrs G King, Wick Farm, Lacock, Chippenham. *Sat Nav:* SN15 2LU. *Tel:* 01249 730887. *Mobile:* 07766 902604. *Water:* One spring fed 3.5 acre lake. *Species:* Carp, Tench, Bream, Pike. *Permits:* Only from the fishery. *Charges:* Day or night permits available. £10 per day. £10 per Night. £15 for 24hr. *Season:* Open all year. *Methods:* No nuts, dogs to be kept on a lead at all times.

DEVIZES

Devizes A.A. (Coarse Lake) &
Contact: T.W. Fell, 21 Cornwall Crescent, Devizes. *Tel:* 01380 725189. *Water:* 6.5 acre Crookwood Lake, well stocked. Major development work will take place September 2013. Please check website for updates. *Permits:* Local tackle shops in: Devizes - Bernies Bait, Snuff St., Devizes, Wiltshire. Tel: 01380 730712. Wiltshire Angling: 5, Timbrell St., Trowbridge, Wiltshire, Tel: 01225 763835. Melksham - Carp Shack, Enterprise Centre, Trowbridge. Chippenham, Calne, Swindon. *Charges:* Please phone for details. All tickets must be purchased before fishing. Adult £5 per day. Junior £2.50 per day. *Season:* All year. *Methods:* Anglers must be in possession of current Environment Agency rod licence. Please remember to take litter home. Please contact in advance if interested in our disabled facilities.

Lakeside Rendezvous
Contact: Phil & Sarah Gleed, Devizes Road, Rowde, Nr. Devizes. *Sat Nav:* SN10 2LX. *Tel:* 01380 725447. *Water:* 2 acre lake. *Species:* Carp - 29lb 4oz, Bream, Roach, Perch, Rudd, Tench. *Charges:* Day tickets not available individually. Hire of whole lake is possible only when no residents and by prior arrangement, can fit up to 20 anglers. - £90 per day. Winter fishing now available from November to end of March. By prior arrangement £10 per day. *Season:* No closed season. *Methods:* Barbless hooks, no nuts. Keepnets permitted in competition only. All nets etc. must be dipped.

MELKSHAM

Chippenham Angling Club (Burbrooks) &
Contact: Kevin Williams. *Mobile:* 07740 723603. *Water:* 1 acre lake between Melksham and Devizes in the village of Bromham. Carp Lake at Corsham. See also entry under River Fishing Bristol Avon. *Species:* Mirror and Crucian Carp, Bream, Rudd, Roach, Perch, Gudgeon and Chub. *Permits:* Full membership only. *Season:* Open all year dawn to dusk. *Methods:* No night fishing. One rod per person. No hooks above size 10. Separate approved nets for Silver fish and Carp.

Leech Pool Lake &
Contact: Rodney Mortimer, Leech Pool Farm, Norrington, Melksham. *Sat Nav:* SN12 8LS. *Tel:* 01225 703615. *Mobile:* 07813 947170. *Water:* 1.25 acre lake. *Species:* Mirror and

Common Carp up to 22lb. Tench 1lb to 2lb, Bream 1lb to 4.5lb. *Charges:* £5 per rod day fishing. £10 per rod night fishing. *Season:* Open all year dawn to dusk. *Methods:* Night fishing by arrangement only. No keepnets. Barbless hooks preferred. Some pegs suitable for wheelchairs with parking close to swims. For more info please telephone.

MERE

Gillingham and District A A (Turners Paddock) &
Contact: Simon Hebditch (Hon. Secretary), 10 Pimpernel Court, Gillingham, Dorset. *Tel:* 01747 821218. *Mobile:* 07990 690613. *Water:* Turners Paddock at Stourhead, Nr Mere. (See also entry under River Fishing Stour). *Species:* Tench 6lb, Bream 7lb, Carp 15lb, Roach 2lb, Rudd 2lb, Hybrids, Perch, Eels 7lb 8oz. *Permits:* Mr P Stone (Treasurer) The Timepiece, Newbury, Gillingham, Dorset, SP8 4HZ. Tel: 01747 823339. Mr J Candy, Todber Manor Fisheries Shop, Tel: 01258 820384. Mere Post Office, High Street, Mere, Wiltshire. Crockers Hardwear, High Street, Gillingham, Tel: 01747 822900. *Charges:* £5 day ticket, £41 season ticket. £20.50 junior and OAP £31. *Season:* June 16th to March 14th. *Methods:* No fish in keepnets for more than 6 hours. Leave no litter. Feeder best for Bream & Tench. Waggler in shallower water. Pole off the dam wall. No balling of groundbait. Groundbait only to be introduced via a feeder or pole cup.

Gillingham and District A A (Two Counties Lake) &
Contact: Simon Hebditch (Hon. Secretary), 10 Pimpernel Court, Gillingham, Dorset. *Tel:* 01747 821218. *Mobile:* 07990 690613. *Water:* 2 acre lake. *Species:* Carp, Tench, Crucians, Roach, Rudd, Bream and Perch. *Permits:* Mr P Stone (Treasurer) The Timepiece, Newbury, Gillingham, Dorset, SP8 4HZ. Tel: 01747 823339. Mr J Candy, Todber Manor Fisheries Shop, Tel: 01258 820384. Mere Post Office, High Street, Mere, Wiltshire. *Charges:* Membership only. *Season:* Open all year. *Methods:* Rules with membership.

PEWSEY

Marlborough and District A.A (Heron Lake)
Contact: Chris Potter. *Tel:* 01672 516587. *Mobile:* 07717 803663. *Water:* Coarse Lake at Wootton Rivers. 35 pegs for members only plus approx 12 miles Kennet & Avon Canal. *Species:* Roach, Rudd, Perch, Pike, Tench, Bream, Carp. Goldfish and Gudgeon. *Charges:* Members only. Full membership £40 plus £5 joining fee, Junior up to 16 £15, O.A.P's £20. *Season:* Open all year. Membership from 1 Jan - 31 Dec. *Methods:* No live baiting. Barbless hooks only on lake. No night fishing or radios. No guests. All nets must be dipped before fishing.

SALISBURY

Langford Lakes (Brockbank Lake) &
Contact: Wiltshire Wildlife Trust Fishery, Duck Street, Steeple Langford, Salisbury. *Sat Nav:* SP3 4NH. *Tel:* 01722 792011. *Water:* Brockbank lake 10 acres. *Species:* Roach, Bream,

Tench, Common Carp, Perch and Pike. *Permits:* Club membership, on application in advance. *Charges:* Full details on application. *Season:* Closed season 16 March - 15 June. *Methods:* No night fishing.

Longhouse Fishery
Teffont, Salisbury. *Sat Nav:* SP3 5RS. *Water:* 6 lakes. *Species:* Common, Mirror, Ghost, Koi, Crucian Carp (to double figures), Roach, Rudd (2.6lb), Perch (3.9lb), Tench (4lb), Bream (4.5lb). *Permits:* Lakeside only. *Charges:* Night fishing by arrangement only. *Season:* All year, only 10 days closed for pheasant shoot (October - January). *Methods:* Only bans are no particles (pulses) other than hemp or corn. No boilies. No large Carp in keepnets. Children under 16, must be accompanied by an adult.

Salisbury and District Angling Club (Coarse Lakes)
Contact: Andrea Topintzis, The Cart Shed, New Bottom Road, Stratford-Sub-Castle, Salisbury. *Tel:* 01722 321164. *Water:* Peters Finger Lakes and Steeple Langford. See entry under Avon Hampshire. East Wellow Lakes. *Species:* Carp to 30lbs plus, Tench to 6lbs, Roach, Bream, Perch and Pike. *Charges:* £94 per season. Concessions for Senior Citizens/ Juniors/Disabled. *Season:* 1 June - 31 March.

Tisbury Angling Club (Coarse Lakes)
Contact: Mr B Broom (membership sec.). *Tel:* 01722 743255. *Water:* See also entry under Nadder (3 mile stretch). Old Wardour Lake (3.5 acre), 2 miles south of Tisbury and Dinton Lake (2.5 acre), 2 miles north of Tisbury. *Species:* Roach, Chub, Dace, Bream, Perch, Crucian Carp, Carp, Brown Trout. *Permits:* £5 p/day guest tickets. Must be accompanied by full member. *Charges:* Adult £35 p/season, OAP £17.50, Juniors £7.50, £8.75 Partners. *Season:* 16 June to 14 March on river and Wardour Lake. Dinton Lake open all year.

Waldens Farm Fishery &
Contact: David & Jackie Wateridge, Waldens Farm, Walden Estate, West Grimstead, Salisbury. *Sat Nav:* SP5 3RW. *Tel:* 01722 710480. *Mobile:* 07766 451173. *Water:* 5 lakes covering approx. 7.5 acres. *Species:* All coarse fish. Specimen Pike Lake. Specimen Carp Lake. 27 peg Match Lake for club or private hire. *Permits:* From the bank. *Charges:* Day (dawn to dusk) tickets Adult £8, Junior/ OAP £6, Evenings from 5pm £5. Match peg fees £6. Night fishing £11 by appointment only. Season ticket £75, Junior/ OAP season £50. *Season:* Open all year. *Methods:* Barbless hooks, net dips to be used, groundbait only in feeders, no boilies, nuts or cereals. Keepnets allowed.

Watergate Farm Lakes
Contact: Charlie Rowland. *Sat Nav:* SP4 7EB. *Mobile:* 07768 515332. *Water:* 2 lakes - 1.25 acre lake and specimen lake. *Species:* 1.25 acre lake - Carp, Tench and Roach. Specimen Lake - Carp up to 33lbs, 4 different known 30's. Mirror, Commons and Ghost Carp. *Permits:* Day tickets on the bank for 1.25 lake. Hills Tackle in Amesbury for specimen lake only. *Charges:* £6 per day 1.25 lake. £15 per day for 2 rods - specimen lake. *Season:* Open all year Dawn to dusk. No night fishing on 1.25 lake. Specimen lake - night fishing available. *Methods:* Full rules at fishery.

Witherington Farm Fishing &
Contact: Eastleigh and District Angling Club. *Sat Nav:* SP5 3QX. *Tel:* 01722 711616. *Water:* 3 well stocked lakes, plus 93 peg match lake at Downton. Toilet facilities for disabled. Most swims accessible to wheelchairs. *Species:* Carp - 27lb, Tench - 7lb, Roach - 2.5lb, Bream - 6lb, Rudd - 0.5lb, Chub - 3lb, Perch - 3lb. *Permits:* From on-site Tackle shop. *Charges:* On application. *Season:* Open 7am - 9pm. *Methods:* No boilies, barbless hooks, all nets to be dipped, no night fishing, keepnets only permitted on Match lake. No cat meat, braided hook lengths, fixed rigs.

SWINDON

Coate Water Country Park &
Contact: Mark Jennings, c/o Rangers Centre, Marlborough Road, Swindon. *Sat Nav:* SN3 6AA. *Tel:* 01793 490150. *Water:* 56 acre reservoir with depth up to 4 metres. *Species:* Carp over 48lb, Pike 30lb, Bream to 15lb, Perch, Roach. *Permits:* On the bank or from Ranger team. There are four types of permit available, Specimen Day Ticket & General Day Tickets which can be purchased on the bank, and 24 & Day season permits which need to be purchased in advance. For details of the 24 & Day season permits contact Mark Jennings on the above. *Charges:* Day Ticket (Specimen) : Non Card £11, Swindon Card £8.40, Conc.1 £5.60 Conc.2 £2.80. Day Ticket (General) : Non Card £5.50, Swindon Card £4.20, Conc.1 £2.80 Conc.2 £1.40 and Junior £2.80.

STILLWATER COARSE

Season: 16 June to 14 March. *Methods:* No live baiting. No barbed hooks. Designated area for disabled anglers.

Mouldon Hill Angling Club
Contact: Kevin Maddison (sec), 33 Castle View Road, Chiseldon, Swindon. *Mobile:* 07961 400 210. *Water:* 1.5 acre lake, 3 islands, 30ft from River Ray. *Species:* Tench 8lb, Roach to 1lb, Perch to 2lb 2oz, Crucian Carp to 2lb, Bream 4lb, Rudd to 1lb, Chub to 3lb, Dace and Gudgeon. *Permits:* Day tickets: Available from House of Angling, Commercial Road, Swindon. Cotswold Angling Centre, Kembrey Street Ind Est, Swindon. Spar Shop, Marigold Close, Woodhall Park, Swindon. Hinders Fishing Superstore Cheney Manor, Swindon. *Charges:* Full membership: Adult (new) £25. Junior (u16) £5. Adult Day £5, Junior £3. April to April. Prices may vary. *Season:* Dawn to dusk, all year, no night fishing and no close season. *Methods:* Barbless hooks only. Carp mesh keepnets to be used. Disabled access can be arranged, please phone.

TROWBRIDGE

Rood Ashton Lake
Contact: Marlene Pike, Home Farm, Rood Ashton, Trowbridge. *Sat Nav:* BA14 6BL. *Tel:* 01380 870272. *Water:* 7 acre lake available for matches - please enquire for details. *Species:* Carp, Tench, Roach. *Permits:* Home Farm and Lake View. *Charges:* Adults 6am - 6pm £6, OAP/Juniors £5. Please enquire for match bookings. *Season:* Open all year. *Methods:* No keepnets (only competitions). No tin cans or boilies, Barbless hooks only. No nuts. No night fishing.

Tucking Mill
Contact: Wessex Water. *Sat Nav:* BA2 7DB. *Tel:* 0845 600 4 600. *Water:* Free coarse fishing for disabled anglers Season 16th June 2013 - 14th March 2014. *Species:* Roach, Chub, Tench and large Carp. *Permits:* The site is regularly used by disabled angling clubs including Kingswood Disabled Angling Club and The Westcountry Disabled Angling Association. Further information about the clubs and matches can be found on the notice board at Tucking Mill. *Charges:* Each disabled angler may bring along an able bodied assistant, who may also fish, but has to use the same pitch. *Season:* 8am to sunset throughout the year except in the close season. *Methods:* No keepnets, barbless hooks.

WARMINSTER

Lavington Angling Club
Contact: Tony Allen (Sec.), 8a Yarnbrook, Nr Trowbridge. *Tel:* 01225 752541. *Water:* Great Cheverell Lake complex. Two 3 acre lakes. One half acre lake. Also river fishing, both Trout and Coarse. *Species:* Carp to 30lb, Tench 4lb, Crucian 1lb, Tench 1.5lb, Bream 6lb. *Permits:* From the membership secretary: Mr Graham Pearce, 4a Holmfield, West Lavington, Devizes. Tel: 01380 818610. *Charges:* £40. Access to locked car park via security number known only to members. *Season:* Two lakes open all year dawn to dusk. *Methods:* Barbless hooks only. Max 1kg groundbait. From June 16 to

September 31 no keepnets between 12 noon and 1pm. No lead core and no braided lines.

Longleat Lakes & Shearwater
Contact: Nick Robbins, Longleat Estate Office, Longleat, Warminster. *Sat Nav:* BA12 7NW. *Tel:* 01985 844496. *Mobile:* 07889 625999. *Water:* Longleat 3 Lakes, Top lake: Carp up to 35lb. Shearwater 37 acres: Carp up to 30lb. Longleat: Middle and Bottom Lake: Perch 4.5lb, Bream 6lb and Roach with Carp up to 20lb. *Species:* Carp, Roach, Bream, Tench, Perch, Rudd. *Permits:* From bailiff on the bank. *Charges:* Day 7 am - 7 pm. Longleat: Day £10 per person, 24 hour ticket £20. Middle and Bottom Lakes: Day £10 per person, 24 hour ticket £20. Concessions for OAP/Junior Day tickets only. Shearwater Lake: Day £10 per person, 24 hour ticket £18. Concessions for OAP/Junior Day tickets only. *Season:* Longleat March - November. Shearwater March - December. For exact dates please contact Nick or check our website. *Methods:* No keepnets or Carp sacks, No nuts, peas, beans on all lakes, No bolt rigs or braided lines. Barbless hooks only. Shearwater has some pegs suitable for disabled anglers with parking close to pegs. Please telephone for further information.

Warminster & District Angling Club
Contact: c/o Steves Tackle, 35 George Street, Warminster. *Tel:* 01985 847634. *Mobile:* 07929 938419. *Water:* 4 lakes - 1 acre each. *Species:* Carp, Tench, Roach, Rudd. *Permits:* Club membership. *Charges:* For prices contact Ian Gallager Tel: 07929 938419. *Season:* All year round.

WESTBURY

Clivey Fishery

Contact: Chris Haines, Clivey Fishery, Dilton Marsh, Westbury. *Sat Nav:* BA13 4BA. *Tel:* 01373 858311. *Mobile:* 07815 937816. *Water:* 1 acre lake - 16 pegs, 0.33 acre lake - 8 pegs. *Species:* Rudd, Bream to 2lb, Perch, Carp to 17lb, Crucians, Tench to 3lb and Gudgeon. Gold Fish, Chub to 2lb. *Permits:* On site Tackle Shop. *Charges:* £5 Day Ticket. *Season:* All year. *Methods:* Barbless Hooks only.

Cuckoo's Rest Fishing Lakes &

Contact: Barry & Eileen Flack, Fairwood Road, Dilton Marsh, Westbury. *Sat Nav:* BA13 4EL. *Tel:* 01373 431472. *Water:* One 4 acre lake and one 2 acre lake. *Species:* Carp 32lbs, Perch 3lbs 10oz, Rudd 2lbs, Bream 8lbs, Tench 6lbs, Roach 3lbs, Chub 3lbs, Pike 24lb. *Charges:* £5 p/ day, £4 Juniors/OAP/Disabled. *Season:* All year 7am to dusk. *Methods:* Barbless hooks. Car Park close to small lake for disabled.

Eden Vale A.A. &

Contact: Geoff Wells, Secretary, 2 Wynford Road, Frome, Somerset. *Tel:* 01373 464777. *Water:* 5.25 acre lake. *Species:* Carp (Common to 15lb, Mirror to 20lb), Bream to 6lb, Roach to 2lb, Perch to 2lb, Rudd to 1lb, possible Pike, Tench 5-6lb, Chub 3lb. *Permits:* Day Tickets from Haines Angling, Dilton Marsh (01373 858311) Wiltshire Angling, Trowbridge 01225 763835. Also from Railway Inn Pub opposite the lake, parking available in pub car park next to fence. *Charges:* Day: £5 adult - £3 junior. Applications to Sec. with S.A.E., must be sponsored by two existing members. Membership senior £25, junior £20, oap/disabled £15. For all new members £10 joining fee. Membership renewable from 1st April. *Season:* Open all year. *Methods:* No fixed rigs, no Carp or Tench in keepnets. Silver fish can be kept in keepnets all year round. Disabled parking in swim next to boathouse up the lane (2 cars). Anglers can park by wire fence in Railway Inn car park. Juniors (under 16) must be accompanied by adult of 21 or over, otherwise not covered by insurance.

Frogmore Piscatorial Group &

Contact: Bruce E Evans, 5 Lanhams Close, Westbury. *Tel:* 01373 864025. *Water:* 10 acre site, 8 acres of water. *Species:* Carp 25lb, Bream 7lb, Crucian 3lb, Roach and Rudd 1lb plus, Tench 8lb, Pike 23lb, Eel 5lb. *Permits:* Yearly membership, no day tickets. *Charges:* £100 full. £75 conc. *Season:* Open all year. *Methods:* No keepnets, barbless hooks. No nights without permission. Full details from club.

White Horse Country Park

Contact: Wiltshire Angling, 5 Timbrell Street, Trowbridge. *Sat Nav:* BA13 4LX. *Tel:* 01225 763835. *Water:* Coarse Lake. *Species:* Carp 32lb, Bream 10lb, Perch 2.5lb, Tench 10lb, Roach 1.5lb. *Charges:* £50 per year. £10 per day Mon to Fri. Sat and Sun £15 per day. *Season:* 1 April to 31 March. *Methods:* Barbless hooks only. No boilies, peanuts, tiger nuts, peas or beans. No fixed or elasticated rigs. No night fishing.

WOOTTON BASSETT

Amalgamated Fisheries Ltd (Tockenham Reservoir) &

Contact: Mrs P Leonard, 48 Abbots Road, Hanham, Bristol. *Tel:* 01179 603378. *Water:* 12.5 acre Tockenham Reservoir at Lyneham, Sabre Lake at Calne plus various stillwaters at Lyneham, Bath and Pawlett near Bridgwater. *Species:* All coarse species including Carp to 30lb, Tench to 7lb, Bream to 8lb, plus Roach, Perch and Crucian Carp. *Charges:* Full Members only at Tockenham. No Day Permits. Adults/Ladies £45. Adult and child £60. Senior Citizen/Disabled and Juniors £25. Available at all Tackle Outlets. *Season:* Lakes open all year. Shackells Lake closed from May 1st to June 16th. *Methods:* Maximum 2 rods, no metal cans or glass allowed on banks, no freshwater fish to be used as livebait. All fishing is from platforms. Good parking facilities.

Stillwater Trout

CALNE

Calstone Fishery

Contact: Estate Office, Bowood, Calne. *Sat Nav:* SN11 0LZ. *Tel:* 01249 812102. *Water:* 0.75 acre reservoir. *Species:* Trout (Brown & Rainbow). *Permits:* Available from the estate office. Season permits only - waiting list. *Charges:* Prices on application. *Season:* April to October. Dawn to dusk. *Methods:* Weekly bag limits - 2 brace. All Browns to be returned. No catch & return of Rainbow after 15th September. First 2 Rainbow must be taken on each visit.

CHIPPENHAM

Pheasant Fly Fishers

Contact: Bruce Low, 8 The Ridings, Kington St Michael, Chippenham. *Tel:* 01249 758260. *Water:* None - A fly fishing club where members fish local waters and go on organised trips further afield. *Permits:* Please contact Bruce Low for more details. Anglers are welcome to attend one of our regular meetings at the Lysley Arms, Chippenham at 8pm on the first Tuesday of each month. Fly fishing beginners welcome. *Charges:* Club membership fees £25. *Season:* Fly fishing trips are organised throughout the year.

DEVIZES

Mill Farm Trout Lakes ♿

Contact: Barbara Coleman, Mill Farm Trout Lakes, Worton, Devizes. *Sat Nav:* SN10 5UW. *Tel:* 01380 813138. *Mobile:* 07500 615396. *Water:* 2 Waters of 3.5 acres each. *Species:* Rainbow Trout. All triploids from 2lb to double figures. *Permits:* Great Cheverell Post Office. One mile from fishery and open on Sunday mornings. *Charges:* 5 Fish £38, 4 Fish £32, 3 Fish £25, 2 Fish £18. (2hrs before dusk only) £10. *Season:* All year, 7.30am to dusk. December and January 8am to dusk. Closed every Monday except Bank Holidays. *Methods:* Fly fishing only.

PEWSEY

Manningford Trout Farm and Fishery

Contact: Malcolm Hunt, Manningford Bohune, By Pewsey. *Sat Nav:* SN9 6JR. *Mobile:* 07544 801844. *Water:* 4.5 acre lake, 1.5 acre catch & release lake and 1.4 acre lake fed by the Hampshire Avon. *Species:* Rainbow Trout to 26lb 8oz. Brown Trout to 19lb 14oz. *Charges:* Details/permits from fishery. 6 fish £40, 4 fish £35, 3 fish £30, 2 fish £25, 4 fish ticket junior £30, 2 fish ticket junior £20. *Season:* Open all year 8am to dusk. *Methods:* Fly fishing only.

SALISBURY

Avon Springs Fishing Lake (Stillwater)

Contact: DJ Dawden, Recreation Road, Durrington, Salisbury. *Sat Nav:* SP4 8HH. *Tel:* 01980 653557. *Mobile:* 07774 801401. *Water:* One 4 acre lake, one 3 acre lake. One mile of upper Avon chalk stream left hand bank, see Wiltshire, River Fishing. *Species:* Brown Trout 15lb 9oz, Rainbow Trout 16lb 8oz (2011). *Permits:* EA fishing licences available on site. *Charges:* £48 per day, £30 junior. Half day £38, junior £28, Eve £28. Pensioners day £43 (Monday only). River and Lake ticket on application. *Season:* Open all year 8.30am to 8pm. *Methods:* Fly only no lures.

Chalke Valley Fly Fishery ♿

Contact: Norman Barter, Vella House, Bishopstone, Salisbury. *Sat Nav:* SP5 4AA. *Tel:* 01722 780471. *Mobile:* 07778 769223. *Water:* 2 spring fed lakes. 'Home' lake 1 acre and 'Marsh' lake 0.6 acres. Max. 4 anglers each lake. *Species:* All Brown Trout Triploids, catch and release. *Charges:* Day ticket booking requested. Wheelchair access for fishing. 8am - 12 noon £20, 12 - 4pm £15, 4pm - Dusk £25. *Season:* Open 15 April until 16 October - 8am till Dusk. *Methods:* Dry fly with barbless hooks.

> Remember a ♿ means the fishery has disabled facilities - contact them direct for further details

Gloucestershire River Fishing

LITTLE AVON

Berkeley Estate Fishing Syndicate

Contact: T. Staniforth, 68 Firgrove, Chipping Sodbury. *Tel:* 01454 881719. *Water:* 6.5 miles of Coarse and Game fishing on Little Avon from Berkeley Castle to Damery-Tortworth. *Species:* Chub, Dace, Roach, Bream, Perch, Brown Trout, and Grayling. *Charges:* Annual membership £55. Guests may accompany members at £7 per day. *Season:* Statutory. *Methods:* Trout season fly only. From June 16 any method. No spinning.

THAMES

South Cerney Angling Club (Duxford Farm)

Contact: Craig Hunt, Fisherman's Rest, Broadway Lane, South Cerney. *Mobile:* 07989 973217. *Water:* Stretch of the River Thames (Duxford Farm). *Species:* Roach, Chub, Barbel, Gudgeon, Perch, Dace and Pike. *Permits:* Permits available from our licensed clubhouse and local tackle shops. Day tickets available. Season permit entitles holder to fish all SCAC waters. A passport photo is required to purchase a season ticket plus valid EA rod licence. *Charges:* Season Permit: £60 Adults, £30 Junior, £35 OAP/Disabled. £40 week licence. *Season:* 16th June - 14th March.

South Cerney Angling Club (Inglesham) ♿

Contact: Craig Hunt, Fisherman's Rest, Broadway Lane, South Cerney. *Mobile:* 07989 973217. *Water:* Stretch of River Thames at Hannington plus stretch at Inglesham. *Species:* Barbel, Chub, Roach, Perch, Pike, Bream, Dace and Gudgeon. *Permits:* Permits available from our licensed clubhouse at Ham Pool and local tackle shops. A passport photo is required to purchase a season ticket plus valid EA rod licence. *Charges:* Season Permit: £60 Adults, £30 Junior, £35 Disabled/OAP. £40 week ticket. *Season:* 16th June - 14th March.

South Cerney Angling Club (River Ray)

Contact: Craig Hunt, Fisherman's Rest, Broadway Lane, South Cerney. *Mobile:* 07989 973217. *Water:* River Ray, Thames tributary (Cricklade). Off the A419 between Blunsdon and Cirencester. *Species:* Stocked with Roach, Chub, Barbel, Gudgeon, Perch, Dace and Pike. *Permits:* Permits available from our licensed clubhouse and local tackle shops. Season permit entitles holder to fish all SCAC waters. To purchase a season permit you are required to supply a passport photo and hold a valid EA licence. *Charges:* Season Permit: £60 Adults, £30 Junior, £35 OAP/Disabled. £40 week licence. *Season:* 16th June - 14th March.

South Cerney Angling Club (Thames Kelmscott)

Contact: Craig Hunt, Fisherman's Rest, Broadway Lane,

South Cerney. *Mobile:* 07989 973217. *Water:* Stretch of the River Thames (Kelmscott). *Species:* Stocked with Roach, Chub, Barbel, Gudgeon, Perch, Dace and Pike. *Permits:* Permits available from our licensed clubhouse and local tackle shops. Day tickets available. To purchase membership a passport photo and a valid EA rod licence is required. *Charges:* Season Permit: £60 Adults, £30 Junior, £35 OAP/Disabled. £40 week licence. Day tickets available. Season permit entitles you to fish all SCAC waters. *Season:* 16th June - 14th March.

Stillwater Coarse

CHIPPING SODBURY

Alcove Angling Club &

Contact: Bryan Cleevely, 31 Roseberry Park, Redfield, Bristol. *Tel:* 01179 392827. *Mobile:* 07938 874330. *Water:* 4 lakes in Bristol & South Glos. Secure gated access to all car parks. Phone for further information and about disabled fishing. *Species:* Carp 28lb, Bream 7lb, Roach, Tench 8lb, Rudd, Pike, Perch and Crucian Carp. *Charges:* Annual memberships only - No Day tickets. Annual memberships Adult £50. Partners of members £10, Children under 12 free, Junior 12 to 17 £16, OAP £28. Disabled £28 (helper £1). Children must be accompanied by an adult at all times. *Season:* No close season. *Methods:* As specified in membership card. Night fishing at Alcove Lido only. Barbless hooks or Micro Barb only. 1 kilo of bait per day.

Bathampton Angling Association (Coarse Lakes)

Contact: Dave Crookes, 25 Otago Terrace, Larkhall, Bath, Somerset. *Tel:* 01225 427164. *Water:* Two lakes at Lydes Farm and Players Golf Club, Codrington. *Species:* Roach to 2.5lbs, Rudd to 2lb, Tench to 6.5lbs. Carp to 20lb plus, Crucian Carp, Bream to 7.5lb. *Permits:* Local fishing tackle shops (members only). *Charges:* Adults £35, Juniors £15, OAP £13. Under 12's free. Additional special day permit at £3 must be obtained before fishing. *Season:* Open from 8am all year round. Closing times vary. *Methods:* Special rules apply - available from secretary and printed on permit.

CIRENCESTER

South Cerney Angling Club (Dab-Chick Lake)

Contact: Craig Hunt, Fisherman's Rest, Broadway Lane, South Cerney. *Mobile:* 07989 973217. *Water:* 8 acre gravel pit (lake 63 - Members only). Spine Road GL7 6DF. *Species:* Stocked with Carp, Tench, Roach, Rudd and Perch. *Permits:* Permits available from our licensed clubhouse, local tackle shops and bailiff on bank. Season permit entitles holder to fish all SCAC waters. A passport photo is required to purchase a season ticket plus valid EA rod licence. *Charges:* Season Permit: £60 Adults, £30 Junior, £35 OAP/Disabled. £40 week licence. *Season:* No close season. *Methods:* Night fishing permitted.

South Cerney Angling Club (Franklins Lake)

Contact: Craig Hunt, Fisherman's Rest, Broadway Lane, South Cerney. *Mobile:* 07989 973217. *Water:* 22 acre gravel pit (Lake 23 - Members only). Access at Wickwater Lane, South Cerney and at Fridays Ham Lane. *Species:* Stocked with Carp, Tench, Roach, Rudd, Perch and Pike. *Permits:* Permits available from our licensed clubhouse and local tackle shops. Season permit entitles holder to fish all SCAC waters. A passport photo is required to purchase a season ticket plus valid EA rod licence. *Charges:* Season Permit: £60 Adults, £30 Junior £35 OAP/Disabled. £40 week ticket. *Season:* No close season. *Methods:* Night fishing permitted. Toilets on site.

South Cerney Angling Club (Gillman's Lake) &

Contact: Craig Hunt, Fisherman's Rest, Broadway Lane, South Cerney. *Mobile:* 07989 973217. *Water:* Small heavily stocked lake (lake 23a - for Members and Day Tickets). Access at Wickwater lane South Cerney. *Species:* Stocked with Carp, Tench, Roach, Rudd, Perch and Bream. *Permits:* Permits/membership available from our licensed clubhouse and local tackle shops. Season permit entitles holder to fish all SCAC waters. Day tickets available on the bank. A passport photo is required to purchase a season ticket plus valid EA rod licence. *Charges:* Season Permit: £60 Adults, £30 Junior, £35 OAP/Disabled. £40 week tickets. Day Tickets available. *Season:* No close season. *Methods:* No night fishing. Toilets on site.

South Cerney Angling Club (Ham Pool)

Contact: Craig Hunt, Fisherman's Rest, Broadway Lane, South Cerney. *Mobile:* 07989 973217. *Water:* 12 acre gravel pit (lake 18 members only). Access at Broadway Lane, South Cerney, Glos, GL7 5UH. *Species:* Carp 38lb, Tench 11lb, Roach 2lb, Rudd 2lb, Crucian 4lb, Pike 30lb+, Perch 2lb, Bream 10lb. *Permits:* Permits available from our licensed clubhouse and local tackle shops. Season permit entitles holder to fish all SCAC waters. Day tickets on bank. A passport photo is required to purchase a season ticket plus valid EA rod licence. *Charges:* Season Permit- £60 Adults, £30 Junior, £35 Disabled/OAP. £40 week ticket. *Season:* No close season. *Methods:* Night fishing permitted. Shower and toilets on site. No loose feeding boilies.

South Cerney Angling Club (Stait Lake)

Contact: Craig Hunt, Fisherman's Rest, Broadway Lane, South Cerney. *Mobile:* 07989 973217. *Water:* Small commercial type lake (lake 23a - Members and day tickets) Access at Friday Ham Lane, South Cerney. *Species:* Stocked with mainly Carp, Roach and Bream. *Permits:* Permits available from our licensed clubhouse and local tackle shops. Season permits entitles holder to fish all SCAC waters. Day tickets available on the bank. To purchase season permit you must supply a passport photo and hold a valid EA licence. *Charges:* Season Permit: £60 Adults, £30 Junior £35 OAP/Disabled. £40 week ticket. Day Tickets available. *Season:* No close season. *Methods:* No night fishing. Toilets on site.

South Cerney Angling Club (Whitefriars)

Contact: Craig Hunt, Fisherman's Rest, Broadway Lane, South Cerney. *Mobile:* 07989 973217. *Water:* 100 acre gravel pit (Lake 26 - Members only). Ashton Keynes, Wiltshire, SN6 6QR. *Species:* Stocked with Bream, Carp, Tench, Roach, Perch and Pike. *Permits:* Permits available from our licensed clubhouse and local tackle shops. Season permit entitles holder to fish all SCAC waters. To purchase a season ticket passport photo is required and proof of a valid EA rod licence. *Charges:* Season Permit: £60 Adults, £30 Junior, £35 Disabled/OAP. £40 week licence. *Season:* No close season. *Methods:* Night fishing permitted.

Swindon Isis Angling Club Lake No1 ♿

Contact: Peter Gilbert, Button Mill, Baunton, Cirencester. *Mobile:* 07785 542795. *Water:* 6 acre mature gravel pit dug in 1955 at Cotswold Water Park (Water Park Lake 19), South Cerney, Cirencester. *Species:* Tench over 10lb, Carp to 35lb, Rudd to 2lb12oz, Crucian Carp to 3lb 8oz, Bream to 10lb 3oz, usual Roach, Perch & good Pike. *Permits:* Tackle shops in Swindon, Cirencester, Chippenham, Cheltenham and Calne. *Charges:* Club Permits: Senior £39. OAP, Disabled and Junior £15. Club permit contains two free day tickets. Year starts 1 April. Half year membership from 1 November Senior £20, Junior £8. *Season:* Open all year round. Club cards start 1st April. *Methods:* No bans.

Wildmoor Waters ♿

The Willows, Wildmoorway Lane, South Cerney. *Sat Nav:* GL7 5UZ. *Mobile:* 07711 826459. *Water:* 2 lakes: Specimen Lake 4.5 acres and Top Lake 0.75 acres. *Species:* Specimen 550 Carp to 38lb. Top Lake: 200 Carp and other coarse fish. *Charges:* Max 2 rods at anytime. £30 for 24 hours. Booking essential. *Methods:* No nuts of any kind. No Lead Core. No fixed leads. Full rules at fishery.

CORSE

Stone End Farm

Contact: Richard Spry, Stone End Farm, Church Lane, Corse. *Sat Nav:* GL19 3BX. *Tel:* 01452 700254. *Water:* Two lakes. Front lake 1 acre - 20 pegs. House Pond 0.75 acre - 12 pegs. *Species:* Common and Mirror Carp to 27lb. Tench to 5lb, Bream to 7.5lb. *Permits:* On site. *Charges:* Day tickets £7. Disabled and children £4. *Season:* Open all year. *Methods:*

Barbless hooks only. No nuts, floating baits, cat or dog meats, no bread. Groundbait allowed in small quantities (no buckets). Soft boilies allowed. No keepnets. Unhooking mats must be used.

GLOUCESTER

Huntley Carp Pools

Contact: John Tipper - Frank Morris, 14 Thoresby Ave, Tuffley, Gloucester. *Tel:* 01452 505313. *Water:* Two 3.5 acre lakes. 1 with Carp to 30lb. 1 with general fish, Carp, Tench, Perch, Bream, Roach, Rudd, Crucian. *Species:* Carp: to 30lb, Bream 4lb, Perch 3lb, Tench 5lb, Roach/Rudd 2.75lb. *Permits:* Only from above. *Charges:* To be advised. *Season:* 16 June - 30 April. *Methods:* No keepnets, barbless hooks.

Lemington Lakes ♿

Contact: Debbie, Todenham Road, Moreton-in-Marsh. *Sat Nav:* GL56 9NP. *Tel:* 01608 650872. *Water:* 5 ponds (4.5, 2.5, 2, 1.25 and 0.5 acres) all with coarse fish. *Species:* Each lake caters for different types of fishing with fish up to specimen sizes. *Permits:* As above. *Charges:* £8 Max two rods (£12 on Westminster Lake) - £6 Children under 14. Night fishing must be booked. *Season:* Open 1st March - 31st October. *Methods:* Barbless hooks only. Disabled toilets on site.

STROUD

Matchplay Angling Association

Contact: James Strafford, Units 3 & 5 Salmon Springs Trading Estate, Cheltenham Road, Stroud. *Tel:* 01453 752242. *Mobile:* 07760 441724. *Water:* Monthly matches at various venues. *Species:* Carp, Roach, Perch, Rudd, Skimmers, Bream, Tench, Chub and Barbel. *Charges:* Adults £7. Concessions £5. *Season:* February-November. *Methods:* Keepnets and main fishery rules.

TEWKESBURY

Hillview Lakes ♿

Contact: Keith Hill, Cherry Orchard Lane, Twyning, Tewkesbury. *Sat Nav:* GL20 6JH. *Tel:* 01684 296719. *Mobile:* 07840 579087. *Water:* 6 lakes covering 4 acres. *Species:* Carp to 22lb. Tench, Bream and Orfe to 4lb+. Perch to 3.5lb. *Charges:* One rod £7. Concessions £6. *Season:* Open all year 8am - 8pm. *Methods:* Keepnets only in matches. Barbless hooks only. No groundbait. Pellets can be loose fed but must be supplied by Hillview Lakes.

WOTTON-UNDER-EDGE

Lower Killcott Farm Fishing

Contact: Mr E Thompson, Lower Kilcott Farm, Nr Hillesley, Wotton-Under-Edge. *Sat Nav:* GL12 7RL. *Tel:* 01454 238276. *Mobile:* 07817 754681. *Water:* 1 acre lake. *Species:* Carp to 21lb, Roach, Rudd. *Charges:* £5 day, plus £1 for extra rod. *Season:* Open all year. *Methods:* Barbless hooks only, no keepnets or boilies.

Stillwater Trout

DURSLEY

Great Burrows Trout Fishery
Contact: Vernon Baxter (Manager), Nibley Green, North Nibley, Nr Dursley. *Sat Nav:* GL11 6AZ. *Tel:* 01453 542343 / 01453 548448. *Mobile:* 07754 502134. *Water:* Two acre lake. Fishing from platform only. *Species:* Rainbow Trout (triploid) stocked from 2lb to 5lb. *Permits:* From V. Baxter on site. *Charges:* 2 fish £20. 3 fish £24. 4 fish £28. 5 fish £32. 6 fish £36. *Season:* Open all year except Xmas day. Fishing from 8am to 1 hr after sunset. *Methods:* Fly only. No lures. Barbless hooks only. Max hook size 14 longshank. No static fishing. No catch and release. Fishing from platforms only. E.A. Licence required. Tuition and equipment available.

GLOUCESTER

The Cotswolds Fishery
Contact: Mrs Celia Hicks-Beach, Witcombe Farm, Great Witcombe. *Sat Nav:* GL3 4TR. *Tel:* 01452 864413. *Mobile:* 01452 863591. *Water:* 3 reservoirs - 15 acres, 5 acres and 2 plus acres. *Species:* Rainbow Trout max weight 8lbs. *Permits:* Witcombe Farm Estate. *Charges:* Seasonal permits available, various prices on application. Day visitor tickets - Full day £45 (6 fish), Half day (6 hrs) £27 (3 fish), Evening £20 (2 fish). Boats £10 Full day, £5 Half day, £3 Evening. Novice 6hrs (max 3 visits) £30. Fish to be paid at £7 each.

Season: 10th March - 27th October, 8am to dusk. *Methods:* Normal game fishing for Trout, No catch and release.

LECHLADE

Lechlade and Bushyleaze Trout Fisheries &
Contact: Tim Small, Lechlade & Bushyleaze Trout Fisheries, Lechlade. *Sat Nav:* GL7 3QQ. *Tel:* 01367 253266. *Water:* Lechlade - 8 acres. Bushyleaze - 20 acres. *Species:* Lechlade - Rainbows to 27lb, Browns to 27lb. Bushyleaze - Rainbows to 17lb, Browns to 17lb. *Charges:* Lechlade: £65 full day, 4 fish. £37.50 half day, 2 fish. £27.50 eve, 1 fish. Bushyleaze: £37.50 full day, 6 fish. £32.50 full day, 4 fish. £30 half day, 3 fish. £22.50 eve, 2 fish. Season tickets available. Discounted day tickets for juniors. *Season:* Open all year. *Methods:* Fly only. Boat hire and float tube hire.

WOTTON-UNDER-EDGE

Tortworth Lake
Contact: Mrs Teresa Lewis, Tortworth Estate Company, Tortworth Estate office, Wotton-under-Edge. *Sat Nav:* GL12 8HF. *Tel:* 01454 260268. *Water:* 14 acre lake. *Species:* Rainbows to 4lb and Browns to 2lb stocked. *Permits:* From Estate Office. *Season:* April to October, mornings (8.30 am to 2.30 pm) and afternoons (3 pm to dark). Two boats available. *Methods:* Fly fishing only. All trolling, spinning, bubble float and/or thread line fishing irrespective of the fly, lure, spinner etc used is prohibited. The use of fish location devices is not permitted.

STILLWATER TROUT

TUITION

TUITION GUIDING COACHING

Not just for beginners - How is your fly casting? it could probably be improved. Make the most of your equipment by booking some tuition to hone your casting skills

David Truran

The Suntrap, 6 Eastcliffe Rd., Par, Cornwall
Tel: 01726 812821
Mobile: 07788 548 009
Email: truranfamily@dsl.pipex.com
www.truranflyfishing.co.uk
Level 2 certificate in coaching/angling
Cornwall PL24 area
All tackle supplied free of charge

Fly fishing tuition and techniques, beginners to advanced.
Fresh and saltwater guiding. All ages and disabled welcome.

Peter Leadsford

Haycorn Cottage, Trerulefoot, Saltash,
Cornwall PL12 5BL
Tel: 01752 851358. Mobile: 07989 421371
Email: p.leadsford@gmail.com
www.haycorncottage.co.uk
Level 2 CCA (Game). ADB Licensed. Member of GAIA
Cornwall/Devon borders, stillwaters and rivers
Quality tackle and permits provided

Tuition for all ages and abilities.
Individuals or groups.

David Pilkington / Tim Smith

Arundell Arms, Lifton, Devon PL16 0AA
Tel: 01566 784666 / Fax: 01566 784494
Email: reservations@arundellarms.co.uk
www.arundellarms.co.uk
AAPGAI qualified instructors
Lifton area of Devon. Based at The Arundell Arms Hotel
Well stocked tackle shop on site

Individual tuition and fly fishing courses.
All types of casting including modern Spey casting.
All aspects of fly fishing.

John Hern

18 Bazley Square, Pinhoe, Exeter EX1 3QP
Tel: 01392 464917 Mobile: 07505 218576
Email: johnhern@virginmedia.com
1st4sport L1CCA, L2CCA UKCC in Game Angling
Devon
All tackle supplied

Tuition and guiding for game fish on
stillwaters and rivers
Angling Trust Licensed Coach

John H Dawson

29 Bourchier Close, Bampton, Tiverton, Devon EX16 9AG
Tel: 01398 331498 Mobile: 07816 453474
Email: info@johndawson.co.uk www.johndawson.co.uk
STANIC - Salmon, Trout and Fly Dressing
Level 2 Certificate in Coaching Angling
AT Licenced
Devon and Somerset
Fishing tackle can be provided

Fly fishing and casting tuition on rivers, stillwaters and
sea. Guiding service. Fly dressing tuition.

Martyn Green

31 Collapark, Totnes, Devon, TQ9 5LW
Tel: (01803) 863279 Mobile: 07704 602180
Email: Martyn.green1@tiscali.co.uk
www.devonfishingguides.co.uk
Level 2 Game & Sea Angling Coach / Instructor
South Devon
Tackle and Bait

All types of sea fishing, especially light tackle, fly fishing
for trout and carp. Tuition for beginners, improvers,
adults, groups, families and children.

Bryan Martin

South Molton, Devon.
Tel: 01769 550840 Mobile: 07759 352194
Email: bryan@devonflyfishing.co.uk
www.devonflyfishing.co.uk
FFF MCI, THCI / APGAI / STANIC / UKCC
North Devon and West Somerset
All tackle provided

Fly casting tuition. Fishing for salmon, sea trout and trout
on rivers & stillwaters. All levels, beginners to advanced.
Saltwater fly fishing. Overseas fishing holidays.

**Fishing in a new area?
On holiday?
Contact a guide to make
the most of your West
Country fishing experience**

Amherst Lodge Academy
Amherst Lodge, St Mary's Lane, Uplyme, Dorset DT7 3XH
Tel: 01297 442773   Mobile: 07753 640737
Email: info@flyfishing-southwest.co.uk
www.flyfishing-southwest.co.uk
Level 2 AT and GAIC / APGAI
Devon-Dorset-Somerset and Cornwall
All equipment and transport provided

*Fly fishing and casting tuition for all abilities and
ages on reservoirs- rivers and stillwaters.
We will teach you the skills required to catch Bass -
Trout - Salmon - Sea trout and Grayling*

John Cheetham
62 Endfield Road, Fairmile, Christchurch,
Dorset BH23 2HU
Tel: 01202 490014 Mobile: 07720 671706
Email: jrcheetham@msn.com
L2 CCA Trout & Salmon
Dorset and Hampshire
Game fishing equipment supplied for Trout and Salmon

*Chalk stream fishing for trout and grayling.
Spey casting. Guiding.
Casting and coaching for all ages.*

Tony King
Wessex Flyfishing School, Lawrences Farm, Tolpuddle DT2 7HF
Tel: 01305 789560   Mobile: 07855 196332
Email: tonykingfishing@googlemail.com www.tkfishing.com
AAPGAI/STANIC/SGAIC/REFFIS. UKCC Level 2.
Dorset, Wiltshire, Hampshire. Trips for Salmon/Seatrout -
Scotland/Norway. Warm water salt fly fishing - Bahamas
All tackle can be provided

*Fly casting - All disciplines. Chalk Stream - Introductions,
Intermediate and Advanced Frome/Piddle/Allen. Still Water -
Introductions, Intermediate and Advanced for Trout & Carp.
Salt Water fly fishing on Dorset coast. MCA Registered boat.*

More on the website.....
● **Learn to fish**
● **Where to fish**
● **Articles & advice
   from top anglers**

WWW.GETHOOKED.CO.UK

Lechlade & Bushyleaze
Trout Fisheries (Tim Small)
Lechlade, Gloucestershire GL7 3QQ
Tel: 01367 253266
Email: tim@lechladetrout.co.uk
www.lechladetrout.co.uk
Team of three Instructors
On site at the fishery
Rods, reels, lines etc.
*Stalking and beginners a speciality.
Please telephone to book.*

The Total Fly Fishing Company Ltd
David Griffiths and James Mills
Tel: 01747 871695
Email: info@totalflyfishing.co.uk www.totalflyfishing.co.uk
APGAI/STANIC Trout, Salmon, Sea Trout

*The Total Experience for:
Expert Casting Tuition (APGAI/GAIA)
Guided chalk stream fishing.
Salmon and Sea Trout fishing in: U.K., and abroad.
Overseas saltwater fly fishing.
Bespoke Corporate days.*

Southern & South West Game Angling
Graeme Lowndes 6 Markson Road, South Wonston,
Winchester, Hampshire SO21 3EZ
Tel: 01962 883803 Mobile: 07595 041202
Email: graemelowndes@tiscali.co.uk
www.sswgameangling.co.uk
Angling Trust Licenced Coach - Level 1 & 2. PAA member
Professional Game Angling Instructor - GAIAC
Hampshire, Wiltshire, Dorset, Somerset and Devon
All game angling equipment available

*Fly fishing tuition and guided fishing days with
Graeme Lowndes. Spey casting a speciality*

Sally Pizii
Tumbleweed Cottage, Curry Mallet, Nr Taunton
Somerset TA3 6SR
Tel: 01823 480710
Email: pizii@btinternet.com
Level 2 C.C.A./STANIC/REFFIS/AT Licenced
Westcountry
All fly fishing tackle available

*Fly fishing and casting on rivers or stillwaters.
Beginners, improvers. Adults, families and children.*

KEY
Name
Contact details
Qualifications
Area covered
Equipment available
Specialities

Game

Coarse

Sea

Publishers of The Get Hooked Guide

Tel: 01271 860183
Fax: 01271 860064
Email: jane@diamondpublications.co.uk
www.diamondpublications.co.uk

Please report injured wildlife to:
RSPCA Tel: 0300 1234 999
www.rspca.org.uk
Don't let fishing litter hurt our wildlife
Please take all your rubbish home!

www.environment-agency.gov.uk

Environmental Incident Hotline:
Tel: 0800 80 70 60

General Enquiries & Regional Offices:
Tel: 03708 506 506

Floodline: Tel: 0845 988 1188

Regional Fisheries & Biodiversity Team offices at:
North Wessex - Rivers House, Bridgwater, Somerset TA6 4YS
South Wessex - Rivers House, Blandford Forum, Dorset DT11 8ST
Devon - Manley House, Exeter, Devon EX2 7LQ
Cornwall - Sir John Moore House, Bodmin, Cornwall PL31 1EB

Purchase your Rod Licence direct:
Tel: 0844 800 5386
www.postoffice.co.uk/rod-fishing-licence

www.anglingtrust.net

Tel: 0844 77 00 616 (option 1)
Email: admin@anglingtrust.net

Dean Asplin SW Regional Officer
Tel: 07854 239731
Email: Dean.Asplin@Anglingtrust.net

Angling Trust Kayak Fishing Safety Course
Tel: 0844 77 00 616 (option 1)

Competitions
Sandra Drew, Competitions & Events Manager.
Tel: 0115 9061 301

Team England Fly Fishing
For details on south west fly fishing including Peninsula Federation and Southern Fly Fishers.
www.te-ff.org Mobile: 07796 017225
Email: j.ball50@btinternet.com

Coaching Qualifications, Level 1 & 2
Email: angela.woodgates@anglingtrust.net
Tel: 0115 9061 313

Angling Trust Voluntary Bailiff Service
To volunteer contact: bailiffs@anglingtrust.net
Tel: 07971 677638

Angling Talent Pathway Programme
Ben Thompson, Senior Competitions and Talent Manager.
Email: ben.thompson@anglingtrust.net

Clubmark Accreditation
Email: clubmark@anglingtrust.net

Child Protection Officer
Ben Snook, Coaching Development Manager.
Tel: 07720 974 811

Building Bridges Project
Helping Migrant Anglers understand UK Angling Law, Culture & Custom. Radoslaw Papiewski, Building Bridges Manager.
Tel: 07886 138072
Email: Radoslaw.Papiewski@Anglingtrust.net

Salmon & Trout Association -
Game anglers for fish, people, the environment.
www.salmon-trout.org
Tel: 0207 283 5838
Email: hq@salmon-trout.org
Dedicated website against unsustainable fish farming: **www.STAndupforwildsalmon.org**

The Atlantic Salmon Trust
Working for wild salmon and sea trout in all their habitats. Tel: 01738 472032
marjorie@atlanticsalmontrust.org
www.atlanticsalmontrust.org

The Riverfly Partnership
Dedicated to the protection & restoration of aquatic flies - Help monitor your local river.
www.riverflies.org Tel: 07590 928842

The Wild Trout Trust
Dedicated to the Preservation of Wild Trout.
www.wildtrout.org   Tel: 023 9257 0985

Game & Wildlife Conservation Trust
The leading UK charity conducting scientific research to enhance the British countryside for public benefit. Tel: 01425 652381
Email: info@gwct.org.uk
www.gwct.org.uk

South West Rivers Association
Email: swra@furniss2733.fsnet.co.uk

The Rivers Trust
The umbrella body of the rivers trust movement.
Tel: 01579 372 142
Email: info@theriverstrust.org
www.theriverstrust.org

South West Rivers Trusts

Westcountry Rivers Trust
www.wrt.org.uk - Tel: 01579 372140

Bristol Avon Rivers Trust
www.bristolavonriverstrust.org

Wessex Chalkstream & Rivers Trust
www.wcsrt.org.uk - Tel: 01794 341874

Action for the River Kennet (ARK)
www.riverkennet.org - Tel: 07880 515859

Personal Support Charities

BDAA
Charity to develop opportunities for disabled people of all ages and abilities to access fishing. Tel: 01922 860912 info@bdaa.co.uk
www.bdaa.co.uk

Wheelyboat Trust
Providing disabled people with the opportunity and freedom to enjoy waters large and small all over the UK.
SW Coordinator Tel: 01822 615953
www.wheelyboats.org

Fishing For Forces
Provide fishing for those returning from Operational Tours.
Bill Howell Tel: 0207 385 2135 / 07850 373760
www.fishingforforces.org

Fishing for Heros
Fly fishing courses as part of a therapy package for veterans and serving personnel.
SW Contact: Mike Thompson
Tel: 07818 062500
www.fishingforheroes.com

SW Fishing for Life
Support network to help breast cancer patients.
Tel: Gillian on 01398 371244
Email: holworthyfarm@aol.com
www.southwestfishingforlife.org.uk

Casting For Recovery UK & Ireland
Provides an opportunity for women whose lives have been profoundly affected by breast cancer to gather on retreat and learn the sport of fly fishing. Contact Sue Shaw.
Tel: 01778 560920 / 07713 476632
Email: info@castingforrecovery.org.uk
www.castingforrecovery.org.uk

Heroes On The Water UK
(HOW UK) is a charity that provides Kayak Angling to our wounded military and members of the public who have suffered whilst carrying out a public duty.
www.heroesonthewater-uk.org

More information within this guide and online at www.gethooked.co.uk

River Game

River Coarse

Stillwater Trout

Stillwater Coarse

ADVERTISERS INDEX

Sea

Tackle